2013

150 Years

Science For A Better Life

BAYER · THE INVENTOR COMPANY

150 Years · Thousands of Innovations · 150 Stories

The Anniversary Book

2013

Bayer headquarters, 2013
A modern enterprise, transparent and open: the Board of Management and the employees of the holding company have worked in the present headquarters building on the Kaiser-Wilhelm-Allee in Leverkusen since summer 2002.

Headquarters, around 1863
The first headquarters building of Friedr. Bayer et comp. (right) on Heckinghauser Strasse in Barmen-Rittershausen (now a district of Wuppertal) was rather modest. Before the company was founded, Friedrich Bayer had used the building to store dyestuffs.

Teamwork, around 1870
Workers from the fuchsine factory in Barmen pose for the photographer (not all of them can keep still for the long-exposure shot). Bayer was known for its employee-friendly policies from an early stage – even before Bismarck's social legislation was passed.

Teamwork, 2003
A large team for a small amount of powder: in 2003, more than 1,200 employees in Berkeley, California, USA, produced "just" 200 grams of powder – the genetically engineered hemophilia drug Kogenate™. This photo appeared on the front cover of the Bayer Annual Report 2003.

Packaging, 2013
State-of-the-art packaging technology for the pharmaceutical of the century: 1,000 Aspirin™ sticks are filled each minute at the Bayer Bitterfeld GmbH facility.

Packaging, 1963
An employee monitors an automated packaging line at the Leverkusen site.

A laboratory in the 1930s
The photo shows Bayer researcher Dr. Kirberg in the Alkydal laboratory in Krefeld-Uerdingen. Bayer started industrial production of the first alkyd resins in 1929. These coating raw materials became known throughout the world by the name Alkydal.

A laboratory in 2000
Bayer employee Erin Chae monitors a protein separation process at a high technology center in the United States. This photo was used in the Bayer Annual Report 2000.

Production today
High-tech: Bayer employees Andreas Werner (left) and Francesco Lo Grande clean and check the control unit of an ointment mixer that is used to manufacture Bepanthen™ skincare and wound ointment.

Production in the early years
Basic: workers mix dyestuffs at the factory in Barmen.

150 YEARS
THOUSANDS OF INNOVATIONS
150 STORIES

The history of Bayer is a history of innovation. For 150 years, we have been researching products to make people's lives better. Bayer is more than Aspirin™ or Makrolon™. It is founded on generations of expertise and social commitment. Bayer is Carl Duisberg and Gerhard Domagk. Our Bayer Cross is both a trademark and a seal of quality – for our medicines, our crop protection products and our high-tech materials.

We have selected 150 stories from 150 years of history. Passion, adventure, willpower and perseverance are the defining terms of our research capability. They frame our emotive portraits of Bayer scientists. Our book tells the personal stories of the people behind Bayer's innovations. They and their colleagues in research and development, production, marketing and administrative functions give their best every day. They are working to make our mission reality: "Bayer – Science For A Better Life."

In stories about our company's significant innovations, we have sought to explain the underlying science and other interesting facts. We hope you enjoy reading what we have put together for you.

THE WORLD OF BAYER

More than 110,000 people work for the Bayer Group worldwide. The company posted sales of €39.8 billion in 2012. Research and development costs totaled €3 billion.

EUROPE

Bayer has many large production sites and research facilities in this region, giving it a broad presence here. The company posted sales of €14.7 billion in Europe and employed 52,300 people, 34,600 of them in Germany.

NORTH AMERICA

In the United States and Canada, Bayer is represented in all strategic business areas. In this region, 15,300 employees generated sales of €9.6 billion.

ASIA • PACIFIC

With its enormous growth potential, this economic area is one of the main markets of the future. With 26,700 employees here, Bayer recorded sales of €8.8 billion.

LATIN AMERICA • AFRICA • MIDDLE EAST

Latin America is a traditional market for Bayer, which has had a presence in the region for 110 years. In Latin America, Africa and the Middle East, 16,200 employees generated sales of €6.7 billion.

The map shows selected key sites around the world (as at December 31, 2012).

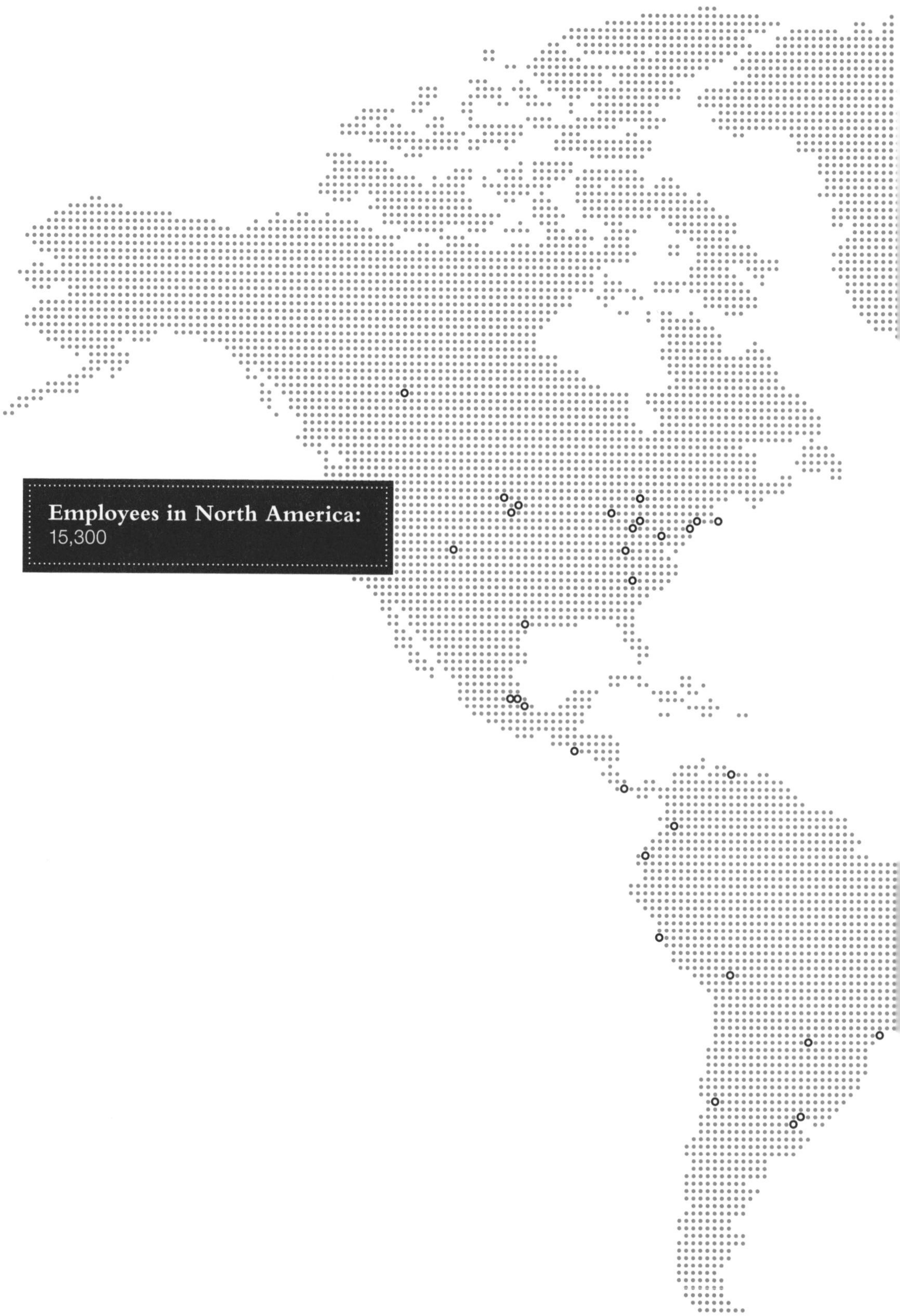

Employees in Europe:
52,300
Employees in Asia / Pacific:
26,700
Employees in Latin America / Africa / Middle East:
16,200

CONTENTS

Chapter 2: ADVENTURE

Profiles: Researchers tell their stories

▬: The Next Generation – introducing young scientists

Chapter 3: WILLPOWER

Profiles: Researchers tell their stories

▬: The Next Generation – introducing young scientists

Chapter 4: PERSEVERANCE

Epilogue: THE FUTURE

CHAPTER

1

PASSION

“

MY MOTIVATION TO FIND A CANCER DRUG IS LIKE A FIRE BURNING INSIDE ME. CANCER AND I – WE STILL HAVE A SCORE TO SETTLE.

”

BERND RIEDL, WUPPERTAL, GERMANY

Page 34

High Salt
Buffer
(PR1) 4
Incorporation
Buffer
(PR2) 5

ONCOLOGY
TRACKING DOWN CANCER

Biology lab technician Sandra Patkovic of Bayer HealthCare, Berlin, Germany, prepares a sequencer. The gene sequences shown on the screen in the background provide valuable information about tumor development that allows identification of therapeutic approaches.

TUMOR ANALYSIS
CLOSE INSPECTION

Irene Hofer scans samples from lung cancer patients which have been marked with different dyes. This special analysis shows whether the tumor cells are responding to a new treatment.

Read more about oncology starting on page 34.

POLYURETHANES
ABSOLUTE PURITY

In the sterile clean room of the Baycusan™ production facility in Dormagen, Germany, chemical production technician Ömer Yildirim (left, in the background Marcus Schuster) prepares a special filter for the manufacture of high-quality cosmetic raw materials. High-purity polyurethanes (PU) from Bayer MaterialScience are used in mascaras and lipsticks and also in hair care and styling products. The raw materials result in skin-friendly cosmetics without solvents or preservatives.

INNOVATION CENTER
ALL ABOUT SHOES

Bayer development engineer Erika Zhu (right) and her colleague Xiang Liu examine shoe soles at the Bayer MaterialScience Innovation Center in Shanghai, China. Scientists there are working on leisure and sports shoe concepts for the future.

Read all about polyurethanes and their many applications starting on page 48.

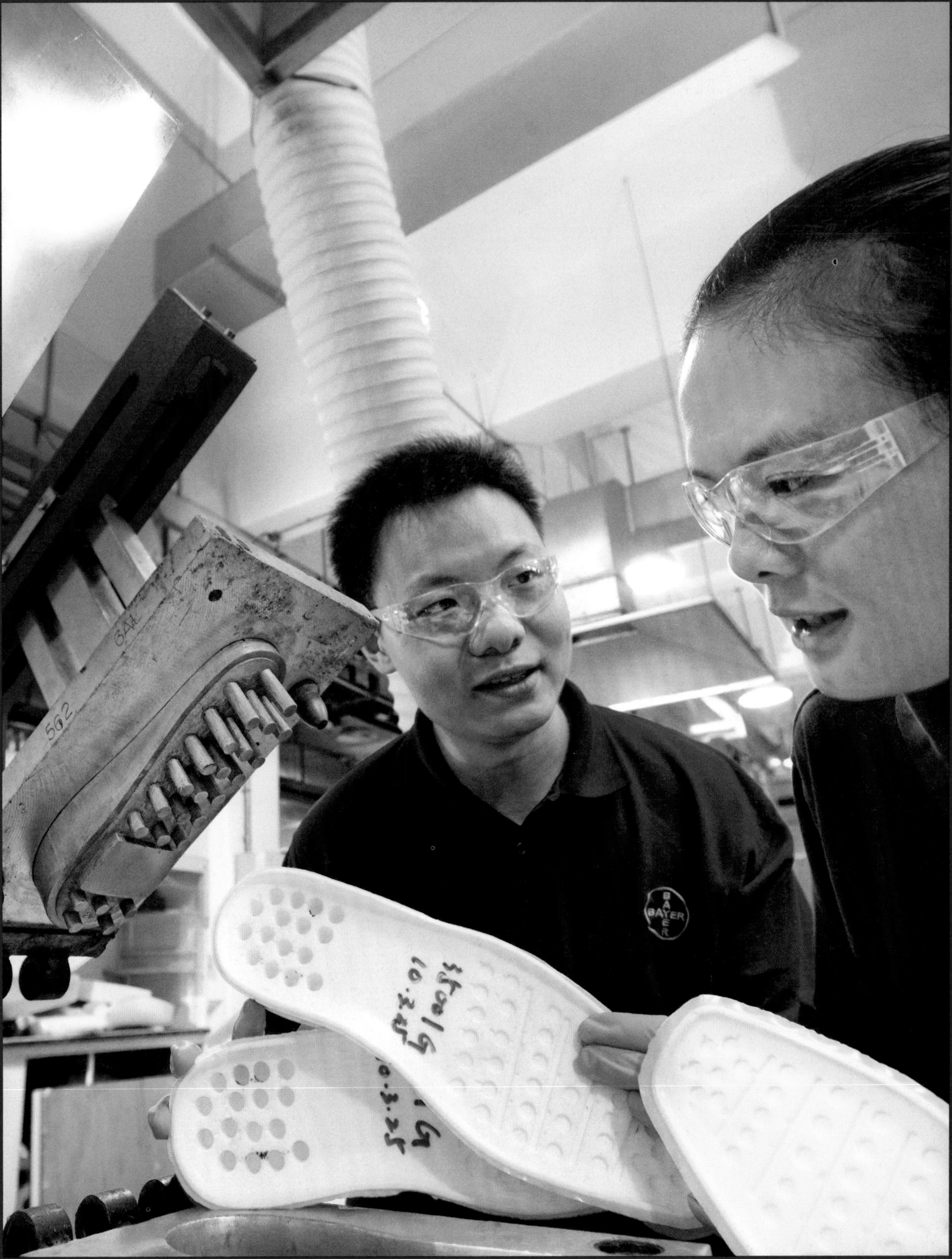

FAMILY PLANNING
CONTROLLED QUALITY

Bayer HealthCare employee Evgeniia Minaeva works in quality control at the Mirena™ production facility in Turku. The workforce there is proud that many steps in the development and production of the innovative hormonal intrauterine system take place in the Finnish port city.

THE PILL
PROPERLY PACKAGED

Bayer HealthCare employee Nancy Lück checks the robot that ensures the Yaz™ product family is properly packaged.

Read more about modern family planning and the first drug product to have a lasting impact on society starting on page 70.

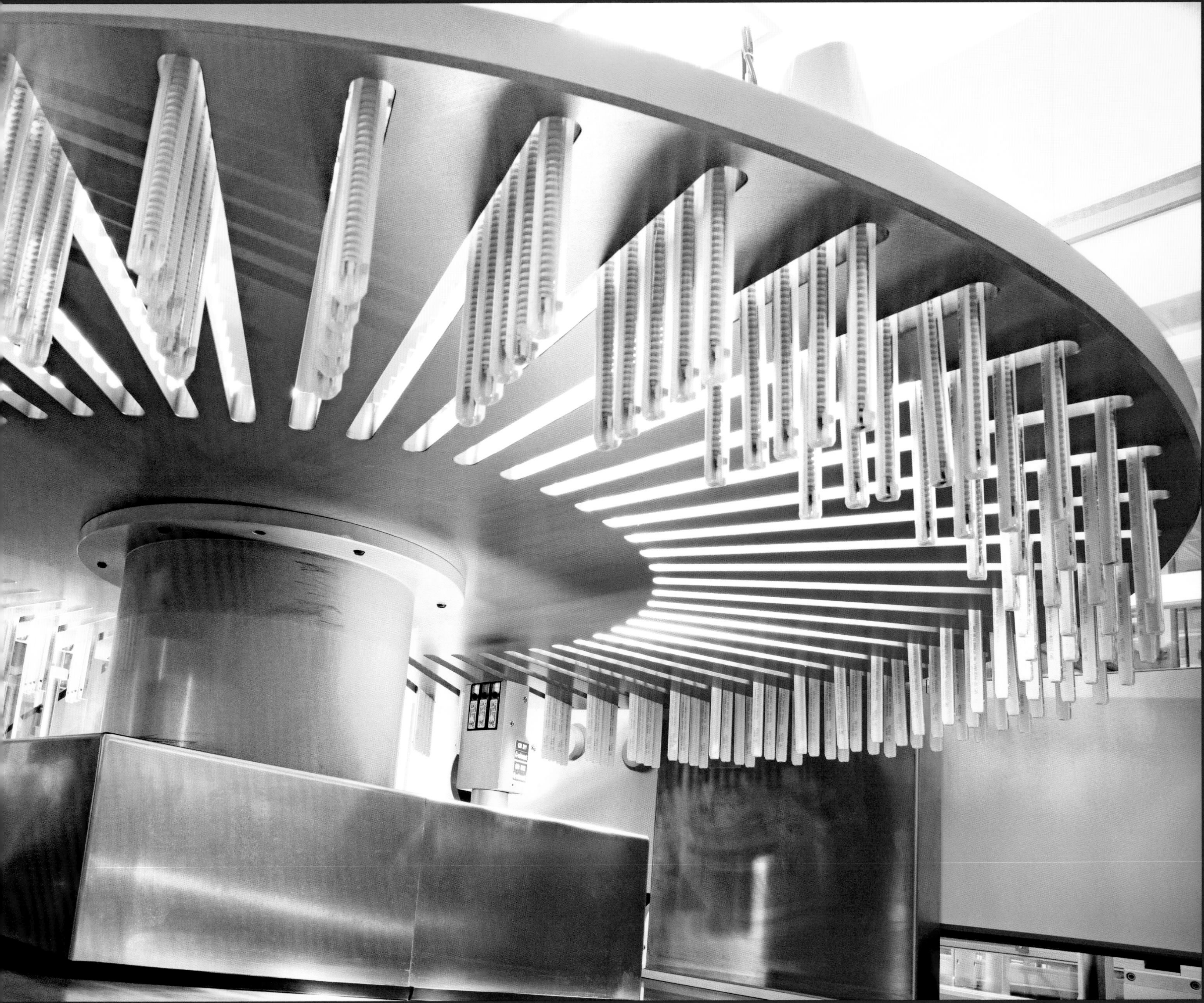

OILSEED RAPE
CROSSBREEDING WITH CARE

Bayer CropScience employees Cynthia Semeniuk and Dr. Godfrey Chongo examine crossbred oilseed rape plants. The plastic hoods ensure controlled growth. At the research center in Saskatoon, Canada, scientists are working to develop innovative oilseed rape varieties.

Read more about oilseed rape starting on page 96.

CORN
CONTROLLING NEMATODES

In the Bayer CropScience laboratory in Research Triangle Park, North Carolina, USA, Laura Schouten examines corn cobs for signs of nematodes. These minute pests are a threat to harvests and controlling them is one of the challenges taken up by scientists at Bayer CropScience.

You can find more information about innovative products for corn starting on page 100.

ANIMAL HEALTH
PROTECTING PETS

Bayer employee Carolin Geier examines roundworms used to test dewormers.

THE ARTIFICIAL DOG

Detlef Karner uses an artificial dog to test active substances for flea control products.

Find out more about animal health starting on page 80.

Bernd Riedl and his favorite toy: riding his motorbike helps the researcher clear his head.

1

Bernd Riedl

Sorafenib

2005

Sorafenib, approved as Nexavar™ in 2005, is an innovative substance for the treatment of liver cancer and renal cell carcinoma. It is taken orally and has a dual mechanism of action. *(See also the profile of Dimitris Voliotis starting on page 38.)*

FULL THROTTLE FOR RESEARCH

As a child he experimented in the cellar at home. Today, Bernd Riedl is one of the leading cancer researchers. When he wants to switch off, this family man turns his engine on.

M**y mother died** of cancer, as did an aunt, an uncle I was very close to and then also a friend. The disease took him within just a few weeks; he was simply gone. Back then, when I was starting out in research, I didn't need to think long when I was asked which area I was interested in. My motivation to find a cancer drug is like a fire burning inside me. It was a strange feeling when I learned for the first time that an active ingredient developed in our laboratory had significantly reduced the tumor in a patient with renal cancer. I felt exhilarated and really light, as if I was electrified. It's hard to describe how total happiness feels. I don't do my job just for the money – that's to support my family, my three children. I'm a researcher above all for ethical reasons. The things we cook up can prolong or improve the lives of thousands of people. Our active ingredient gives sick people hope and that's what counts as far as I'm concerned.

A researcher has to be a combination of boxer and plumber. A boxer because you have to be able to take defeat – and there are plenty of those. And a plumber because you have to be as pragmatic as a clever handyman. I don't care how we reach our objective. The main thing is that we reach it. You need to constantly question every detail and look at apparently insignificant little things that can't be explained. That's where the solution sometimes lies. And you constantly have to work at motivation – your own and that of the entire team.

We have to keep going, on and on, even if we're running on the spot. I make very sure there's a good atmosphere and I believe that open discussion sessions are important. A cheerful evening at the local Italian in Wuppertal may be more important than an international congress in New York. What we do is not plannable. Developing medicines is different to making cars or building houses. We don't work in a sausage factory. Success can't be planned.

"Teamwork is crucial in research. The soloist is not so important – it's the orchestra that counts."

I knew what career I wanted to pursue after my first chemistry lesson in ninth grade at high school in Wasseralfingen in rural southern Germany. Our teacher was a stern academic with gray hair who experimented with ammonia water and hydrochloric acid and made a fog generator from a washing powder tub. This kind of experiment would today attract attention from the state prosecutor but boredom and excessive caution in the modern teaching curriculum are another subject. Back then, I immersed myself in the world of minute particles, read everything that came into my hands, studied structural formulae and lost myself in the encyclopedias my grandpa gave me. I got one volume from him every month. I wanted to understand why things are the way they are. Chemistry still explains a lot to me – understanding the smallest things helps me see the big picture. I find some molecular structures esthetically beautiful – like works of art. As a teenager, I also found other aspects of chemistry interesting. We made a rocket from a fire extinguisher. Take-off was brilliant, then it brushed a rain gutter and continued several hundred meters before coming down in a nearby wood. I also enjoyed being able to pass on my knowledge, especially to the girls in my class who came to me for extra tuition.

"The lad will manage it," was what my father said when he put me forward for my high-school diploma, which was still an exception at that time in the rural area where I grew up. I studied chemistry in Stuttgart. Following my PhD, which already dealt with a natural substance that is effective against cancer cells, I spent a few years researching antibiotics. Together with a colleague, I headed an international project group on the U.S. East Coast, where we looked for compounds to switch off the enzymes that play an important role in the division of tumor cells. Teamwork is crucial in research. On the day-to-day level the soloist is not so important – it's the orchestra that counts. In every project and every phase, "perhaps" prefaces so many answers, it can drive you mad. There's always a risk that you can go down the wrong track. Very few people know how we research scientists work, how difficult it is to find an active ingredient, how complex, how rarely we succeed, how many imponderables we have to deal with, how tough progress usually is. Failure is our reality. Failure, setbacks, the feeling of not getting any further.

In the case of sorafenib, which Bayer HealthCare developed together with U.S. company Onyx, one problem troubled us. We had screened and investigated several hundred thousand compounds and synthesized thousands of derivatives that in tests actually seemed to be effective against cancer. However, further tests then showed that many of

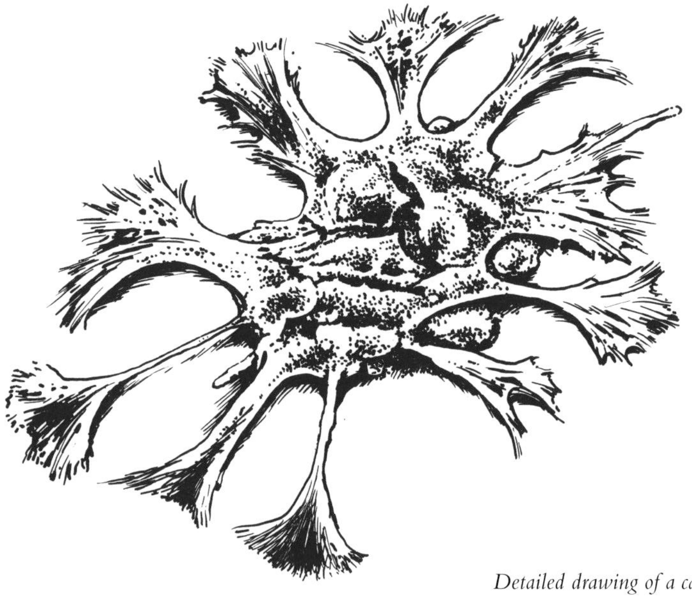

Detailed drawing of a cancer cell

them had adverse effects. Most active ingredients fail on the way from test tube to tablet. They have to survive exposure to gastric acid, make their way through the bloodstream to the tumor, penetrate its cell wall and then hit the right target. If a molecule is active anywhere else along this route, it may cause side effects.

We were so close and yet still didn't make it across the finish line, we brooded and pondered. Toward the end of the project, we came up with a matrix of more than 50 compounds, in the hope and firm conviction that one of these was the right one. We finally made the breakthrough – not with a sudden flash of inspiration and a triumphant shout like in the movies. Development candidate BAY 43-9006 became sorafenib. This attacks the cancer cell in two ways: it cuts the blood supply and blocks the signal pathway that stimulates the cell's ceaseless division and causes the growth of a tumor.

Two things help me clear my head, two things that men love: aged Scotch whisky and a motorbike. I discovered this passion while I was still at college. There's nothing better than spending a week riding twisting alpine roads. At my peak I had six motorbikes. Today, I still have four and my favorite is a Yamaha XJR 1300. I don't drive fast, I enjoy the ride. Apart from the time I spend with my children, these are the hours when I'm not thinking about my molecules and the laboratory. Researchers rarely switch off – our work is part of our lives. I also try to find out what happens to our inventions and developments, how a new active ingredient performs in clinical trials. I sometimes read blogs and Internet forums in which cancer patients report that they are doing better. It means a lot to me to know I've helped. When my wife and I are invited to friends, I'm sometimes asked: When will science finally beat cancer? When will it happen? I can't answer this question – no-one can – but we're working to check the disease. Cancer and I – we still have a score to settle.

Bernd Riedl

Dr. Bernd Riedl, born in 1961, is considered to be the discoverer of multi-kinase inhibitors, a novel class of cancer drugs. He has won numerous prizes for his work, including the Otto Bayer Medal and the UCB Award for Excellence in Medicinal Chemistry from the European Federation for Medicinal Chemistry. Bernd Riedl is married and has three children. He lives with his family in Wuppertal, Germany.

One of his favorite places:
Dimitris Voliotis enjoys strolling with his family through Liberty State Park, New Jersey, USA, with views across to the New York City skyline.

2

Dimitris Voliotis

Nexavar™

2005

Dimitris Voliotis is head of clinical development for cancer drugs like Nexavar™, which was approved in 2005 (see also the profile of Bernd Riedl starting on page 34). The tolerability and efficacy of every new substance is tested in extensive trials which may involve thousands of patients in hospitals around the world.

A MOMENT OF HAPPINESS

Dimitris Voliotis is head of clinical development for various cancer drugs, including Nexavar™, testing and optimizing each drug product in extensive trials before market launch. Sometimes, the pressure and effort and research work of many years culminate in one single moment.

I **used to be** a hands-on practicing physician and have worked in internal medicine, oncology and intensive care medicine. During those years of bedside work and proximity to patients, I learned to pay attention to details. Today, I'm in charge of clinical development for various cancer drugs and therefore responsible for the studies needed before a new drug can be introduced to the market. We have to prove that our new substance really does help. The studies we have to run are extremely complex, often cost many hundreds of millions of euros and may involve thousands of patients in 25 or more countries. Patients are monitored closely for many years. Overall, we have selected hundreds of hospitals and clinical sites worldwide as our partners. We need a global perspective for our work. This also means that I spend a lot of time on airplanes.

The fate of individual human beings can easily be reduced to just numbers owing to the mass of data that is processed in each study. Marketing authorization for a new drug is about statistics so the human aspect may become secondary. But this is not something I would want to just accept. Behind each number is a personal story – the serious illness of someone's loved one: a child, spouse, parent, family member or friend. As physicians, we are repeatedly confronted with cases and personal fates that stay with us. I still remember one young man who was taken by cancer within just a few weeks and a young girl who did not stand a chance. On the other hand, I've also experienced many moments in which patients did not lose their courage, kept fighting and were able to beat their disease in the end. You can't do this job unless you manage to build a protective wall around yourself and your private life. This kind of work has changed my attitude towards life. I try to live more consciously in the present, to enjoy what I have, the seemingly small everyday moments with my family. We drive over to New York City, stroll through Battery Park, have lunch in downtown Manhattan or take the kids to the movies. What is often important is not thinking ahead, but cherishing the moment. I'm motivated by being able to help many patients – actually thousands of them. I'm still primarily a physician, even though I now spend most of my time at an office desk.

"I try to live consciously in the present."

We work closely with the researchers who have discovered a new substance. We test its efficacy, we optimize and we do everything we can to make sure it helps patients in the best possible way. These tests typically involve three phases which are monitored by the regulatory authorities and an independent committee. During the last stage (phase III), several experts analyze the available data and then we are invited to a conference to be informed about any possible issues. The new substance is typically tested against a placebo or against the best available product, if there is one already approved for a particular indication. I will never forget one day in a hotel in Manhattan. A typical conference room in a large U.S. hotel: no windows, thick carpet, long tables, the noise of the air conditioning. The subject was our cancer drug Nexavar™, which was in the crucial phase III. The participants withdrew for consultations and then the committee chair informed us: "Ladies and gentlemen, we have to stop the trial."

At that moment, I thought the world had come to a standstill. Until he continued: "The results are positive!" The active ingredient was to be made available to all patients as soon as possible now that it was clear how effective it was.

In such an official setting, you can't let your emotions run free but we high-fived under the table – and later toasted each other with a glass of champagne. Because of the time difference, we woke up our colleagues in Germany when we called them, but no-one minded. One colleague had tears of joy in his eyes. You have to realize that the pressure of many months or even years, the expectations, the tension, the skepticism and the doubts disappeared all at once. Everything culminated in that one moment. We had the certainty that, from now on, many patients would be able to benefit from our drug. A wonderful energy was released – and this is what keeps me going every day.

Dimitris Voliotis

Dr. Dimitris Voliotis was born in Aachen, Germany, in 1963. He divided his childhood and teenage years between Athens, Greece, and Germany, before studying medicine in Cologne. After his military service, he took a position at Cologne University Hospital and moved to clinical pharmacology at Bayer in 2001. A passionate runner, Dimitris Voliotis is married and has three children. He lives in New Jersey, USA.

"Good" radiation

AN ACTIVE INGREDIENT THAT TARGETS BONE METASTASES

Prostate cancer is a disease that primarily affects men of old age. If diagnosed at an early stage, it can often be successfully treated by surgery or radiation. If it is not detected by screening, however, prostate cancer can be life-threatening. More than 250,000 men die from the disease every year. In the advanced stage, the cancer spreads daughter tumors throughout the body via the blood. The patient's bones are the main site of spread, which causes extreme pain.

An alpha-particle emitting substance named Xofigo™ (active ingredient: radium-223 dichloride) could offer a new form of treatment. Because it is very similar to the bone mineral calcium, it is easily absorbed by the body in the skeleton rebuilding process. The active ingredient accumulates in the newly formed bone substance where it releases alpha radiation that specifically targets the cancer in the bone.

The drug product was developed by radiochemist Roy Larsen and cancer specialist Oyvind S. Bruland. Following initial studies, their company Algeta in Norway looked for an international partner with experience in oncology and found one in Bayer HealthCare. Many experts believe that Xofigo™ could be a significant innovation. In fact, the alpha radiation drug has several special features. Following intravenous administration, the product takes just a few minutes to find its way into the patient's skeleton. As a result, the organs and tissues are exposed only briefly to radiation. The half-life – the length of time it takes for half of the radionuclides to decay – is less than eleven-and-a-half days.

3

Xofigo™

2013

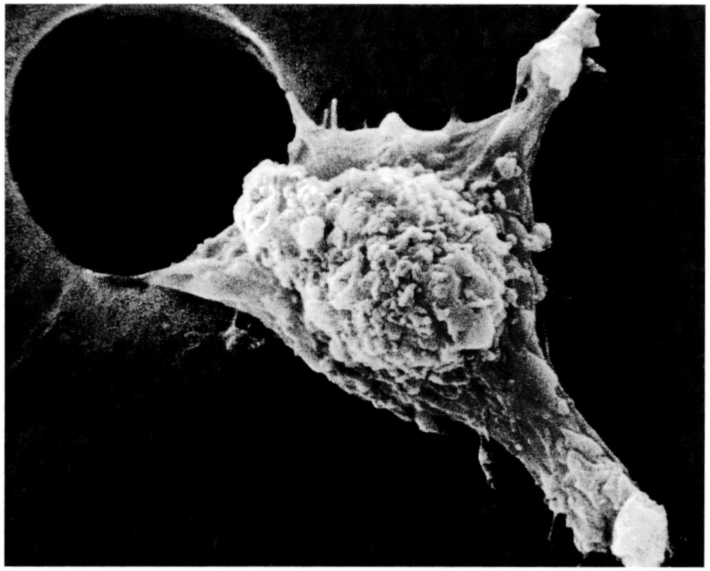

Life-threatening: a metastasizing cancer cell, shown here through an electron microscope

Unlike other radiopharmaceutical active ingredients that also harm the surrounding tissue, Xofigo™ selectively targets the metastases. And, because it reaches the gut quickly, it is excreted from the body again within just a few hours. A large-scale international phase III study has indicated to researchers that the drug could give patients the prospect of a markedly improved life expectancy and less pain. Furthermore, the drug has a favorable safety profile. Many patients are able to carry on with their daily lives while undergoing treatment. Bayer received regulatory approval for the drug product in May 2013.

A well-traveled scientist: Xin Ma has lived on various continents during her career. Her present home is Berlin, Germany.

4

Xin Ma

Global Drug Discovery Innovation Center China

2009

The Global Drug Discovery Innovation Center China in Beijing brings together scientists from around the world to research innovative therapies and new active ingredients. It was opened in 2009.

A GLOBETROTTER

After years abroad, Xin Ma returned to her home country to work on an ambitious project. Its success was due to her tenacity – and to Bayer's excellent reputation in China.

A**t the start,** when I began building a network to establish the Global Drug Discovery Innovation Center China (GDD ICC), I was traveling a lot. I say – half in jest – that I spent one month of the first year in the air. The aim was to attract the brightest minds for our project in Beijing. That meant I had to familiarize myself with the innovation environment in China. Meet, listen to, get to know and convince decision-makers. There was no day that was boring. At first, we had nothing more than an idea and a small group of highly motivated people. There were four of us, to be exact, scientists from Germany, the United States and Asia. You don't attract bright minds with funding alone but, above all, with ideas, a shared vision and a long-term outlook. What helped us in our search was Bayer's very good reputation in China. Bayer stands for quality and trust.

Even as a young girl, I loved chemistry. I was fascinated when, for example, a yellow liquid turned blue as a result of a chemical reaction. It was magical to me. My older brother brought home reagents, vials and apparatus from a laboratory and I would experiment in my parents' bathroom. I was once very fortunate when I mixed hydrochloric acid and sulfuric acid and it caused an explosion. I'm glad that no scars remained and today wonder at my youthful recklessness.

My interest in chemical investigation remained unbroken. I majored in polymer chemistry at the Dalian University of Technology and then turned to organic chemistry for my master's degree. I came to Germany on a scholarship from the Max Planck Society and then spent two years in research at the State University of New York.

After almost two decades in the United States (where I worked in West Haven, Connecticut, researching and developing new medicines in the areas of oncology and diabetes) and in Europe, I finally returned to my home country in 2009. To my joy, I found that life there had changed dramatically. I was amazed by the speed of this transformation.

> ***"I don't mind where my office is. What is really important is to have a creative team."***

As a result of my career path, I've come to know new countries, different cultures and a range of roles and responsibilities. I was trained to quickly adapt to a new environment. I don't mind where my office is. What is really important is to have a creative team that captures the strengths of diverse people. Early in my career, a former supervisor showed me the value of recognizing employees' potential and of fostering and utilizing this in the best way. If you get the right combination of people with the right attitude, things are so much easier. Perhaps I've acquired a feel for this during my travels around the world.

Today, the Innovation Center we established in Beijing is working with the most renowned universities, hospitals and institutes in China. A fantastic team has come together. In the meantime, I've moved on to a new position in Berlin, where I now work in strategic marketing.

> ***"When I started my career, I thought I would grow old in the laboratory."***

When I started my career, I thought I would grow old in the laboratory. I couldn't imagine any other job. My career began in research; one could say it started where the ideas are. Today, I'm at the other end of the value creation chain, helping to commercialize our products. It's almost like coming full circle. Change has been the only constant throughout my career. I've learned how valuable it is to be able to move between different worlds.

Xin Ma

Dr. Xin Ma was born in 1963 in Wuhan, China, and studied polymer and organic chemistry at the Dalian University of Technology in Beijing, China. She came to Germany to study for her doctoral degree with a scholarship from the Max Planck Society and then became a researcher at the State University of New York. She joined Bayer HealthCare in 1998. Today, she heads the Strategy & Portfolio Management Department in the General Medicine Division. Xin Ma lives in Berlin, Germany.

Total spending on research and development at Bayer HealthCare in 2012

€1,962,000,000

Bayer

2nd cause of death

in the western industrialized countries: cancer. The rate is falling in industrialized countries but increasing in developing countries, in part due to the adoption of a westernized lifestyle (smoking, lack of exercise, overeating).

WHO

The long road to developing a drug

Substances investigated during the development of a new active ingredient:
5,000–10,000

Active ingredient development

Average length of time taken to develop a new drug product:
12 years

Average cost of developing a new drug product:
approx. €1,000,000,000

Bayer

Number of years of life that are lost worldwide due to cancer (measured on the basis of average life expectancy):

169,000,000

WHO

Number of people who die of cancer each year: 7,900,000

GLOBOCAN

Number of new cases of cancer worldwide each year

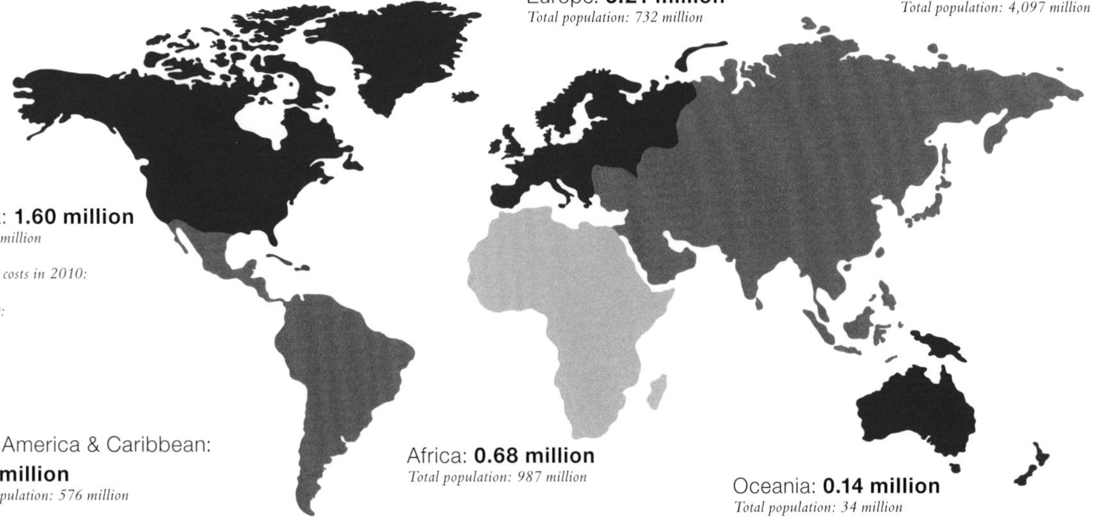

Europe: **3.21 million**
Total population: 732 million

Asia: **6.09 million**
Total population: 4,097 million

North America: **1.60 million**
Total population: 345 million

Cancer-related medical costs in 2010:
US$ 153,697 million
Projected costs in 2030:
US$ 218,322 million

Latin America & Caribbean: **0.91 million**
Total population: 576 million

Africa: **0.68 million**
Total population: 987 million

Oceania: **0.14 million**
Total population: 34 million

GLOBOCAN 2008

More interesting facts about human health can be found on pages 123, 211 and 229.

Number of types of cancer:
More than 100; every part of the body can be affected.
WHO

Projected new cases of cancer worldwide in 2030: 21.5 million

WHO

New cases of cancer worldwide by type, 2010

Lung cancer:	**1.69 million**
Breast cancer:	**1.45 million**
Colorectal cancer:	**1.30 million**
Stomach cancer:	**1.04 million**

WHO

In her free time, Konstanze Diefenbach tries to find the right way to the top. She has enjoyed climbing since her teenage years.

THE NEXT GENERATION

Konstanze Diefenbach

Berlin, Germany

Bayer HealthCare

SCALING THE FACE

Teamwork, mutual trust, achieving a goal: Konstanze Diefenbach finds she can apply many aspects of her hobby in her job.

I**'ve been fascinated** with climbing since I was at high school in Dresden. I liked a lot about the sport: the teamwork, the physical effort, the natural beauty of the sandstone hills of Saxon Switzerland where we climbed. The feeling we were pursuing a goal. Writing my name in the summit book after finishing a climb. On the face you're alone and have to find your own way to the top. Yet you also learn that there are different ways to reach a goal, that you can rely on others and that you need to take risks. Some of this experience can help in both private and professional situations.

When I moved to Beijing with my young daughter to establish the Department of Clinical Pharmacology in Asia, my climbing experiences certainly helped me. The department's objective is to find out whether active ingredients that have been developed and tested in Europe and the United States have the same effect in Asian populations. It was an exciting task – a bit like climbing a rock face in some ways and anything but easy in places. But I knew I could rely on a good Bayer team.

One afternoon, I went to an indoor climbing center with my new co-workers. Although many of them were skeptical at first, they all enjoyed it. And, most importantly, climbing welded us into a team.

Konstanze Diefenbach

Dr. Konstanze Diefenbach was born in Dresden in 1972. She is head of Clinical Pharmacology Oncology. Konstanze Diefenbach has one daughter and lives with her family in Berlin, Germany.

DREAM FOAMS: THE MATERIAL OF UNLIMITED OPPORTUNITY

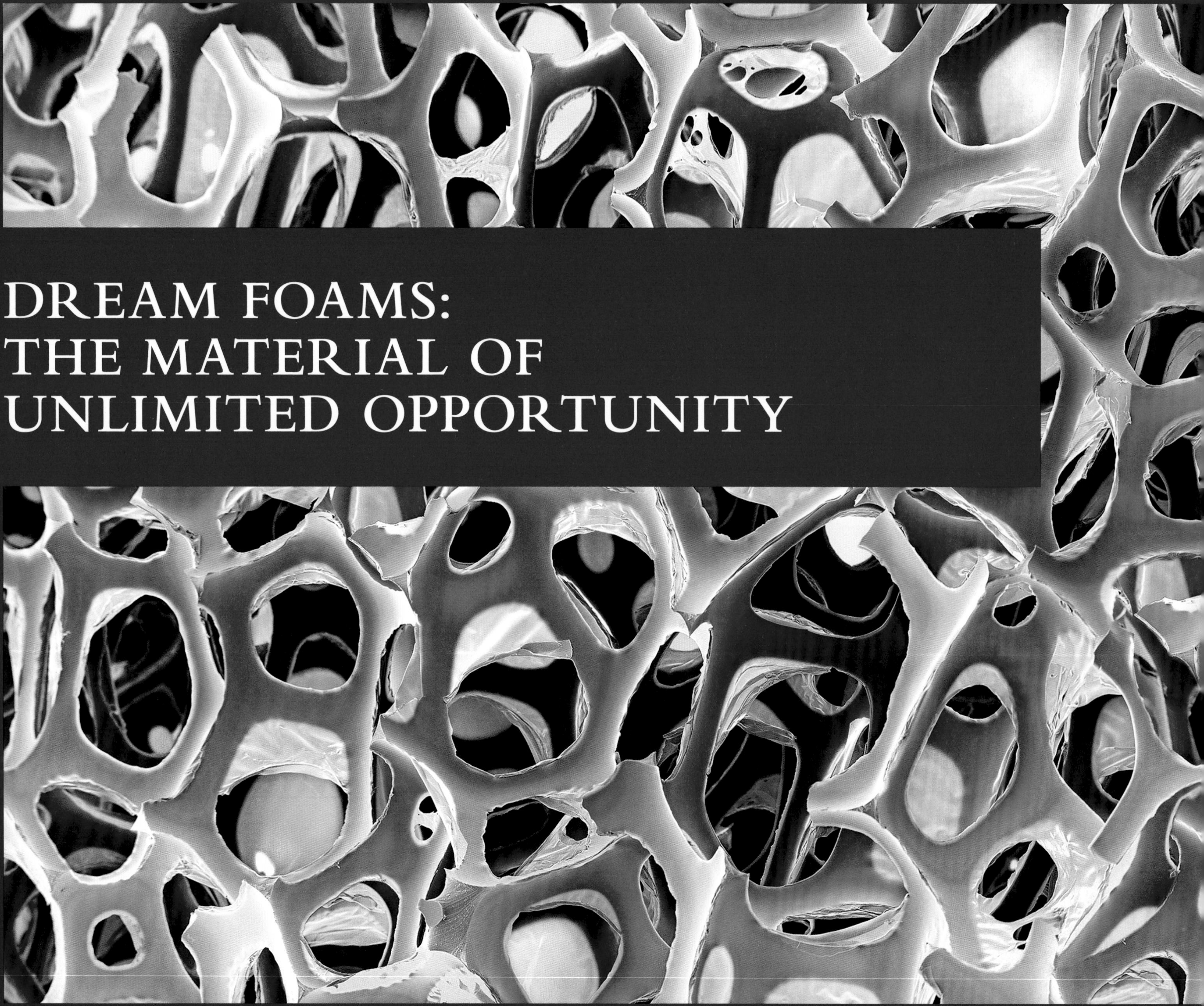

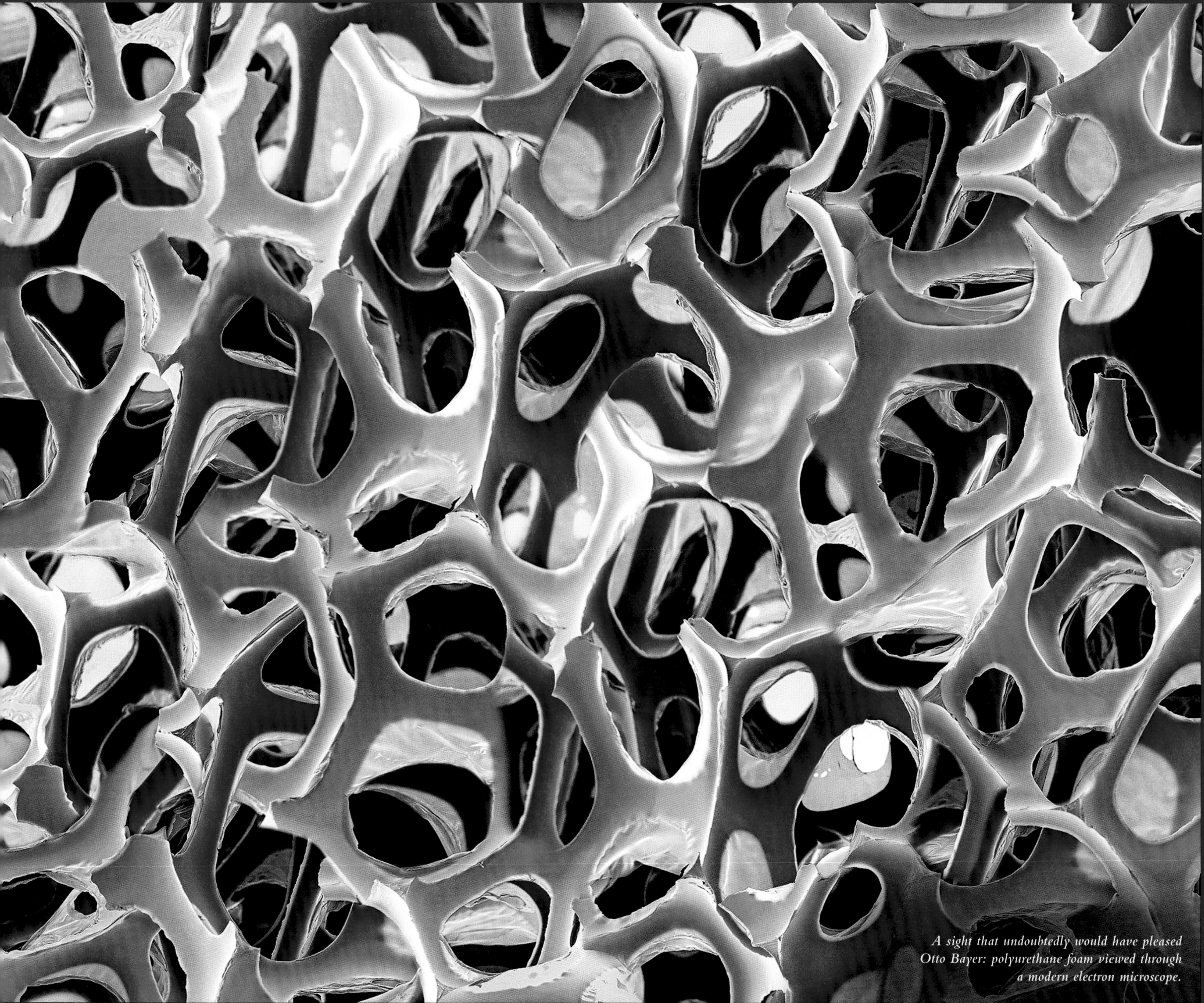

A sight that undoubtedly would have pleased Otto Bayer: polyurethane foam viewed through a modern electron microscope.

A scientist through and through: Professor Otto Bayer was also popular as a supervisor, because he was known for his modesty despite all his achievements. The photo shows him in his laboratory in 1952.

THE FATHER OF POLYURETHANES

Otto Bayer changed the face of the world. His inventions made it possible to use plastics in a variety of applications, from automobiles to footwear. It all began with an experiment, the results of which reminded critics of Swiss cheese.

5

Otto Bayer

Polyurethanes research

1927

Otto Bayer (not related to the company's founder), who joined the company in 1927, had a major influence on many areas of scientific development, but he is best known for his pioneering research in the field of polyurethanes. Over 400 patents bear the name Otto Bayer, and he received many awards.

Professor Dr. Dr. hc. mult. Dr. E. h. mult. Otto Bayer, honorary chairman of the Supervisory Board of Bayer AG and one of the most successful researchers in the chemical industry, passed away on August 1, 1982. Six German universities and colleges had conferred an honorary PhD on the Frankfurt native.

That was what the newspapers reported. A team headed by Bayer succeeded in synthesizing oil-resistant rubber. He influenced the manufacture of acrylic fibers, advanced the development of crop protection products and co-developed optical brighteners for laundry detergents, anti-tuberculosis drugs and reactive dyes. Above all, Otto Bayer went down in history as the father of polyurethane chemistry.

How did this man with the strong features and combed-back hair manage to achieve so much? Polyurethane chemistry, his greatest success as a scientist, would never have been possible without his optimism and boundless passion. Bayer's chemical vision was initially considered unfeasible, but he clung stubbornly to his belief. Today, "the method for making tailor-made plastics," as polyurethane chemistry was described in the United States, shapes our lives.

Otto Bayer was born on November 4, 1902, in Frankfurt am Main, Germany. Even as a teenager he was an enthusiastic inventor. Bayer graduated from Klinger Secondary School in 1921, which also had been attended 24 years earlier by Otto Hahn, the pioneer of radio chemistry and Nobel Laureate. Bayer was not an outstanding student; he was only interested in chemistry. By today's standards, his final grades would not

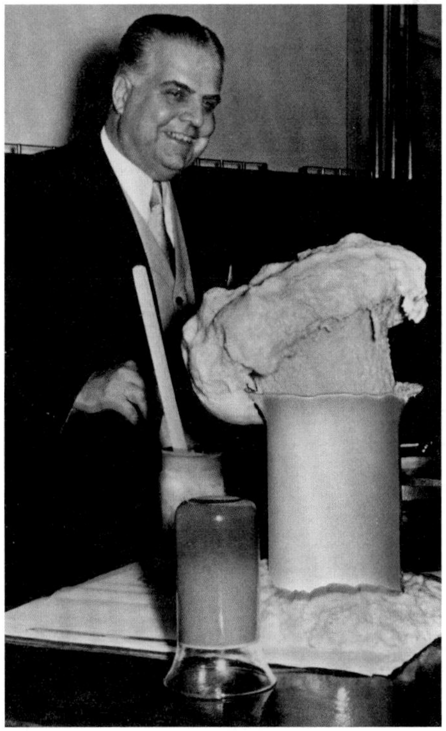

Critics compared his results to Swiss cheese, but Bayer's experiments – here a PU trial in Göttingen in 1965 – changed the world.

His passion and optimism are legendary. These characteristics enabled him to realize a vision that revolutionized an entire industry.

As a young man in the Central Scientific Laboratory, 1933

Momentous occasion: the founding meeting of the Supervisory and Management Boards of Farbenfabriken Bayer AG on December 19, 1951

have got him a place at university. Bayer studied in his home city. Because money was tight, he attended mostly special lectures, believing that he already had a thorough command of organic chemistry. He chose Julius von Braun as his doctoral adviser and continued to work as the latter's assistant for two-and-a-half years after receiving his PhD.

Thanks to a recommendation from Braun, Bayer was given a position with the Cassella Farbwerke chemical company in 1927. He was made a head of department there in 1931. In 1933, Fritz ter Meer, a member of the Board of Management of I.G. Farbenindustrie AG, suggested him as head of the Central Scientific Laboratory, supervising 60 chemists. Bayer was not yet 32 years old. When he first heard, he thought the appointment was a joke. Bayer was cordially received in Leverkusen. His philosophy at the time of taking up his position sounds pretentious: "Much more important than solving the technical problems of the present, it appears to me, is to further expand basic research in the field of high-molecular materials." What Bayer meant was that he was seeking new territory, specifically in the field of macromolecules.

Bayer legends: Otto Bayer talks with Nobel Laureate Gerhard Domagk at a celebration in 1952 marking Bayer's 25th anniversary in company service.

He put together a team of young chemists, who from 1933 began to untiringly conduct one experiment after another in the Central Scientific Laboratory. At some point, bubbles formed in the matrix due to the release of carbon dioxide. However, the first foams in history would have to wait over ten years before they were manufactured industrially. Bayer's next successful process was polyaddition, a method that set standards and changed the world of plastics. It created thousands of jobs and, because it was less problematic than condensation and polymerization, it helped to cut costs significantly. "Chance is the most essential part of discovery," wrote philosopher Friedrich Nietzsche, "but most people do not encounter chance." Otto Bayer recognized chance immediately and grasped it.

With his hallmark cigar: Bayer in 1958

In his private life, the descendant of south German farmers was a very sociable person, with a preference for good wine, cigars and the Munich Oktoberfest. He collected Roman, Syrian and Greek artifacts, Augsburg silver and Nuremberg goblets. Otto Bayer was both respected and popular as a supervisor, in part because he always remained modest despite all his achievements. Wherever possible, he had his name listed last on patent applications. How he maneuvered the Central Scientific Laboratory through the confusion of the war years, saving his people from service at the front, and how he rebuilt the laboratory after the war in buildings that had no roofs are a testament to his willpower and organizational skill. Otto Bayer was characterized by drive. He also understood how business worked, and had a good feeling for the psychology of the stock market. In this he reminded many of Carl Duisberg. What Otto Bayer, who became a member of the Board of Management of Farbenfabriken Bayer AG in 1951 and was Chairman of the Supervisory Board from 1964 to 1974, also had in common with Duisberg (see page 238) was his dedication to research and education.

A microscope reveals the fine structure of a polyurethane foam.

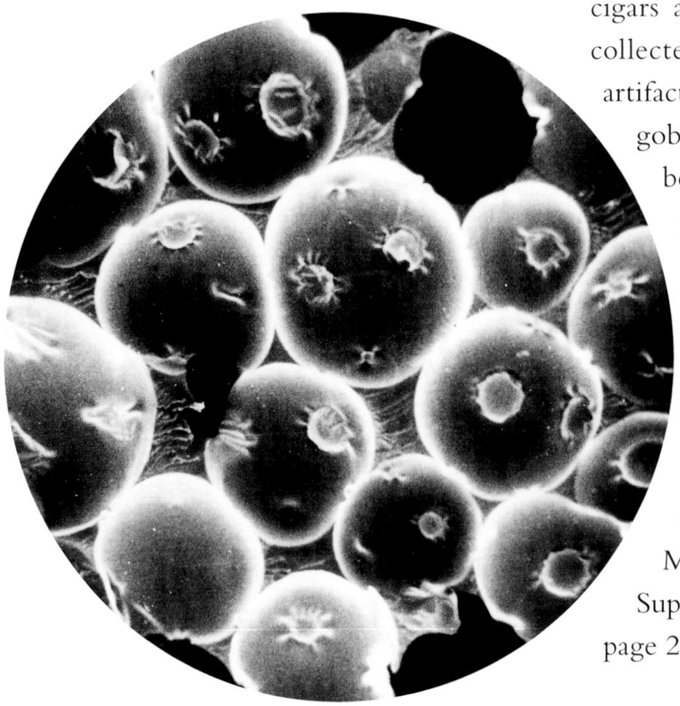

One of the greatest innovations

THE TRIUMPH OF "IMITATION SWISS CHEESE"

They are diverse, versatile and almost infinitely variable. They can be rigid or brittle, soft or elastic, dull or tacky. They can also be foams, the chemist's dream material, the material with unlimited uses.

Polyurethanes (PU for short) are plastics or synthetic resins formed by a polyaddition reaction between polyols and polyisocyanates. They are constant companions in our lives. We sit, walk and stand on them. They are found in car seats, dashboards and fenders, as synthetic fibers in clothing, as insulation in freezers; they are in mattresses and bathtubs; they are used to make coatings, toys, shoe soles, sound absorbers, adhesives, seals, thermal insulation in buildings, tires, wheels, prosthetic devices and traction bandages – and those are just some of the applications.

6

Polyurethanes

1937

Otto Bayer was appointed head of the Central Scientific Laboratory in Leverkusen in 1934, where he first spent his time researching and developing dyestuffs. But as a chemist, Bayer knew that the economic success of the company whose name he shared would depend on new fields of business. Decades later, Bayer recalled: "I wanted to shift research ... to two primary areas: crop protection and macromolecular chemistry."

Everything back then revolved around macromolecular chemistry. Scientists had learned to make large chain or lattice molecules from simple compounds. These resulted in novel materials, which could be used to make lots of different things. Otto Bayer began looking for a fully synthetic fiber. He thought this could be made by combining two low-molecular compounds in a polyaddition reaction.

It all started with a mistake that marked the birth of foam.

Reactions to Bayer's plans were sobering. "Crazy idea," criticized one of his closest co-workers. "Maybe you aren't the right man to manage this laboratory after all," his supervisor commented. But in 1937, Otto Bayer and his team found a highly viscous material that could be drawn to form threads. It led to the patent for all polyurethanes, Patent Specification No. DE 728981. Four years later, a mistake made in an experiment yielded molding compounds made of polyester and diisocyanates that were full of pores caused by carbon dioxide bubbles. This mistake marked the birth of foam.

The test laboratory in Leverkusen described Bayer's first polyurethanes as "imitation Swiss cheese." It would be more than ten years before the foams could be industrially manufactured with different levels of hardness, in part because suitable processing and production equipment had to be found for the new material. Thereafter, however, no field of chemistry developed more rapidly. From polyether polyols and integral foams to extremely strong elastomers, RIM technology and viscoelastic foams: developments have been never-ending.

Today, Bayer researchers are working on producing PU raw materials from the greenhouse gas CO_2. And no-one would ever call that a "crazy idea!"

A sports car made by Bayer: the zaZen concept car was built entirely from polyurethanes. This photo was taken in 2006.

On a healthy footing

IN THE BEGINNING WAS THE PLATFORM SOLE

The summer of love. Flower children. It is 1968, and young people are wearing long hair, brightly colored shirts and miniskirts. But the real hit of the season are shoes with platform soles. The chunky heel is made of wood or cork. Wood is heavy; cork is not resistant to abrasion. Bayflex™, a newly developed integral foam that, like all polyurethanes, would come to be used in a variety of applications, did not share these shortcomings. The foam and the strong outer layer were manufactured in a single processing step.

7

Bayflex™

1968

The platform sole was soon forgotten, but the industry remembered the multifunctional material. Gone were the days of thread, nails and glue. Even today, Bayflex™ bonds to leather or textile uppers to create a product that stands for comfort, durability and style. Bayer covers the entire range of applications with its Bayflex™ Footwear line. Bayflex™ Safety is for durable, wear-resistant safety shoes; Bayflex™ Lightweight goes into lightweight, elastic athletic and casual shoes; Bayflex™ Fashion enables fashion designers to make high-quality, uniquely shaped shoes that can be flexibly adapted to the latest trends.

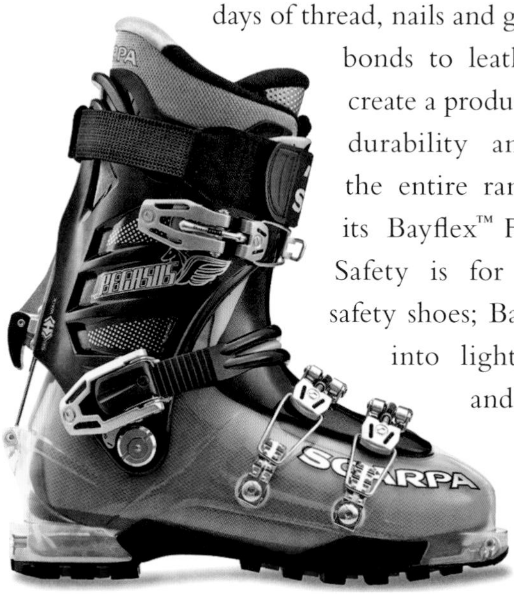

Downhill specialist: the Scarpa ski boot made from Desmopan™

People buy five pairs of shoes a year on average, and polyurethanes ensure they are increasingly lightweight, comfortable and abrasion-resistant. And not to forget, polyurethanes are resistant to moisture aging and microbes. Polyurethane insoles can even be treated with a fungicide to prevent athlete's foot. Bayflex™ has long been synonymous with innovation in the shoe industry. The latest invention: the EcoTrekker™, a concept shoe made of 90 percent renewable raw materials, such as corn starch and by-products from the sugar industry.

For goal scorers: modern soccer shoes made of Desmopan™

Unlimited possibilities

CHAMPION OF VERSATILITY

What do shift lever knobs in cars have in common with ski boots, or flexible road posts with ID tags for animals? What links waterproof, breathable films for rain jackets with sheathing for power cables on oil platforms? And how is it possible that virtually the same material is used to make soccer shoes, transparent vegetable packaging, inflatable boats and transport rollers for the mining industry? In 1962,

8

Desmopan™

1962

Bayer introduced a line of rubber-like elastomers that bridged the gap between rubber and rigid plastics. They were thermoplastic polyurethanes (TPU). The product name: Desmopan™. Their appearance: transparent to white granules. Their most outstanding characteristic: the rigidity and flexibility of the different grades can be varied widely, making them stable over a broad range of temperatures. They are design-friendly and chemically resistant. They are resistant to scratches, tears, cuts and abrasion, but still flexible. Bayer MaterialScience currently offers some 90 grades of this champion of versatility – simply by varying the manufacturing process and the starting materials.

The magic of a Danish chair

BEAUTY IN EVERY LINE

The Danish designer and architect Verner Panton experimented in the mid-1950s with a chair he called the "S Chair." Working with Vienna-based furniture manufacturer Thonet, Panton made the chair from a single piece of plywood shaped under steam pressure. After trying for several years to transfer the principle to plastic, he finally succeeded in 1960 using a styrene copolymer: acrylonitrile styrene acrylate (ASA). The chair went into volume production seven years later. The material used to make it was Baydur™ 60, a rigid polyurethane foam from Leverkusen. The "Panton Chair" is one of the first successful combinations of outstanding design with durable materials. It made Panton famous and gave Bayer the opportunity to tap new markets with its Baydur™ product family. Those capable of rendering Panton's ambitious and bold design in polyurethane no longer needed to compete with traditional materials such as wood, metal or other plastics. Baydur™ soon became synonymous with cost-efficient fabrication, stability, strength and functionality.

9

Baydur™

1960

The number of applications in which the material is found today is endless. It is used extensively in housings, plugs, power chargers and sheathing for electronic and electrical components, in motor vehicles of all kinds, in athletic and recreational articles, in loudspeakers, light columns, tanning beds, cable sleeves, medical devices, sewage pipes, video projectors, snowboards, furniture and much more.

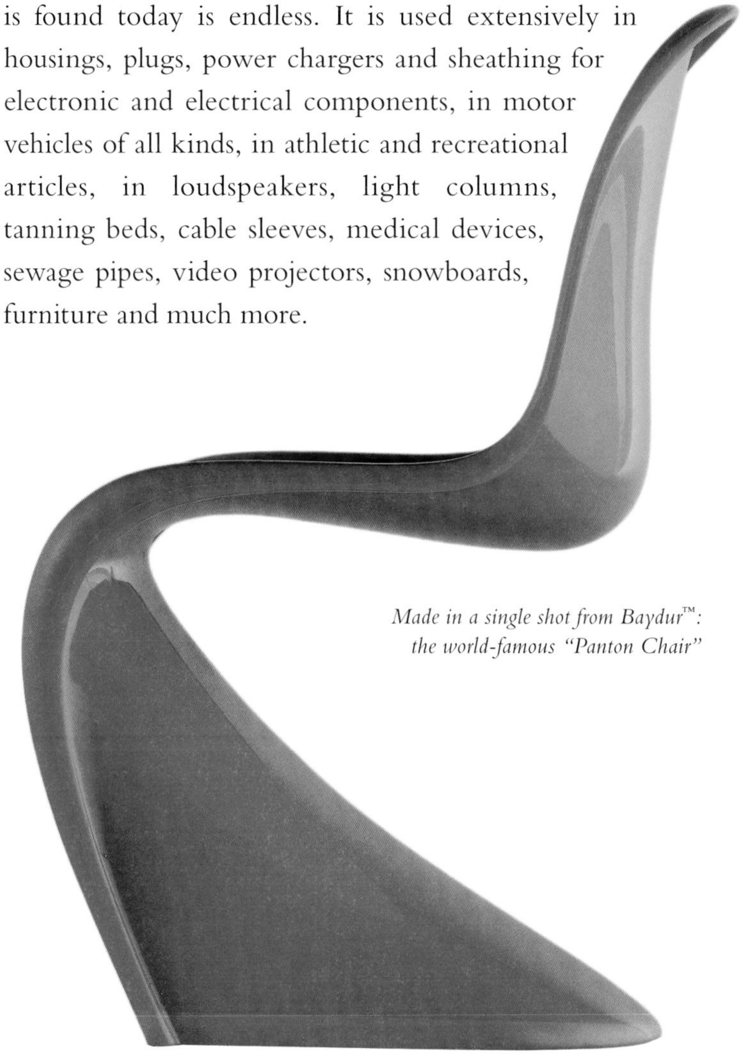

Made in a single shot from Baydur™: the world-famous "Panton Chair"

Polyurethane applications

WHAT HELPS TO GET CARS UP TO SPEED?

Where to start, where to stop? Polyurethanes are everywhere: in acoustic foams, armrests, instrument panels and roof liners. They are found in the chassis, fluid reservoirs, cable sheathing, lamp housings and coatings; in headrests, shift lever knobs and windshield wiper mounts; and naturally in seats and cushions. Modern cars would be inconceivable without polyurethanes, which fulfill all expectations of a vehicle.

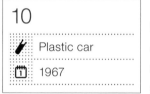

10

Plastic car

1967

Durability: unlike rubber, polyurethanes are resistant to abrasion and chemicals. And they don't rust. Safety: polyurethanes not only provide comfortable seats but also protection against injury in the event of an accident. Good looks: polyurethanes give designers greater freedom. They are easier to process and manufacture, and they improve the drag coefficient (cd value). Eco-friendliness: polyurethanes reduce the weight of a car, cutting fuel consumption and helping to protect the environment.

It all started in the 1950s, when cellular Vulkollan proved its effectiveness in motor vehicle spring elements. Over time, polyurethanes revolutionized the automotive industry. The first DD coating systems came into use in 1958 (see page 192); flexible molded foams for car seats were introduced in the late 1960s; the first sports car with a plastic body (license plate: LEV-K 67) was introduced in 1967; bumpers made of Bayflex™ forced the industry to rethink material standards in 1969. 1971: polyurethanes in roof liners and steering wheels; 1980: interior car trim made of glass fiber-reinforced Baydur™; 1986: polyurethane foams for noise protection; 1989: energy-absorbing foams from the Bayfill™ product line for interior trim; 1995: the first instrument panels made of Bayfill™, Baydur™ and Desmopan™, manufactured using the powder slush process; 2000: fender made of Bayflex™ using RIM technology. In 2007, Bayer developed a new cold-curing foam with polyol components containing a high proportion of renewable raw materials.

Developed in 1971, RIM stands for reaction injection molding. It is used to manufacture large components in a single production step. The technology was extended in 1975 with the development of reinforced reaction injection molding (RRIM), used to produce glass-fiber reinforced components with coatable surfaces. In 1983, General Motors unveiled the Pontiac Fiero; its RIM exterior parts mounted on a steel frame were considered a sensation. By 1985, 75 percent of all cars produced in the United States were equipped with RIM parts in the front and rear.

Wonder world of chemistry

Bayer's developments alone since then are almost too numerous to mention. If consumers wanted to know exactly what they are driving, they would need a degree in chemistry. Take Bayer's polyurethane systems for lightweight engineering applications which are processed in combination with fillers and short, long or continuous fibers to make molded parts or coatings. This technology is a vast wonder world of chemistry. It takes only 90 seconds to manufacture a RRIM fender, and the finished product is so light it can be lifted with one finger.

License plate number LEV-K 67: the first sports car made of plastic, developed by Bayer in collaboration with Gugelot Design GmbH, Waggon- und Maschinenbau AG and BMW AG, is shown parked near the Rhine bridge at Leverkusen in 1967.

Use in surgery

IMPROVED WOUND CARE

Following major surgery in hospital, patients hope most of all that their wounds will heal as quickly and painlessly as possible. Researchers at Bayer MaterialScience have developed raw materials for a new polyurethane foam that can be used to manufacture particularly soft and supple wound dressings. These are both flexible and stable and rapidly absorb wound secretions. Combined with a thermoplastic polyurethane film, the wound dressings are also skin-friendly. They keep dirt and microbes out but allow wounds to breathe – thus facilitating rapid healing. Modern wound management can reduce the duration of treatment, especially after surgery – something which patients, doctors, therapists and health insurance companies all wish to achieve. It also facilitates a faster transition from hospital treatment to non-hospital care. The patent for the new polyurethane technology was registered in 2008.

11

Baymedix™

2008

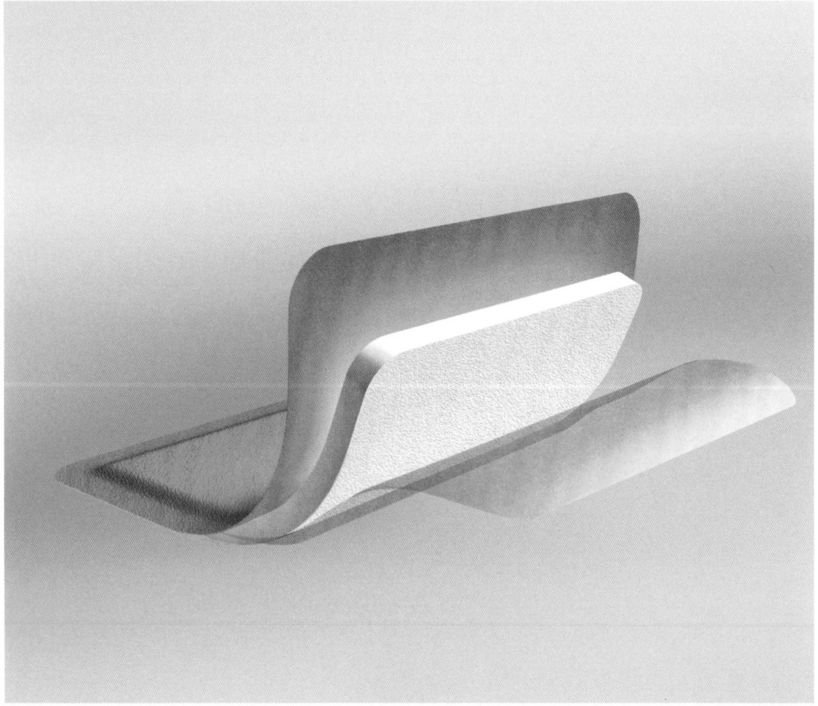

Rapid recovery: modern wound dressings made from polyurethane raw materials are skin-friendly and promote healing.

Polyurethane for the skin and hair

POLYMERS FOR COSMETICS

A familiar situation at the beach. You reach for your sun lotion to protect your skin from harmful UV radiation. And then there's that unpleasant sticky feeling. Many products with a high sun protection factor (SPF) are difficult to rub in. An innovation from Bayer MaterialScience can help. Baycusan™ C 1000 is a polyurethane dispersion that keeps high-protection sun lotions creamy. It is also water-resistant and has an additional feature of interest to sun lotion manufacturers – it has been proven to boost the effect of the sun protection factor.

12

Baycusan™

2008

Bayer polyurethanes are used in hair products as well. Baycusan™ C 1008 helps to repair split ends, providing a combination of care and styling properties. It protects the hair against heat, enhances gloss and gives natural-looking hold, making the hair smooth to the touch. Baycusan™, which was launched in 2008, is also used as an additive in world-famous luxury-brand mascaras, eyeliners and lipsticks.

Modern insulating materials

FOR A PLEASANT CLIMATE AT HOME

Thermal insulation is not a new concept. It basically involves wrapping air – like in a down comforter. We can't wrap our homes in comforters but we can install rigid polyurethane foam insulation panels. The principle is the same: air – or a gas – is locked into tiny pores that prevent the molecules from transferring their kinetic energy.

13

EcoCommercial Building

2009

During production, the liquid raw materials are foamed with blowing agents such as CFC-free pentane gas or CO_2. The foam compound is tacky before curing and can be bonded to a facing suited to the subsequent use.

The finished rigid foam components are used in roofs, walls and floors, and in building and technical systems. Around one-third of all polyurethanes produced worldwide are used to insulate homes. They don't melt at high temperatures; they retain their shape; and they are dimensionally stable, compression-resistant, durable and water-repellent. Rigid foams are used to prevent energy loss and thus also minimize CO_2 emissions – in private homes and industrial buildings, particularly in the United States, where the materials are being manufactured increasingly from renewable raw materials.

Bayer's researchers have a clear goal: to make the insulation panels thinner. This reduces the additional weight a building has to carry and creates more living space. In conventional polyurethane insulating materials, the pores measure roughly 100 to 150 micrometers. The air molecules inside still move minimally and transfer energy. The most recent development: microfoams with tiny pores that restrict the thermal exchange between cold and warm spots even more. Applications for Baytherm™ Microcell include novel refrigerated containers (see also page 66).

If researchers manage to make the pores even finer, the volume of the elements could be reduced further still. This is why Bayer is working on nanofoams, which would make it possible to significantly increase insulation effectiveness.

For the children: EcoCommercial Buildings (ECB) are climate-friendly, energy-optimized structures. They incorporate innovative construction and insulating materials with the aim of reducing emissions. Built in 2009, the Bayer CropScience day care center in Monheim was the first ECB in Germany.

An elder statesman of polyurethanes in his favorite place: the garden of his home in Leverkusen. Günter Oertel was President of the Alliance for the Polyurethanes Industry and is considered to be one of the preeminent researchers in this field.

14

Günter Oertel

Polyurethane chemistry

1960

Günter Oertel's research findings resulted in more than 90 international patents – the first in 1960 – numerous publications and many commercial products. He is considered to be one of the pioneers in the field of polyurethanes. He was admitted to the Polyurethane Hall of Fame in 2003.

LOVE OF FREEDOM

His bust is in the Polyurethane Hall of Fame in the United States. On the road to becoming an internationally renowned researcher, Günter Oertel had to overcome major obstacles – and even escape from the East German secret police.

The men who were waiting for me at the entrance to the University of Dresden were wearing leather coats and had tough, grizzled faces. They looked exactly the way you would imagine the secret police in a cliché-ridden movie. They flashed their IDs: State Security. A car pulled up and took me to a gray basement on the outskirts of the city. I was led into a dark room and made to stand under a bright light. The interrogations began. I was told that one of the audio engineers who worked at the university radio station, for which I did announcements because I had a distinctive voice, was operating an underground radio station aimed at sabotaging the East German regime. I barely knew the man. I may only have spoken to him once or twice in the hallway, but that was enough. Now he had escaped to the West. It was 1952, the era of the Stalinist purges. Desperate parents would often stand in front of the university, begging for information and holding photos of their sons who had disappeared. I had been forced to join the FDJ, the Communist youth movement, but I didn't belong to any other party organization. I had been aware for some time that the police were tailing me, not least because of the footprints in the front yard my landlady had complained about.

The interrogations, in which they asked me the same questions over and over again although I could not answer, went on for several days. They kept at it until I was so exhausted I simply couldn't go on. After several days of questioning, they presented me with a list of ten names. "We're giving you the opportunity to prove your patriotism," said one of the officers. I was expected to spy on these ten classmates from that day on. They gave me a few days to think about it. The next morning, shortly before Christmas 1952, I went to see my parents at their farm in Thuringia to say goodbye. They were horrified, but they understood why I was leaving. It would be 12 years before I saw them again. I just couldn't live with the system. I had witnessed a lot of suffering, violence and bloodshed. I had survived an air attack on a train. During the Volkssturm, Hitler's last-ditch attempt to defend Germany, I was trained as a 12-year-old junior platoon leader to operate an anti-tank weapon in the fight against the advancing U.S. troops.

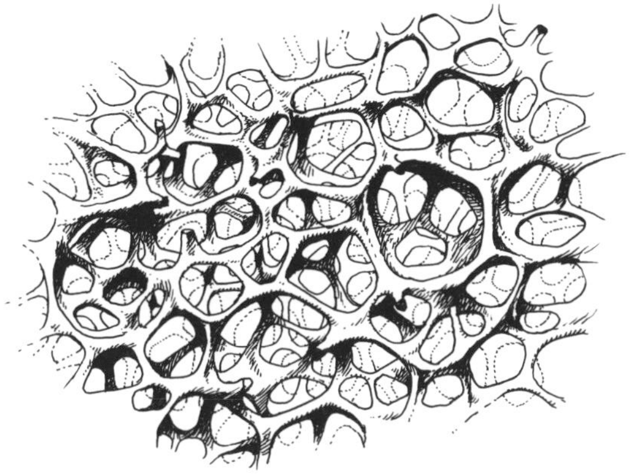

Lattice structure of polyurethanes

After the interrogations by the secret police, my mind was made up. I could have put up with the East German government and I would not have fled, but betraying my friends was simply not an option. I had to get out. I went as far as I could by train and then hitchhiked my way around the Berlin Ring. I finally made it the rest of the way to West Berlin on foot without being arrested. The Berlin Wall hadn't been built yet, and going to West Berlin was discouraged but not yet prohibited. However, you couldn't risk attracting the attention of the East German police if, like me, you were on the "wanted list." I was lucky. I spent the next few weeks in a refugee camp where I was repeatedly interrogated for long periods by the British and U.S. intelligence services, and then flown from Tempelhof to West Germany. My next stop was the former Heidemoor concentration camp, which held almost 5,000 young men between the ages of 15 and 25. Hygienic conditions there were terrible. It was infested with bedbugs and lice. Because of overcrowding, boredom and a general feeling of hopelessness, fights were common, although I somehow avoided the violence. The problem was they wouldn't release you unless you had a place to live and a job. They offered me jobs mining coal in the Saarland and in agriculture. I declined. I had studied chemistry in Dresden, and that was the career I wanted to pursue, not end up a miner or farmhand. In the camp I met a friend from college whose cousin was living in a seminary in Bamberg. We wrote him a letter requesting his help, and a few days later we were on a train to Bavaria.

After a few weeks in the seminary, where they took good care of me, my health – which had suffered during my time in the camp – had improved to the point where I wanted to try to resume my study of chemistry. To earn a little money, I worked nights shoveling coal and handling freight at the Bamberg train station. And then bureaucracy threw up more obstacles. First they wouldn't recognize my high-school diploma from East Germany. To retake the exam, I had to cycle five hours overnight to Nuremberg because I didn't have the money to buy a train ticket. Because I only had provisional identification papers from the City of Berlin, I was classified as "stateless." After a great deal of effort and with my father's help, I finally had my birth certificate, and then they demanded a "political clearance certificate." And how was I supposed to get that as long as I was on the East German police "wanted" list?

I don't know how my story would have turned out if I hadn't been inspired to write a letter to the "Untersuchungsausschuss freiheitlicher Juristen," a human rights organization in Berlin that issued me a certificate stating that I had no undesirable political history or affiliations. Finally I was able to go back to college – and got my PhD six years later. My thesis supervisor – Professor Walther Noddack, the discoverer of the element rhenium and Nobel Prize nominee – was friends with legendary researcher Otto Bayer. Other people might have been nervous to meet the inventor of polyurethanes, but I wasn't afraid of anything any more. Bayer, a tall, powerfully built man who smoked like a chimney, came across to me like a friendly father figure.

"I'm especially proud of my international team."

"Young man, would you like to come to work for us in the Organic Chemistry Department?" he asked me as we sat in his office and he enveloped me in a cloud of smoke from his fat cigar. "No, thank you," I replied. My passion was inorganic chemistry, and at the time I was working on a very promising process to isolate rare earth elements.

Bayer looked at me with astonishment and repeated the question as if he thought he hadn't heard me correctly, but I replied "No" a second time. Back in Bamberg, Noddack temporarily threw me off his program because I was conducting secret experiments outside the scope he had defined for my PhD thesis. But his anger softened when he saw the results – the method was innovative and the result groundbreaking: I was the first person to successfully isolate rare earth elements in industrially usable quantities. It was a pioneering achievement. Rare earth elements, especially the metals, are only now becoming economically important again because they are used in smartphones and superfast computers, among other things.

Otto Bayer didn't let up trying to bring me to Bayer. After a probationary period, I overcame my objections to organic chemistry and dived into polyurethane research. Decades later, after a career in which I filed many patents and ended up on the Board of Directors, I was honored with admission to the Polyurethane Hall of Fame in Arlington, Virginia. There is probably something made of the material our team developed in every home and every car in the world: mattresses, refrigerators, bumpers, steering wheels, dashboards, shoes – the list of applications goes on and on. It is a pleasant feeling to be able to look back on it all at the end of my life. I'm especially proud of my international team, with whom I kept in touch long after I retired. If you want to create an atmosphere conducive to innovation and lead a creative team, you have to inspire your people by your own example. And you have to stand up for what is important to you.

Günter Oertel

Dr. Günter Oertel was born in 1932 and is considered to be the elder statesman of international polyurethane research. He is the author of the standard work on polyurethane chemistry and technology. He is also an avid golfer. Günter Oertel has four children and lives in Leverkusen, Germany.

Microfoam improves insulation

FOR A MORE EFFICIENT REFRIGERATION CHAIN

F**resh foodstuffs need** to be stored properly and that requires energy. Around one-fifth of electricity consumption in a modern household is used to power refrigerators and freezers.

Over recent decades, insulating materials made from rigid polyurethane (PU) foams have significantly improved the energy efficiency of these appliances. The foam is filled into the cavity between the outer skin and the inner lining. Improving the insulation reduces the amount of energy needed to maintain a low temperature inside an appliance. Worldwide, few refrigerators or freezers are now produced without the use of polyurethane insulation.

15

Baytherm™

1973

The components required to make rigid polyurethane foam are Baytherm™, on the market since 1973, and Desmodur™. They are ideally suited for insulating refrigerators and freezers. But milestone victories like these haven't stopped the researchers from working to optimize their products and solutions.

Their most recent achievement is Baytherm™ Microcell, a new material with an especially fine-pored structure. The pore size is a crucial factor in the material's insulating properties. The finer the pores, the better the insulation is.

The pores of the new microfoam are not much larger than a human hair – making them 40 percent finer than in conventional rigid foams. As heat passes through the material, it is reflected more often by the numerous small pores than it would be in a foam with a coarser structure. This reduces the thermal conductivity of the Microcell foam by as much as ten percent compared with a standard material. The new insulating material therefore further cuts the refrigerator's electricity consumption – and thus also the user's annual bill.

Foam insulation cuts energy consumption and saves money.

This development benefits both consumers and manufacturers. The latter are expected to further improve the efficiency of household appliances, cutting energy consumption and thus also CO_2 emissions. And because Microcell foam can be processed in the same way as a conventional rigid foam, manufacturers do not need to invest in new production technologies – ensuring excellent insulation properties at a reasonable price.

In the future, this could benefit private households and various other participants in the upstream refrigeration chain. The material is already used in virtually all refrigerated containers, for example, hundreds of thousands of which are shipped all over the world.

And Bayer's researchers have their eyes set on new targets. They are already working to further reduce the foam's pore size – from the micro to the nano range, which is around one millionth of a millimeter. This could make it possible to double the material's insulating capacity and halve energy consumption.

Well-cooled by polyurethane: the high-tech plastic is also used in refrigerated containers. Produce can be transported at sub-zero temperatures and is still fresh when it reaches the consumer.

Taking a dive: Thorsten Dreier - shown here in the BayArena, Leverkusen - could have had a career in soccer. He doesn't regret being part of a different team at Bayer.

THE NEXT GENERATION

Thorsten Dreier

Leverkusen, Germany

Bayer Technology Services

A TEAM PLAYER

Thorsten Dreier faced a choice: professional soccer or a chemistry degree? What remains is his team spirit – and his enthusiasm for a grass soccer field in the fall.

My interest in chemistry was aroused in the first lesson when our teacher – his name was Dr. Komossa and he had a gray beard – detonated electrolytic gas. My other passion was that elementary thing which fascinates most boys: soccer. I was no use on the field but I was good in goal. My home club in Dülmen put me forward for various selection squads and I made it into the youth team at Borussia Dortmund and then into the Preußen Münster squad. I sometimes dreamed of being a professional soccer player and often went straight from the auditorium to the soccer field. I trained with Stefan Klos, who went on to win the Champions League with Borussia Dortmund and a series of championships with Rangers Football Club in Glasgow. One day, a second league club called wanting to sign me as a reserve player and I had to make a choice between the soccer field or the laboratory. I've never regretted my decision. My job as the head of a department in polyurethanes process research is exciting and offers me a global playing field. From my time as an active soccer player, I've come to value team spirit – and the ability to go that extra mile to achieve one's objective. Even today, I still enjoy running across freshly mown grass on a fall morning.

Thorsten Dreier

Dr. Thorsten Dreier was born in Münster in 1972. He studied there and in West Virginia, USA. The PhD chemist is the father of a young daughter. He and his family live in Düsseldorf, Germany.

Manja Ahola enjoys relaxing on Ruissalo Island, a skerry covered with enchanted oak forests that is close to her workplace.

16

Manja Ahola

Levonorgestrel

1990

The Mirena™ hormonal intrauterine system, approved in 1990, is a small T-shaped piece of plastic with a cylinder containing levonorgestrel. It reliably prevents pregnancy for a period of up to five years. Manja Ahola is the co-inventor of a new generation of Mirena™.

THE PRIDE OF TURKU

Manja Ahola from Finland has been developing contraceptives for many years. She sees it as more than just a job. She found her way into research thanks to some well-meaning advice from her mother.

I **come from** a small fishing village on the west coast with its jagged skerries and dense forests. In the past, people from our village often learned a trade. The men became lumberjacks in the forests or went to sea; the women became teachers or stayed at home with their families. I originally wanted to be a nurse, like my mother, but she advised me against it: "Don't do it, child! Believe me, the job won't be enough for you. You've got other talents." Looking back, I'm grateful for her warning which was to change my life. I found the sciences and also math easy at school and later studied biochemistry. Job prospects weren't particularly good in Finland back then. When I finished my PhD, I was very happy to get the chance to work – at that time with Schering – in Turku.

I've been researching contraceptives for women for many years. I myself am the mother of a son and it's a fantastic feeling to have helped bring to market the hormonal intrauterine system, supporting millions of women with their family planning. The hormonal intrauterine delivery system is a flexible T-shaped piece of plastic with a cylinder that evenly releases tiny amounts of the hormone levonorgestrel. The physician inserts the device directly in the uterus. It functions very simply in theory but the mechanism is actually highly complex. Body fluids penetrate the silicone in the device, gradually releasing the active ingredient stored there. A very effective method because the tiniest amount of levonorgestrel – one twenty-millionth of a gram – is sufficient to reliably prevent pregnancy.

The hormonal intrauterine system is the result of a development collaboration spanning the globe from the United States to Berlin. We in Turku are particularly proud that a lot of the development work – from research through to production – happens here. Access to some of the labs and production areas is restricted to protect our know-how. The plant is on the outskirts of the city, close to the port. What I really appreciate is the good spirit of cooperation between my colleagues. We have a warm working atmosphere. Communication is easy and friendly and we don't put much emphasis on hierarchies. Getting help on tricky questions? No problem at all. Some while back, I had the chance to live and work in Berlin for eight months. It was an interesting time for me because I learnt a lot there.

"I visit the sauna several times a week. That's just something we do in Finland."

Every now and then, my job can be stressful. The best way for me to clear my head is to exercise. I like jogging. My family is very keen on sport and we're avid soccer fans. Our son Otto – not a typical Finnish name but we didn't name him after Otto Bayer – plays midfield for FC Kaarina. Sometimes we travel a whole day northward for away games. What I do several times a week to relax is to go to the sauna. That's just something we do in Finland.

Model of the hormone levonorgestrel, the active ingredient in Mirena™

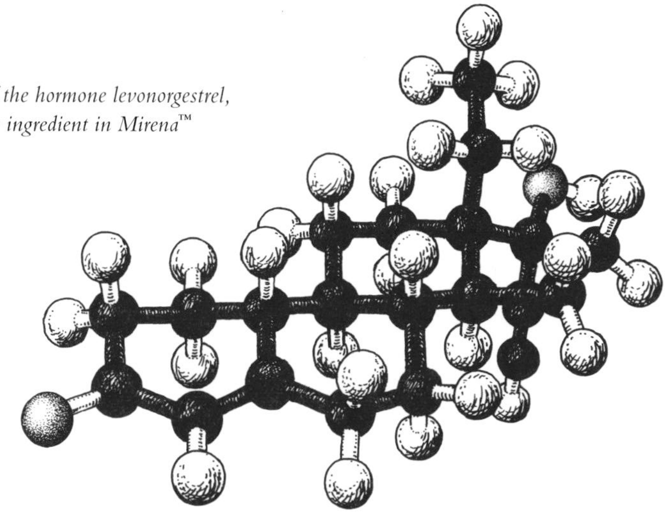

We in Turku – an old port city with a canal and ships lying downtown – are a little idiosyncratic. Throughout our history, Sweden, Russia and Finland often fought over sovereignty. Even today, the city is officially bilingual – Finnish and Swedish – which has resulted in the people developing a strong awareness for their region. We have our own dialect, known as *Turun murre*, and there is a saying that you can't become a Turku native but are born one.

From my office I can cycle to Ruissalo Island, a recreational area with wonderful enchanted oak forests. My family and I have spent many evenings after work down on the jetty, have swum in the sea or gone for walks. It's especially idyllic on Midsummer's Eve and greatly reminds me of my childhood.

Manja Ahola

Dr. Manja Ahola, born in 1967, was awarded the Otto Bayer Medal in 2012. She lives in Turku, Finland.

The story of modern family planning

A DRUG THAT HAS HAD A LASTING IMPACT ON SOCIETY

17

The birth control pill

1960

Anne Purcell Higgins was 49 years old when she died of tuberculosis. It was the end of a terrible life of hardship, poverty and destitution with 11 children from 18 pregnancies. Her sixth child, Marie Luise, was 19 at the time and drew her own conclusions. At the funeral, she walked up to the man she held responsible: her father, a strict Catholic. "It's your fault," said Marie Luise. "Mother is dead because she had too many children."

The death of her mother in 1899 was a turning point in the life of Marie Luise Higgins, who later called herself Margaret and took the name of her husband, William Sanger. As a nurse, she dedicated herself to helping pregnant women, talking with them about their sexuality.

Tireless fighter for women's rights: Margaret Sanger

In 1912, she began writing a column for the *New York Call* entitled "What Every Girl Should Know," in which she explained the menstrual cycle and coitus interruptus. She also published *The Woman Rebel*, a magazine in which she appealed to women to claim the right to their own bodies. And she founded the first family planning center in the United States. What this feminist was trying to achieve required courage and tenacity, because sex education was virtually non-existent anywhere in the world at the time.

Family planning was a utopian dream. Societies were conservative, as were legislators. The Comstock Act adopted in the United States in 1873 made it illegal to distribute any "obscene, lewd and lascivious material" – including information about contraception. It was even illegal to distribute condoms if they were not prescribed by a physician. This had far-reaching consequences, especially for women in the lower social classes.

In 1925, Margaret Sanger received a letter from Englishtown, New York. A pregnant woman wrote: "I am 30 years old and have 11 children. I suffer from kidney and heart disorders. My children are undernourished. We are poor. Now my monthly bleeding is several weeks late again. My doctor says I will go crazy if I keep this child, but he does not want to do anything for me. I would rather die than have another child." Margaret Sanger's conclusion: "Women need a reliable contraceptive pill that is as easy to take as Aspirin." Several decades would pass before her idea became reality, and Schering AG, Berlin, Germany (now Bayer HealthCare Pharmaceuticals) played a pivotal role. Walter Hohlweg and Hans Herloff Inhoffen were researchers at the company who were among the pioneers of family planning.

The scientific development of the pill began in 1919 in Innsbruck, Austria. The physiologist Ludwig Haberlandt discovered during an experiment with rats that an existing pregnancy in the animals prevents renewed fertilization. His logical conclusion was that giving pregnancy hormones to women could make them temporarily infertile. Haberlandt was motivated by two circumstances. The economic depression that followed the First World War caused large families the most suffering. Also at that time, Vienna-based psychologist Sigmund Freud was suggesting: "It would be one of the greatest triumphs of humanity if we could raise the responsible act of procreating children to the level of a deliberate and intentional activity."

Haberlandt recognized the principle but lacked sufficient quantities of hormones suitable for the human organism. It was not until 1929 that the necessary scientific breakthrough was made in this field by the biochemist and later Nobel Laureate Adolf Butenandt. He succeeded in isolating the female sex hormone estrone. Things then moved fast. In 1933, Schering AG, Berlin, Germany introduced Proluton™, the first biological progestogen drug. Working in the company's main laboratory, chemists E. Schwenk and F. Hildebrand synthesized estradiol in 1934, laying the foundation for modern hormone therapy products. That same year, Butenandt and other scientists isolated progesterone. The ovulation-inhibiting effect of this progestogen was proven in 1936. And in 1938, Walter Hohlweg and Hans Herloff Inhoffen developed ethinyl estradiol, the world's first orally active estrogen which is still a common ingredient in oral contraceptives. Schering AG, Berlin, Germany was considered at that time to be the global leader in this field of research. On March 1, 1961, it launched Anovlar™ in Australia, and three months later in Germany and the rest of Europe (see page 78). Shortly before, on May 11, 1960, Enovid was the first oral contraceptive to be introduced to the U.S. market – and Margaret Sanger was again involved. At a party in 1951 she met the biologist and physiologist Gregory Pincus, a hormone specialist. Sanger asked him what it would cost to develop such a drug – Pincus estimated about US$125,000. Sanger was friends with women's rights activist Katharine McCormick, heiress to a combine harvester empire, who donated a total of US$2 million over the next few years.

The first orally active estrogen

Pincus's pill was followed less than a year later by Anovlar™, an improved version with a significantly lower hormone content. Soon after that came the micro-pill, which contained less than 30 micrograms of ethinyl estradiol, and then the estrogen-free pill, which contained only the active ingredient desogestrel. The monophasic products were followed by biphasic and triphasic pills in which the active ingredient combination is adapted to the

New York, 1929: Margaret Sanger (third from right) also faced court in the fight for greater rights. In this case, she was accused of distributing "obscene, lewd and lascivious material" – and that included information about contraception – which was illegal in the United States.

Women in the 1960s: the introduction of the birth control pill marked the start of female-controlled family planning, giving women new perspectives in modern society.

fluctuating hormone levels in the female body during the monthly cycle. The birth control pill was one of the first drugs to directly trigger social change. Few other things have influenced the modern world as much as this tiny pill, which exploits the interaction between estrogens and progestogens during a woman's monthly cycle. Estrogen suppresses the maturation of new egg cells and ovulation. Progestogens also suppress ovulation and make the cervix impenetrable to male sperm.

The pill accompanied the sexual revolution of the 1960s. It contributed significantly to emancipation and gave women increased access to education and professional employment, because it provides a nearly 100-percent reliable method for avoiding unwanted pregnancy. It thus prevents innumerable illegal abortions with their dramatic emotional and physical consequences, and occasionally fatal outcomes. The pill also greatly influenced demographic trends, particularly in industrialized western societies. Declining birth rates and aging populations now present new challenges for welfare states.

The launch of the pill triggered contradictory reactions.

In Germany, the launch of the pill triggered broad public debate and contradictory reactions. Conservative political and social elements protested, fearing a loss of morality and the collapse of family life. Knowledge of the contraceptive pill was restricted to selected gynecologists, who initially could prescribe it only for married women and then only with their husbands' consent. However, news of the innovation quickly spread. The 1970s saw a growing shift in women's gender roles in industrialized societies. An increasing number of women started working outside the home. Claudia Goldin, Professor of Economics at Harvard University, saw the pill as a key cause in the evolution of a new economic role for women. They found it emancipating, but politicians and large sections of western societies criticized the decline in moral values.

The pill has changed a lot.

The pill is one of the greatest achievements of modern medicine. According to one study, 63.2 million women worldwide between the ages of 15 and 49 were taking an oral contraceptive in 2008. Few other drugs have been scientifically studied and their effect documented so closely. And few other drugs have evolved so rapidly. The pill has changed a lot, but tremendous challenges remain. The World Health Organization (WHO) has found that 38 percent of all pregnancies worldwide are still unwanted. Especially in developing and emerging countries with high mother and infant mortality, women still do not have sufficient access to health care and contraceptives and half a million women die every year during pregnancy or childbirth. These are among the reasons Bayer works with government and non-government organizations in 135 countries. As a result, 16 million women in sub-Saharan Africa were supplied with contraceptives in 2010, for example.

Margaret Sanger witnessed only the beginnings of the contraceptive pill's success in the western world. She died in 1966 at the age of 88, a few months after the U.S. Supreme Court legalized birth control for married couples.

Bayer also provides family planning support to women in developing and emerging countries. Sister Jane Maenaria is explaining contraceptive methods at a clinic in Kenya.

Birth of the pill

A MAJOR STEP TOWARDS FAMILY PLANNING

Small as a lentil, green as a pea and shrink-wrapped in tinfoil. The product that first appeared on pharmacy shelves on June 1, 1961, in a green pack with a white stripe, selling for 8.50 German marks, might have looked nondescript, but it was the subject of extensive and often euphoric commentary. Germany's *Stern* magazine reported: "We can say with certainty today that we have now taken a major step forward in solving one of the most urgent problems in the coexistence of man and woman: the problem of birth control and family planning."

England, 1961: the newspaper photo shows male employees in a pharmaceutical factory making "the pill." They are wearing inflatable protective suits to avoid contact with female hormones.

Anovlar™ is the name of the first oral contraceptive that Schering AG, Berlin, Germany (now Bayer HealthCare Pharmaceuticals) introduced in Germany. It is an active ingredient combination of the estrogen ethinyl estradiol and the progestin norethisterone acetate.

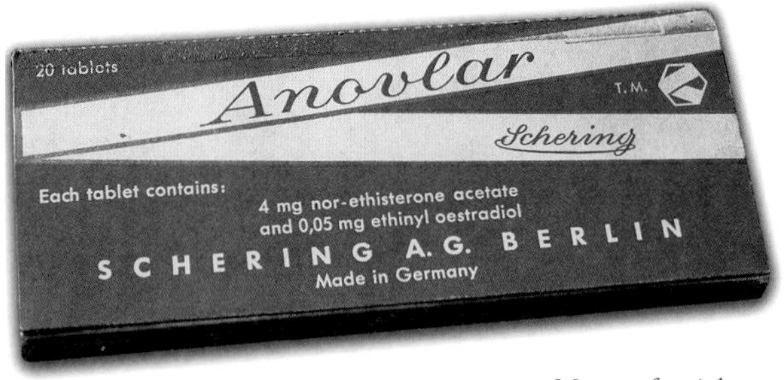

Means of social change: Anovlar™

Belgian gynecologist Ferdinand Peeters was among those involved in testing the product. In his extensive tests on 50 patients, there were no pregnancies and the women's menstrual cycles were regular.

Anovlar™ basically means "no ovulation." However, the drug was initially advertised as a treatment for menstrual disorders and was prescribed only to married women – the manufacturer's response to prevailing cultural and political attitudes. In 1960, every movie that even hinted at nudity still caused a scandal. Nevertheless, Anovlar™ soon became established in the market. The first calendar pack was introduced in 1964, making it easier to ensure the pill is taken regularly. When German magazine *Konkret* asked its readers in 1968 to send in the addresses of doctors willing to prescribe Anovlar™ to unmarried women, the response was overwhelming. The editorial office was flooded with letters. Times eventually changed. Birth control with oral contraceptives became the norm and a new word entered our language: the pill.

18
Anovlar™
1961

Adapted to the hormone cycle

THE TRIPHASIC PILL

Six days of estrogen and progestogen, followed by five to six days of estrogen and progestogen in a slightly higher dose and then ten days of reduced estrogen and elevated progestogen: this is the formula for the so-called triphasic contraceptive. The world's first product of this kind was introduced in 1976. Its name: Triquilar™. What's so special about Triquilar™ is that the active ingredients have been adapted to the female hormone cycle.

19

Triquilar™

1976

The female organism does not release a constant quantity of estrogens and progestogens. Estrogens dominate the first half of the cycle and progestogens the second. These fluctuations were not yet thoroughly understood when the pill was introduced in 1961.

In ethinyl estradiol, researchers had found an estrogen that reliably fulfilled its primary function of suppressing follicle development in the ovaries. It was more difficult, however, for them to find a progestin. Levonorgestrel, registered in 1970, was the first to fulfill all these conditions.

A long time in development

A NEW PROGESTIN

Drospirenone is a progestin developed by Schering AG, Berlin, Germany (now Bayer HealthCare Pharmaceuticals) that has been combined with ethinyl estradiol estrogen in various contraceptives since 2000. Studies have shown that it can counteract water retention in body tissue. In combination with estradiol, it is also used for hormone replacement therapy during the menopause.

20

Drospirenone

2000

Researchers at Schering AG, Berlin, Germany synthesized drospirenone back in 1976, but it took nearly a quarter of a century before its pharmacological potential was fully recognized. The active ingredient was brought to market in 2000.

Carefree togetherness: the pill simplifies family planning for couples.

A place at the table: Hubert Dorn misses his sick friend Terry Hopkins. The two researchers worked together for many years.

21

Hubert Dorn

Flumethrin

1980

Hubert Dorn and Terry Hopkins made major contributions to the development of several products. Flumethrin, registered as Bayticol™ in 1980, largely overcame the problem of the Australian cattle tick. Drontal™ Plus and Drontal™, dewormers that are effective against all relevant types of worms in dogs and cats, were a global innovation when they were launched. The development of Advantage™, a flea control product for dogs and cats, is considered a masterpiece. Kirkor Sirinyan also contributed significantly to this product (see his profile starting on page 90).

FRIENDSHIP FOR LIFE

Together with Australian Terry Hopkins, Hubert Dorn developed products to control ticks, fleas and flies. But the research collaboration yielded much more than products.

W**hen I think** about our friendship, I recall a waterhole named Kalkheuwel in the Etosha National Park in northern Namibia. Photographers love it because you can get particularly close to the wild animals. You sort of squat down among them while they're drinking. If lions come to the waterhole, the other animals wait and you have to be a bit careful. It was during our vacation, sometime in the 1990s. We were already sitting with a clipboard and tape recorder at our observation post shortly before seven in the morning. Terry wanted to know how many animals come to the hole each day and so we counted – hour after hour. The first giraffe came by at seven thirty. A herd of zebras – 141 in all – trotted up between ten and eleven, and then things got a little crowded because 40 antelope and 21 springbok appeared at the same time. Shortly after three, we were impressed by three elephants but the hyenas worried us slightly. When we left our post at just after five in the afternoon, slightly stiff from our long vigil, we had 610 wild animals on our list. I still have the statistics Terry typed into his computer – tidily, as is his way.

I would like to talk about Terry Hopkins, one of the most important inventors at Animal Health, who can no longer tell his own story because he is seriously ill. I've known him since 1970, the year both of us started working for Bayer. I grew up in Hoffenheim, a village near Heidelberg, and studied veterinary medicine after graduating from high school. In my first year at Bayer, I was asked if I wanted to move to Australia. I, a country boy who had worked with farmers, moved to Surfers Paradise on the Gold Coast! The research station was about 30 kilometers inland. So it wasn't far to the famous beaches and it was the start of a wonderful time.

"We were a good team, Terry and I, and our time together didn't stop in the lab."

I met Terrence Hopkins, whom everyone called Terry. We became friends. Terry is accurate, objective, reasonable and unbelievably thorough and reliable. He also has a wonderful sense of humor. It's a pleasure to get to work with someone like him. Incidentally, Terry is the only Australian I know who doesn't like beer.

Following my return to Germany, Terry took over the station and made it a research facility that was highly regarded not only at Bayer but also by veterinary faculties in Australia. "You can rely on Australia" was something you often heard at Animal Health. I couldn't say how many times I've traveled Down Under over the years. Terry came to Germany at least once a year. It's said that opposites attract. I also remember one argument we had, in Rio de Janeiro. We were at a parasitologists' congress and I'd gone for a few beers with colleagues – all in the interests of international research cooperation. The following morning I was slightly hung over and overslept, missing a paper we had registered for – and Terry, the Australian Prussian, was mad at me. "Hubert, what a disgrace," he hissed at me when we met in the corridor. I promised to do better in the future. The following day, we were sat punctually in the front row.

Terry doesn't feel so comfortable in a large group of people. He isn't an entertainer, he's almost shy and doesn't really enjoy receptions. He also doesn't feel at home in the marketing world and if he doesn't like something, he can be slightly awkward. When he retired, he could have had a big party but he had only a modest celebration with a small number of people. We were a good team, Terry and I, and our time together didn't stop in the lab. We went on vacation together with our wives – we visited the Grand Canyon, hiked through Yosemite National Park and went on safari in Kenya and South Africa. Terry loves animals – and I don't just mean the ones we cooked during long evenings spent round the barbecue.

Hubert Dorn

Dr. Hubert Dorn was born in 1941 and grew up in Hoffenheim. He is an enthusiastic chess player who even forced a draw in a simultaneous game with legendary world champion Boris Spassky. Hubert Dorn was awarded the Otto Bayer Medal f or his research work. He is married and lives in Wuppertal, Germany.

Protection against ticks and fleas

NO CHANCE FOR THE FLEA CIRCUS

Four-legged friends who play outdoors are exposed to dangers that their owners may not be aware of. Fleas are not just unpleasant for the animals – they can be a real danger. These parasites irritate our furry friends by making them itch or causing pain. Above all, however, they can transmit serious diseases which may affect the animals' human owners too. People who want to enjoy walking their dogs without having to worry about these biting pests need to examine their pets regularly, take the necessary precautions, and find out about the risks that could be waiting outside.

Flea bites can transmit cat-scratch disease, leukemia viruses and dangerous bacteria such as Rickettsia, for example. If a dog bites and swallows a flea when it's grooming, it can become infected with tapeworms which use fleas as intermediate hosts. A flea can lay up to 50 eggs per day on a dog or cat. A single female flea can lay up to 2,800 eggs in just eight weeks!

This is why the primary task of an effective flea product is to quickly eliminate an existing flea infestation. In 1985, researchers at Bayer synthesized an active substance which does exactly that: imidacloprid, a compound that is also used in crop protection applications (read the profile of inventor Shinzo Kagabu starting on page 326). In 1996, imidacloprid was approved for use in Advantage™, a flea control product for dogs and cats. The spot-on solution is simply applied as drops to the skin using a pipette. The active substance quickly spreads all over the animal's body. Fleas on a dog or cat are eliminated within just a short time. Collars incorporating the active substance are now also available.

22
Advantage™
1996

If a flea comes into contact with imidacloprid, the active substance penetrates the insect and attacks its nervous system, where it blocks the synapses within a few minutes. The flea's nerve cells are overstimulated, causing the pest to die. The active substance is tailored exactly to the receptors in the flea's nervous system, so it damages only the pest and not the host animal. Imidacloprid is also effective against larvae in the immediate surroundings of the treated animal, a vital secondary property that prevents the fleas from establishing a new colony. Advantage™ ensures that companion animals and their owners need not fear fleas and the associated risk of the illnesses they carry – either outdoors or in the home.

All-round protection for four-legged family members

Descended from a family of foresters, Axel Haberkorn enjoys walking in the woodlands around Wuppertal.

23

Axel Haberkorn

Toltrazuril

1986

Toltrazuril, marketed as Baycox™, has a broad spectrum of effectiveness against all types of coccidia (single-celled intestinal parasites). The active ingredient is effective in the treatment of piglets, calves and lambs. It was first launched in 1986 for use in poultry. It is considered a pioneering achievement, especially in the area of piglet production, and was approved in Europe for the treatment of pigs in 2003.

THE PARASITE HUNTER

For centuries, his ancestors were foresters in the German state of Hesse. It was down to chance that Axel Haberkorn wore a white lab coat to work rather than a green loden coat. And it fits his theory that life is a long sinus curve.

P**arasites are something** wonderful. At least they are when you're looking at them through an electron microscope. I was fascinated by how they can adapt to their host. I've researched and analyzed them and uncovered their secrets because I wanted to control them. I was actually supposed and wanted to become a forester. I can trace my ancestry back to 1099 when a Haberkorn went off to Jerusalem as a crusader. I know this so exactly because I spend a lot of time investigating my family history. Some of my ancestors were knights but above all they were foresters. For more than 300 years, Haberkorns worked in the forests around the Vogelsberg in the German state of Hesse. I wanted to continue this tradition. Even as a child, I recognized birds by their song and could identify every tree. The first years of my life weren't very happy overall. My father died when I was two. During the war, my mother, brother and I had to flee. We children searched the bombed city of Giessen looking for people buried under the rubble and found many bodies. These memories have stayed with me until today, now I've reached old age.

We fled north from the battle zone on the platforms of military trucks and found refuge in a village near Verden in Lower Saxony, where we moved into a mill. A short time later, that small place also came under fire – and our mill of all things was hit. A farmer in the district took us in.

We slept on hay in the barn and worked in the fields for our food and board. The farmer's wife, old Mrs. Behrens, wasn't a bad cook but she often left meat out for a long time. Following one meal, my brother almost died of food poisoning. The doctor who treated him helped us move into temporary accommodation.

Dream job: forester

My mother encountered her childhood sweetheart again in Giessen, a former general who had lost his wife in the war. They married. I got on really well with him because I shared his interest in ancestry and sometimes showed him old coats of arms. I wanted to be a forester, that was definite. I was accepted for Vogelsberg, everything was going to plan. The tradition was to continue. But when I came home after a party with my friends from school to celebrate our graduation, I found a letter. The Forestry Ministry informed me that preference had been given to a candidate from Hesse. Now what?

In desperation, I began an agricultural apprenticeship but quickly came to a crossroads. I was advised I could become a teacher with the qualification or I could marry into a farming family. My own farm? No chance. I decided to follow my heart and study what had always interested me: biology. I enrolled at the University of Hamburg. My stepfather was skeptical about my career plans. To pay my college fees, rent and food, I worked on the docks as a stevedore. I hauled boxes and sacks from freighters. The hourly pay was 1.50 German marks and the working day was long.

I did an internship at the Tropical Institute on Bernhard-Nocht-Strasse in Hamburg's St. Pauli district. Parasites became my area of expertise. An acquaintance arranged for me to join Bayer and I started work there in 1963, when the company celebrated its 100th anniversary. I was immediately able to contribute my interest to research. And quite successfully, one could say with hindsight. One of the things we did was find the first active ingredient to treat Chagas disease. We also discovered a substance that is effective against coccidia in all stages of development. And I found out that almost all native bird species are infected with malaria pathogens. People say that I radiate great harmony and a deep inner peace. That may have something to do with my approach to life. I believe that life takes the form of a long sinus curve. Sometimes you're at the top and sometimes at the bottom. One should always remember that these are just moments in time. It is a thought that helps me when things get tough. You have to keep going, just keep going.

Axel Haberkorn

Professor Axel Haberkorn was born in 1933 and grew up in rural Lower Saxony. After graduating from high school in Lüneburg, he did an agricultural apprenticeship and then studied biology. Alongside his research activities at Bayer, Axel Haberkorn was a guest lecturer at various universities and at the Bernhard Nocht Institute for Tropical Medicine in Hamburg from 1972 to 1997. In 1987, he was appointed an honorary professor at the University of Bonn. He is an honorary member of the German Society for Tropical Medicine. His contribution to Baycox™ was rewarded with the Otto Bayer Medal. Axel Haberkorn is married and has two daughters. He lives in Wuppertal, Germany.

Antibiotics for animals

STOPPING BACTERIA IN ANIMALS

Baytril™ is a jack-of-all-trades among the veterinary antibiotics. It eliminates the bacteria which cause respiratory and intestinal diseases and puts a stop to E. coli and Salmonella too. It is effective in companion animals such as dogs and cats and in cattle, pigs and poultry. It has become firmly established in animal husbandry in particular. Farmers value the product because it is effective in treating their herds. The active ingredient enrofloxacin was first marketed in 1987: a yellow crystalline powder which inhibits the growth of bacteria and thus prevents them from multiplying in an infected animal. Development of this active ingredient was based on an innovation in human medicine: the discovery of the quinolones. About one year after completing the development of ciprofloxacin – a highly successful broad-spectrum antibiotic – researchers chose to develop the derivative enrofloxacin for veterinary use. A very modern approach since now more than ever, Bayer's research and development work focuses on the life sciences – human, animal and plant health.

24
Baytril™
1987

Whether in pigs or cats: antibiotics help cure serious illnesses.

New drug product

HELP FOR OUR FURRY FRIENDS

Cats can get a cold, dogs can get a bladder infection – there is nothing unusual in that. And if an animal has had surgery, the wound may become painfully inflamed. Over the years, a number of antibiotics have been developed specifically for animals. Their active ingredients attack the DNA strands of bacteria and kill them. In 2011, Bayer HealthCare launched Veraflox™, a next-generation quinolone with a broader spectrum of activity and reduced development of resistance.

25
Veraflox™
2011

Thanks to its innovative formulation, Veraflox™ is sold as an oral suspension. Its good tolerability makes it especially suitable for treating cats. The active substance is pradofloxacin.

Not to be taken lightly: leishmaniasis

STOP PARASITES FROM BITING

The problem of transmittable infectious diseases is still not well-known to many dog owners. One such disease is leishmaniasis, which is transmitted by sandflies and may go undetected for many years. Researchers from Bayer HealthCare have been working to find a solution. Their aim was to stop the parasites before they even reached the dog's skin. This scientific work showed that Advantix™ kills ticks, fleas and other ectoparasites like sandflies. The treatment of infectious diseases is otherwise lengthy and difficult. Often it is only possible to suppress the symptoms.

26

Advantix™

2002

If left untreated, leishmaniasis is fatal to dogs. Advantix™, which received regulatory approval in 2002, kills the vector and reduces the risk of transmitting diseases. In humans, leishmaniasis is considered by the World Health Organization (WHO) to be a neglected tropical disease. It is endemic in Central Asia, East Africa and South America – and now also in most of the Mediterranean region. Worldwide it threatens more than 350 million people in 88 countries. It is estimated that there are up to two million new cases each year. The disease progresses in similar ways in humans and animals, affecting both the skin and the internal organs.

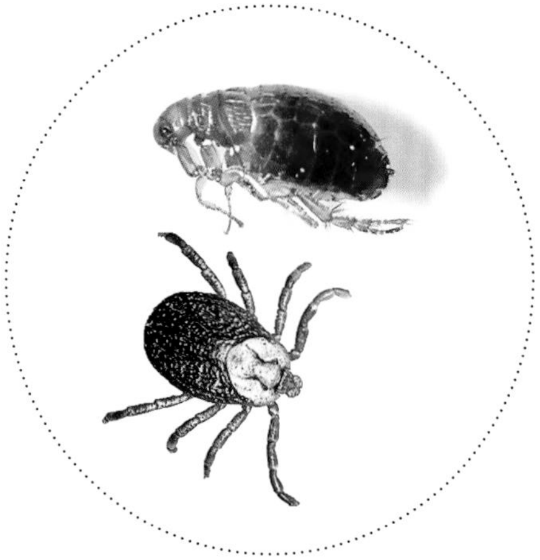

Annoying and dangerous tenants: ticks and fleas

Protection against ticks and fleas

LOW DOSAGE, STRONG EFFECT

Seresto™, a product launched by Bayer HealthCare in 2012, is not a conventional collar intended for attaching a dog to a leash – it's a drug product that repels ticks and fleas for up to eight months. The active substance combination is also lethal for biting lice. The innovative collar is made from a special polymer matrix containing the active substances imidacloprid (to control fleas) and flumethrin (for ticks). Most ticks are effectively repelled before they can bite and transmit any diseases. Flea bites, which are highly allergenic, can also be avoided.

The active substances are released as soon as the collar is fitted to the animal and spread in small quantities across the natural lipid layer of the animal's skin and fur. The dosage is kept at a constant low level which maintains continuous efficacy. Natural oils which are kind to the skin ensure that the coat and skin don't suffer. The collar is not affected by rain, although the animal shouldn't be bathed with shampoo to avoid washing off the active substance. The collar is available in two sizes for cats and small dogs and for large dogs. Seresto™ means that the tick season during the warmer months doesn't have to be a problem, either for dogs or their owners.

27

Seresto™

2012

An underestimated danger

KEEPING ANIMALS WORM-FREE

The earthworms you see in the yard are harmless. They are in fact useful, breaking down the soil or providing anglers with bait. Other tiny worms are dangerous parasites which infest the intestines of animals and humans. They lodge in the digestive tract, feed on their host's intestinal contents and blood and cause painful infections which, if left untreated, can kill. Many species can be transmitted from dogs and cats to their owners.

Tapeworms and roundworms cause many different symptoms, resulting in digestive problems and nutrient deficiencies which weaken the host animal. Hookworms attach themselves firmly to the mucous lining of the intestines and feed on their host's blood, causing serious damage. Roundworms have a negative impact on puppies' development. Toxocara canis, the scientific name for these roundworms, are a widespread global problem. The worms' eggs are extremely resistant so many parks are infested with worms. Various types of worm, including the cucumber tapeworm, fox tapeworm and roundworms, have a serious health impact if they are transmitted to humans when they are at certain stages of development. In Europe, fox tapeworm infection is the most severe and deadly form of parasite infection in humans.

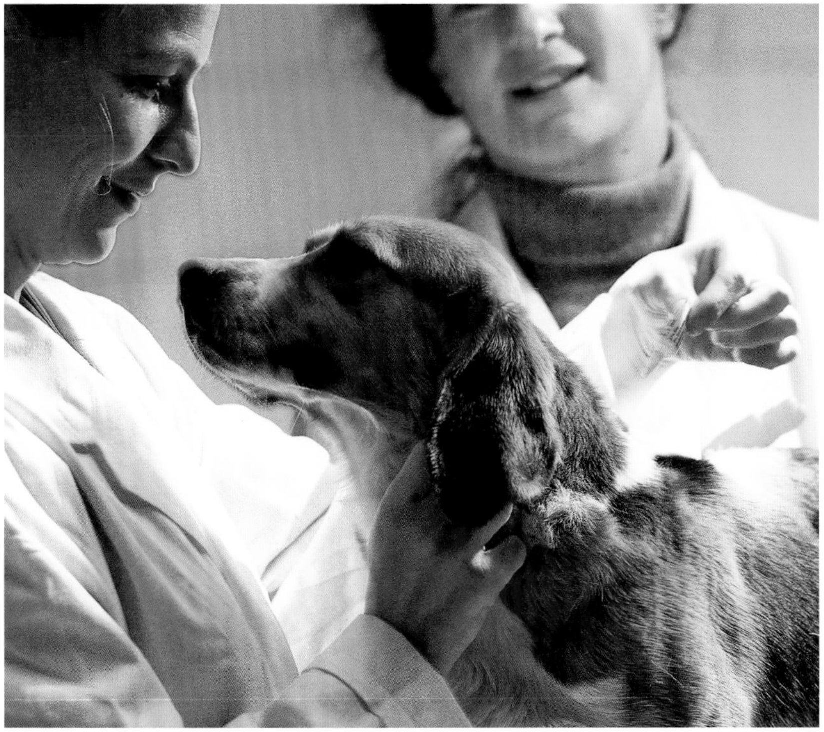

Regular checks by a veterinarian help keep an animal healthy.

28

Droncit™

1976

In the mid-1970s, scientists from Bayer and E. Merck developed an active ingredient which can be used to control tapeworms and flukes in humans and animals. This substance, called praziquantel, opens calcium channels on the worms' skin, flooding their nervous system with stimuli and paralyzing them. The immobilized worms die and are excreted. The active ingredient was first marketed as Droncit™ for veterinary use in 1976. Five years later, it was used as the active substance in Biltricide™ to treat schistosomiasis, a worm-borne disease that is particularly prevalent in Africa and Asia. Even today, millions of people in developing countries are treated with praziquantel, saving many lives. Subsequently, praziquantel was used in combination veterinary products: Drontal™ Plus for dogs (1988) and Drontal™ for cats (1994). Drontal™ Plus is the only product considered effective against all relevant intestinal worm species in dogs.

Dog lover: Kirkor Sirinyan, shown here at the research center in Monheim, has a soft spot for animals.

29

Kirkor Sirinyan

Advocate™

2003

Advocate™, which received regulatory approval in 2003, provides broad protection against a large number of parasites which can infect dogs and cats. Just one spot-on application is necessary. The effect lasts for a month. Advocate™ is effective against ear mites, fleas, worms, sarcoptic mange and demodicosis.

GONE TO THE DOGS

Kirkor Sirinyan was raised in Istanbul's jewelry quarter. He came to Leverkusen via the divided city of Berlin and found his place in veterinary product research. A varied research career.

M**y father's gems** aroused my interest in chemistry. Father was a jeweler in Istanbul's jewelry quarter. His shop was in one of the old city's crooked alleys, close to the Blue Mosque. Through gemology I wanted to know more about the relationships between natural things. Unusual for my family with its long merchant tradition. I went to the Austrian High School in Istanbul and was generally raised in an international environment. My parents were Christians of Armenian origin.

Father's shop was fine and clearly laid out, perhaps 50 square meters, with three sales counters. I earned my pocket money helping out there and saved for my studies. I learned a lot about life and there was absolutely no preferential treatment for me because I was the boss's son. I also learned a lot about respect when dealing with employees and customers. I don't know if father was a little sad that I went my own way. I believe he was also a little bit proud. I moved to Berlin in the winter of 1971, in the middle of the Cold War, and it was a very cold winter too. I lived in a student room in the city's Wedding district, quite close to the Wall, which I could see from my window. There was a tension in the city, an energy I found stimulating. You could meet a lot of interesting people and have exciting conversations.

Berlin pulsated during these years. I earned my living as a translator for a bread factory, helping out the guest workers there and writing work schedules. I was quickly promoted and soon had personnel responsibility for more than 300 people. An attractive job for a young man but I resisted the temptation to seek my fortune in the bread business. Instead I wrote my doctoral thesis in chemistry.

"My grandmother always advised me: carpe diem – seize the day."

The first contacts with Bayer, the discussions with my later supervisors, were very convincing. I was assigned to the plastics division, to polymers research. I worked on modifying the surfaces of engineering plastics but then I "went to the dogs." I got to know a colleague from Kiel, from the animal health production facility. I didn't even know that Bayer had this activity in its portfolio and the new field interested me. I'm attracted by new things, always have been. There were only a few products for small animals and I thought I could do pioneering work. Also, I like animals. I grew up with a Labrador and a cat, which lived at our country house. "I'll do something good," was my first thought. Manufacturing and logistics in Kiel were in the hands of a team of open and enthusiastic people. Everybody did everything and my experience as a "manager" at the bread factory came in useful. Flat hierarchies, fast decision-making, high individual commitment. I followed my grandmother's advice of carpe diem – seize the day. In my view, there is no good and no bad. You have to take things as they come.

To me, innovation means creating a network at the right moment to implement an idea. You need the right brains for that. A company that wants to be successful must attract creative minds. This is the only way to get enthusiastic people and it's enthusiasm that counts. That's also how it was when we started our research. There were a few obstacles to overcome with the first flea treatments but we were successful because we were able to take an unconventional approach. We worked together with colleagues in Kansas City in the United States and were given a lot of freedom by our supervisors. I still remember the comment made by our clinical director, who sighed during a long meeting and then said: "OK, I don't think it'll work but if you all think so, then give it a try." And the result: we were successful. Alongside research, it was always important to me to see the business side of a product in order to achieve commercial success. There is still something of the merchant in me after all.

Kirkor Sirinyan

Dr. Kirkor Sirinyan was born in Istanbul, Turkey, in 1951. In his free time he enjoys history and hiking. In 2006, he received the Otto Bayer Medal. He is married, has one son and lives with his family in Bergisch Gladbach near Cologne, Germany.

Number of companion and livestock animals worldwide

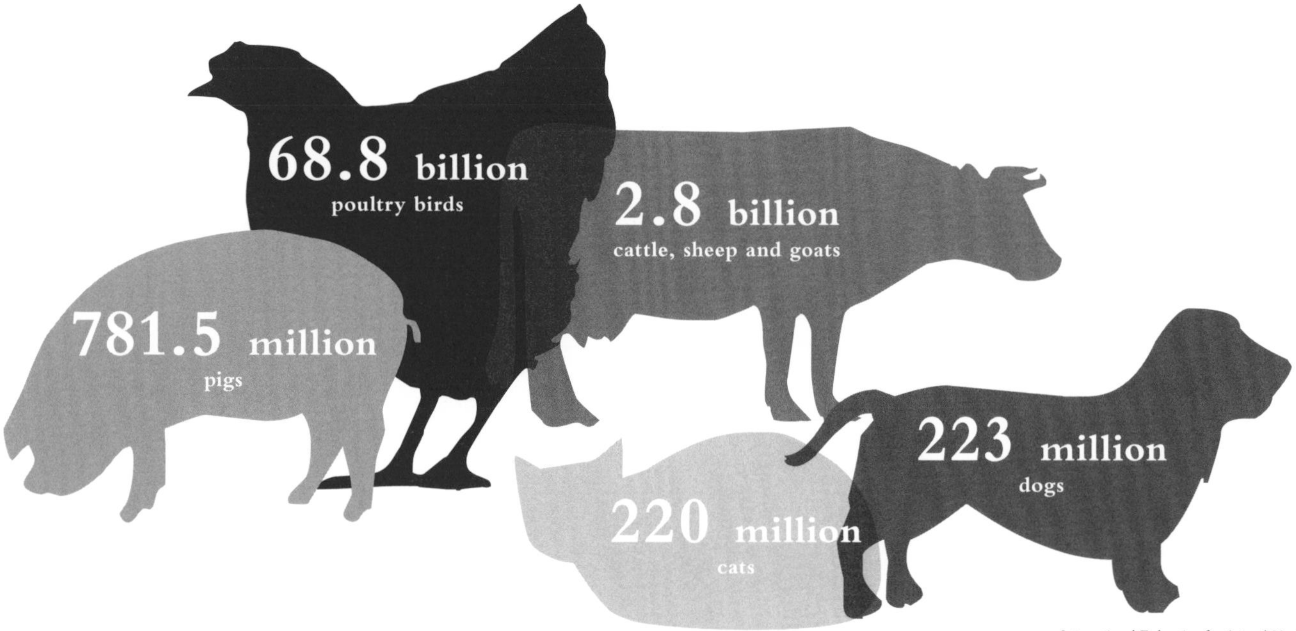

International Federation for Animal Health

1,200,000
Number of horses kept in Germany

13,300,000
Number of horses kept in the USA

FAO

Number of companion animals (million)
Top five European countries (2011)

Russia:	**38.9**
Germany:	**31.0**
Italy:	**29.2**
France:	**27.8**
United Kingdom:	**23.9**

Euromonitor, IVH

900
Amount (€) spent by a German dog owner on his/her animal each year

1,136
Amount (€) spent by a U.S. dog owner on his/her animal each year

VDH

Proportion of the world cereal and soybean harvests used for animal feed (2011):

70% of soybean harvest
36% of cereal harvest

Bloomberg, FAO

Flea facts

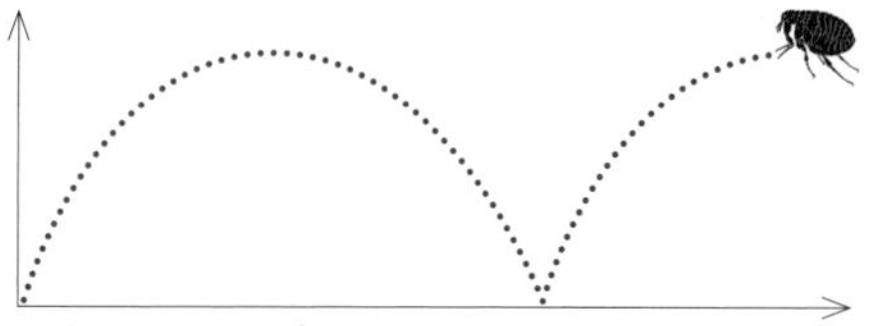

Bayer

Fox tapeworm:
Mortality rate in humans if left untreated: 90 %

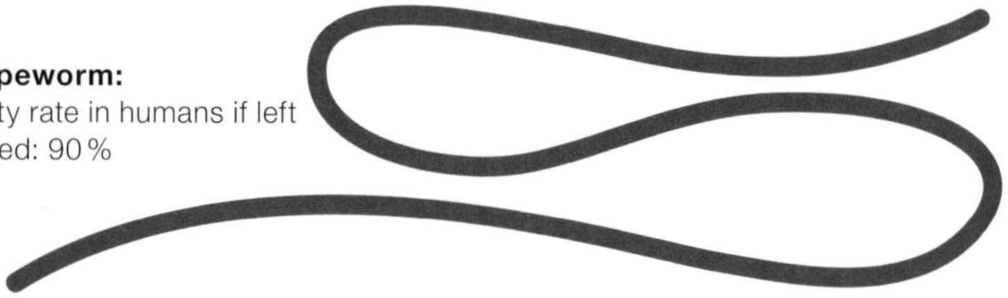

Heartworms colonize the right heart and large blood vessels. Length: up to 30 cm.

Length of a **cucumber tapeworm** in dogs:
70 cm (3 mm wide)

Bayer

11

Number of years a soft tick can go without food

Bayer

In her free time, Sabine Bongaerts enjoys bike tours with her family. Her home is close to the Rhine and to the fortified town of Zons.

THE NEXT GENERATION

Sabine Bongaerts

Monheim, Germany

Bayer HealthCare

TURNING KNOWLEDGE INTO REALITY

Sabine Bongaerts was determined to make a difference.
Today, she heads the global research department at Animal Health.

Even as a child I wanted to be a researcher. I wanted to make a lasting impact and help society by inventing medicines and curing diseases. But some of my teachers advised me against studying biology because at that time there was a surplus of specialists. Now, as the Global Head of Animal Health Research, I'm glad I was determined enough to stay on my own path. People tend to excel the most in the fields they find interesting and fun, and that has certainly been true in my case.

I have my dream job. Working in research, we constantly ask ourselves how innovations can contribute to a better life. At Animal Health, we also have the added excitement of collaborating with researchers at CropScience and Pharmaceuticals to share results. Together we are demonstrating the advantages that new molecules can have for the health of companion animals, livestock, people and plants. Today, I also have the opportunity to encourage other people who are interested in research to have the willpower and determination to get their dream job and do their part to make a difference to our world.

Sabine Bongaerts

Dr. Sabine Bongaerts was born in Neuss in 1968. She studied biology, with the focus on biochemistry, and obtained a doctorate from the University of Mainz. Sabine Bongaerts is married and has two children. She lives in Dormagen, Germany.

In a Canadian oilseed rape field: Hieronim Polewicz moved from Eastern Europe to the prairies of Canada. He loves his job at the research station in Saskatoon.

30

Hieronim Polewicz

InVigor™

1996

InVigor™, which was approved in 1996, is a high-yielding hybrid oilseed rape variety. Hieronim Polewicz is a member of the research team that is working to increase crop yields, improve oil quality and enhance plants' resistance to stress, diseases and insect pests.

LIFE ON THE PRAIRIES

From Eastern Europe to the Canadian prairies: oilseed rape breeder Hieronim Polewicz experienced a culture shock when he changed workplaces. A story about people wearing shorts in frosty weather, vast open spaces with very large farms and a paradise for anglers.

O**f all Bayer's** many sites around the world, I work at one of the most exotic. Saskatoon in the province of Saskatchewan is in the middle of the Canadian prairies. The province is almost twice as big as Germany but only around one million people live here. Saskatchewan is a paradise for anglers. I've worked out that if you wanted to fish a different lake every day, you'd be busy for more than 273 years. It's about 600 kilometers along a straight interstate from Saskatoon to the cities of Calgary and Edmonton. If you arrive by air, you see nothing but fields of oilseed rape and wheat. It can get very cold. In the winter, we sometimes leave the engines of our cars running so they don't freeze. If a polar wind is blowing, the thermometer can show temperatures of minus 30 degrees Celsius for weeks. If you live at the northernmost end of the world, you have to be tough. During the winter frost, I've seen young people walking across the street in shorts just because the sun was shining and the temperature went up to minus 20. When I moved here 18 years ago, I met very friendly people who welcomed us warmly. We felt happy here right from the first day.

Some years, there is snow on the ground through to May. The short summers are the challenge for us breeders. What flourishes here, can flourish anywhere. I was glad to move here because Saskatoon is the global center of my expertise: oilseed rape breeding. I felt like a skier who was allowed to live in the Alps or a cook who moved to the gourmet city of Lyon.

You can imagine what my teenage daughters thought about exchanging Poznan in Poland for the Canadian prairies. Saskatoon is a city of conferences and festivals – each year we have a jazz festival and folk festival. The city is vibrant and growing at a great pace, which is due to agriculture, potash and uranium deposits. Saskatoon is flourishing and has also been named the sunniest city in Canada.

"From the big city to the Canadian prairies. My daughters weren't too happy."

To visit our research station, you have to head northeast out of the city and then turn left at a gas station. There's no street name. I have to give visitors the geographical coordinates for their GPS. People with a poor sense of direction have experienced a minor adventure by the time they drive onto our parking lot. You can say this is where oilseed rape is developed for all continents. We experiment with the plants and develop new varieties with improved agronomic characteristics and resistance to diseases or pests. The building is a sort of high-security prison for seedlings. Working with genetically modified plants requires strict procedures and stewardship measures. I like my job because every day is different. A lay person might wonder what's exciting about oilseed rape breeding. I would say: a great deal! Every day I talk with exciting people and we often discover new concepts. I travel a lot because we have breeding sites and test stations in Chile, Australia, Asia and Europe that I have to visit. I work in my dream job.

"Am I still a Pole or already a Canadian? I have to think about that for a while."

Plants have fascinated me since I was a child. My father, an engineer, supported my enthusiasm and I studied agriculture after finishing high school. Very few people know how important Poland is to oilseed rape. The country is to oilseed rape breeding what Brazil is to soccer or Germany to automotive engineering. I got a job at a government institute. Then I joined Bayer and moved to the prairies. That was in the mid-1990s and I now feel so much at home here that I have to think for quite a while when I'm asked if I'm still a Pole or already a Canadian. I sometimes miss the cultural life and diversity of Europe. But when, for example, I'm sitting for hours in traffic on my way from Ghent to the airport, then I long for the empty highways of Saskatchewan. Here on the prairies, life has a different rhythm. Everything is a little more relaxed.

Hieronim Polewicz

Dr. Hieronim Polewicz was born in 1954 and grew up in Poznan, Poland. In 2006, he received the Otto Bayer Medal for his research. He is married, has two daughters and lives in Saskatoon, Canada.

Innovative canola variety

FOR HEALTHY VEGETABLE OIL

Canada is the second-largest country on earth and one of Bayer CropScience's biggest markets in the oilseed segment. The weather on the prairies is changeable and the temperature differences are enormous, ranging from short hot summers to long icy winters. All this means that only innovative, high-quality crop plants can thrive there. Many of the farms in the prairie provinces of Alberta, Saskatchewan and Manitoba are giant enterprises covering vast tracts of land. Researchers have to think in large dimensions in order to satisfy the needs of farmers, consumers and the global market.

31

InVigor™ Health

2008

That is why scientists developed canola, a high-yield variety of oilseed rape. Bayer launched its hybrid seed InVigor™ in 1997; this is now grown on an area of 2.8 million hectares and produces excellent yields every year. Innovations like this are developed at the company's Canola Breeding Center of Innovation in Saskatoon, Saskatchewan. Bayer CropScience researchers (see the profile of Hieronim Polewicz starting on page 96) are working to combine new technologies with existing know-how. They are developing plants with a higher yield and greater stress tolerance. Seed quality is also an increasingly important factor. One of their successes is InVigor™ Health, on the market since 2008, a seed that produces a more healthy oil with a lower oleic acid content that remains stable even at the high processing temperatures common in the food industry.

Analyzing a canola plant in the laboratory

A gardener at heart: Günter Donn loves working in and caring for the oasis behind his house. Watch a tree being felled? He can't.

32

Günter Donn

Glufosinate-ammonium

1997

Glufosinate-ammonium is a herbicide that has been sold as Liberty™ since 1997 and is combined with LibertyLink™ seed. The system is used for non-selective weed control in key crops such as cotton, corn, oilseed rape and soybeans which are resistant to glufosinate-ammonium herbicides. This makes cultivation easier and sustainable.

THE RAINBOW MAN

Günter Donn loves trees. Whether in the garden behind his house or on trips to Ireland, the researcher – one of the pioneers of green genetic modification – feels most comfortable when he's surrounded by plants.

I **love plants.** This is not just something I say. It's really true. I can't bear to watch when a tree is being felled. It breaks my heart and makes me feel physically unwell. You can ask my wife about how we sometimes argue if I'm supposed to tidy the garden behind the house. Our garden blooms in all seasons and in stages. It's part of my job to understand plants and how they work. I can grow a tree from a single plant cell. That occasionally also helps in my garden work at home. When my favorite tree, an American aspen, had to be removed (much to my sorrow) because it was taking up too much space, I quickly made a few backups.

Even as a child, according to my mother, I put plants around my sand castles. I knew and recognized everything that grew in the garden and flower beds. So well that, as a four-year-old, I helped with the weeding because I could distinguish at a glance between the vegetable seedlings and weeds. My grandfather worked as a gardener in Hamburg and taught me a lot in the greenhouse. Since then, I have always admired the ability of cacti to survive the harshest conditions: heat, cold and drought. Also the bonsais, which are unbelievably adaptable. Later, I was fascinated by orchids, the seeds of which attract a fungus which is otherwise dangerous to plants. They then digest this fungus when it penetrates the cells of the seedlings. In other words, they use the parasite to support their own growth.

> *"It now makes me smile to think about the pomato experiment to cross a potato and tomato."*

After graduating from high school, I plunged into the study of biology and chemistry. I literally lived in the laboratory. My curiosity was insatiable. My PhD subject was the fava bean. University work held little attraction for me. I wanted to go into industry so I could achieve something. I often forgot the time when I was working. Eight, ten or more hours had often flown by when I left the laboratory. There were other projects in my field which with hindsight make me smile. Like the attempt to cross a potato and tomato to make a "pomato," with the potato growing beneath the soil and the tomato above it.

Some people consider me to be one of the pioneers of green genetic modification in Germany and perhaps there's some truth in this. What is now routine and largely accepted, once provoked very different reactions. Some colleagues thought of me as slightly exotic because I proposed modifying the plants themselves rather than applying crop protection products. Others viewed what I did with the same suspicion as alchemy. This only changed when we registered the first patents and it became clear that our area of research was where the future of crop protection lay. I sometimes find the public debate about genetic modification hurtful. You're branded in a certain way and encounter a lot of anger. There were times when the phone would ring in the middle of the night. What has always annoyed me is the half-knowledge – or even quarter-knowledge – and hollow emotion that were the basis for attacking us. You feel powerless when those that shout the loudest are the ones who get heard. As a scientist, I would rather stick with the facts. It is a fact that we have to ensure an adequate supply of food for a growing world population in a changing climate. In discussions, I'm often asked whether man has the right to modify the genetic material of plants. I answer that this has been happening for centuries – ever since people began growing crops and breeding plants. The difference is that we can work far more precisely today.

In my free time, I try to interest young people in science. I go to my grandchildren's pre-school, to elementary schools and to middle schools. I bury PET bottles in sand and produce a volcanic eruption using baking powder, dishwashing liquid, some vinegar and a pinch of red food coloring. I explain to the children what happens in nature during each season or I make them a small rainbow. I call it my guide to being curious.

Günter Donn

Dr. Günter Donn was born in 1949 and raised in the Black Forest. He studied biology and chemistry at the University of Hohenheim. Günter Donn worked for German agrochemicals companies for more than three decades and is considered one of the most eminent experts in the fields of plant genetics, biotechnology and cell biology. He has been involved in volunteering for many years. He is married and has two married sons. Günter Donn lives near Frankfurt, Germany.

Universal protection

FREEDOM TO GROW

The product name says it all: Basta™. Basta means finished, the end, no more weeds or grasses. And it's all thanks to an active substance based on glufosinate-ammonium, which was developed back in 1976. Glufosinate belongs to the family of glutamine synthetase inhibitors. It disrupts the ammonia metabolism of weeds, which greatly inhibits their photosynthesis. Within just a few days, the weeds start to wilt and die. However, the success of Basta™ is not due solely to its rapid and effective action, but also to its versatility. First approved in 1984, Basta™ is one of the great all-round performers in crop protection and one of Bayer CropScience's best-known herbicides.

33
Basta™/Liberty™
1984/1997

As a rule, most herbicides have a selective action which means they are only effective against certain weeds. Then there are the broad-spectrum herbicides which inhibit the metabolism of almost all plants. One of the best-known products of this kind is Liberty™, approved in 1997, which is also based on glufosinate-ammonium. It causes ammonia to accumulate in plant tissue, reaching toxic levels within just a few hours.

Corn: a tasty food for both humans and animals

Effective weed control

PROTECTING THE CORN

Popcorn, steak and tortillas would seem at first glance to be very different foodstuffs. But they have one thing in common: corn, the second most important cereal after wheat. Slightly more than half of global corn production is used to make animal feed, with world demand for meat steadily rising. In the fields, the problem is the number of weeds that are difficult to control. They are becoming increasingly resistant to substances such as glyphosate which are then ineffective. As a result, the weeds compete with the corn plants for light, water and nutrients. There is a risk that entire harvests will be lost.

Bayer CropScience has developed an innovative and highly effective method of controlling weeds during the growing season.

The company's scientists used a biotechnological trick to make corn plants resistant to the new active substance. The combination of the non-selective herbicide Liberty™ and Liberty™-tolerant LibertyLink™ plants, which received regulatory approval in 1997, has cleared cornfields of weeds. The active substance can also be used to protect soybeans, cotton and oilseed rape.

34
LibertyLink™
1997

The multipurpose insecticide

LONG-TERM EFFECT

Let's look at Gaucho™, first approved in 1991 as an insecticide for pelleting beet and vegetable seeds. In this process, seed is coated with a nutrient-rich mass. Gaucho™ 70 WS is used in feed and sugar beets to provide protection against pigmy mangel beetles, beet leafminers and virus-transmitting aphids. In onions, it protects against onion flies and thrips. In cabbages, it is used to control cabbage aphids and the turnip flea beetle. It protects lettuce against aphids and is also used in corn.

Controlling insect pests in various crops

This list demonstrates the importance of the Gaucho™ product family in crop protection. In companion animals such as dogs and cats, the active substance is used to control lice and fleas (see page 83).

The active substance underlying this success is imidacloprid, an effective contact and oral poison. It is easily taken up by the roots of plants and transported to the leaves, which are then protected from chewing and sucking insects. If applied directly to the leaves, it spreads to both sides and is transported to newly formed leaves. Imidacloprid is broken down only slowly by the plant. A small quantity is therefore sufficient to produce a long-term effect. Imidacloprid was first synthesized in Japan in 1985. It is found in a wide range of products that are sold in many countries.

35

Gaucho™

1991

Help for amateur gardeners

CONTROLLING APHIDS

They are just a few millimeters in size – and yet they can destroy entire crops. Aphids exist in many different shapes and colors. They have long antennae and like to colonize the undersides of juicy young shoots and leaves. Whether they choose hops, apples, tobacco, ornamental trees or grapevines – aphids use their proboscis to suck nutritious plant juices from the phloem.

They also damage the plants with their excretions – known as honeydew – which cover the leaves with a sticky coating that is highly susceptible to mold. In this way, the aphids pave the way for undesirable fungus infections like sooty mold. Many types of aphid also transmit virus diseases.

36

Confidor™

1991

Protection against aphids and other sucking insects

Confidor™, which is based on imidacloprid (read about its inventor Shinzo Kagabu on page 326), protects plants against aphids and other sucking insects such as whitefly – which is actually a kind of aphid that needs to be eliminated from all vegetable crops. Amateur gardeners are also familiar with whitefly because they feed on the flowers they have lovingly planted on balconies and patios and in garden beds.

Today, Confidor™ (first registered in 1991) is used worldwide in more than 100 different crops including fruit and vegetables, soybeans, cotton, potatoes, corn and rice.

Ready for harvest: corn fields cover about 170 million hectares worldwide, 24 percent of the available arable land, and yield annual harvests of 883 million tons, or 34.1 percent of the global cereals harvest. The main producer is the USA with a share of 35.5 percent, followed by China (21.8 percent) and Brazil (6.3 percent).

In a corn field in South Africa: Bayer Sales Manager Curtis Troubert (left) talks to farmer Stefan Ferreira.

All-round protection

SUPPORT FOR CORN IN DIFFICULT CLIMATE ZONES

Z**ea mays is** the scientific name. A species from the genus of grasses, diverse, annual, monoecious and sturdy. As a field crop, it can grow to a height of three meters. Its round stems are covered with smooth leaf sheaths. They are crowned with cob-shaped fruit containing rows of whitish, golden yellow, red or even purple kernels. These contain protein, fat, carbohydrates, fiber, minerals, vitamins A and B and valuable amino acids – and they taste simply delicious.

37

MaisTer™

2003

Corn has been cultivated for many thousands of years and there are some 5,000 known varieties. Today, it is grown all over the world, even in regions where climatic conditions are not ideal for the plants.

In central Europe, for example, corn faces early pressure from weeds which compete with the crop for water. Along with light and warmth – temperatures between 20 and 30 degrees Celsius are ideal – water is the main prerequisite for a plentiful yield.

Bayer CropScience has developed a product that helps to solve this dilemma: MaisTer™. First registered in 2003, this herbicide contains two active substances. Foramsulfuron controls all relevant grasses and many other weeds, while iodosulfuron provides efficient protection against broadleaf weeds. The herbicide thus offers all-round protection and has been helping farmers to optimize the productivity of corn crops for a decade.

Bio-protection against nematodes

BAD NEWS FOR NUTRIENT ROBBERS

The scientific name of this pest somehow sounds mean: Diabrotica virgifera. The Western corn rootworm looks innocuous but causes annual harvest losses totaling US$1 billion in North America alone. It is now increasingly prevalent in Europe as well. In August and September, each insect lays up to 200 eggs in the top soil layer, from which larvae than hatch in spring. They drill their way into the roots of plants, causing severe damage and restricting the uptake of nutrients and water. The plants yield less, wither or collapse altogether.

38

Poncho™/Votivo™

2003/2010

Help comes from Poncho™, a seed dressing based on clothianidin that was approved in 2003. This active substance can be used in cereals and sugar beets, for example, where it is effective against other chewing and sucking insects. Studies have shown that applying Poncho™ in corn can increase yields by up to 60 percent. A key benefit of the seed dressing is that only about one percent of the arable land actually comes into contact with the active substance – much less than is the case when using leaf herbicides.

Poncho™/ Votivo™, launched by Bayer CropScience in the United States in 2010, is the first example of an efficient combined biological and chemical crop protection product. The story of Votivo™ began in Israel, where a company called AgroGreen discovered a strain of the soil bacteria Bacillus firmus which produces organic substances in the form of enzymes and phytohormones. The bacterium is capable of restricting the reproduction of nematodes and AgroGreen initially used it in a soil management product. When Bayer CropScience acquired a number of biological products from AgroGreen, its researchers pursued a different goal. They wanted to use the substance as a seed treatment – with success, as the first tests soon showed.

Seed treated with Bacillus firmus repels the tiny nematodes which can cause so much damage. As the roots grow, the protective bacteria in the soil multiply, feeding on the roots' excretory products, for example. The nematodes, which are normally attracted by these same excretory products, no longer receive the signal which triggers their voracious feeding. The larvae hatch late or not at all and can no longer penetrate the already lignified root tips. The combination of Poncho™ and Votivo™ provides excellent protection.

The seed dressing Poncho™ protects oilseed rape plants against insect pests.

CHAPTER

2

ADVENTURE

“

I’M CONVINCED
THAT EVERYTHING IS POSSIBLE
IF YOU PUT YOUR MIND TO IT
AND WORK HARD.

”

HELEN FREE, ELKHART, INDIANA, UNITED STATES

Page 120

SOYBEANS
PREVENTING RUST

A Bayer CropScience employee checks the results of a test with soybeans in a greenhouse at the research center in Raleigh, North Carolina, USA.

Find out what Bayer's researchers are doing to control soybean rust starting on page 168.

TROPICAL DISEASES
PROTECTION FROM BITES

Bayer researchers Dr. Karin Horn and Dr. Günther Nentwig under a LifeNet™. It provides effective protection against the Anopheles mosquito which transmits malaria. An insecticide is incorporated into the polypropylene fibers of the net. The mosquitoes die on contact.

Read about this innovation and tropical diseases starting on page 130.

DIABETES
A HANDY HELPER

An oversized model of a handy helper for people with diabetes: blood glucose meters from the Contour™ product family need just 0.0006 milliliters of blood and display the results of the analysis in five seconds. The photo shows a model of a Contour™ product from 2006.

Read about this innovation starting on page 120.

SKIN
THE HEALING TOUCH

Bayer employee Andreas Werner checks the stirring rods in an ointment mixer used to produce Bepanthen™. The spotless equipment is shown on page 12.

Read more about the skin starting on page 138.

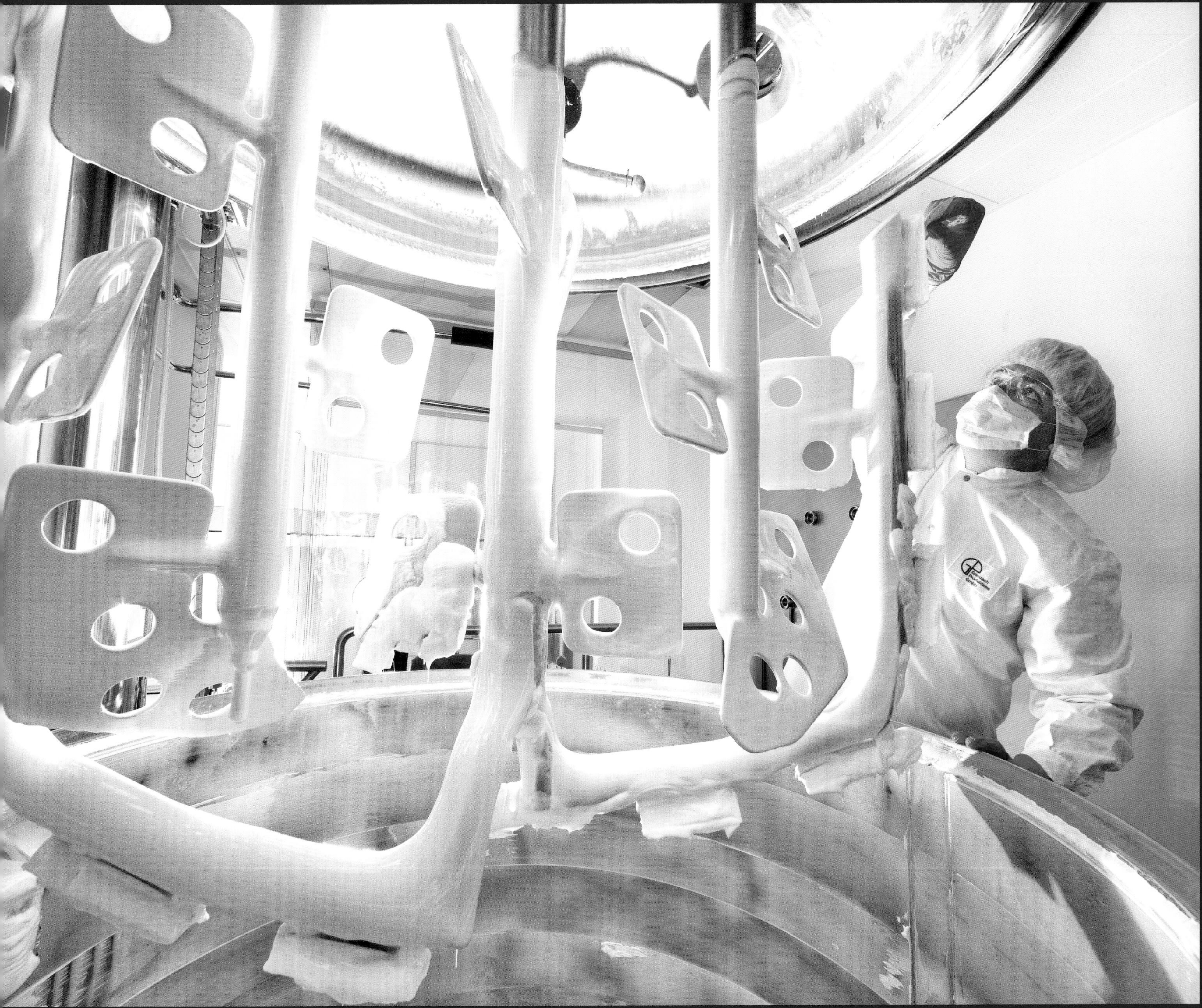

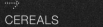

CEREALS
CRITICAL APPRAISAL

In Australia, Bayer employee Richard Dickmann and Vanessa Gillespie of the Commonwealth Scientific and Industrial Research Organisation (CSIRO) inspect a new wheat variety which should produce higher yields.

GROWTH
A LIGHT TOUCH

Jan Temmerman, a Bayer CropScience technician at Astene, Belgium, checks the growth and development of test plants in a greenhouse.

Read how Bayer researchers around the world are working to improve cereals and safeguard food supplies starting on page 144.

200 ml
200
150

ASPIRIN
PROVEN NEW FORMULATIONS

Julin Tong tests new formulations of the active ingredient in Aspirin™, acetylsalicylic acid, at the Bayer HealthCare laboratory in Morristown, New Jersey, USA.

Read the incredible success story of the pharmaceutical of the century starting on page 178.

ANALYSIS
RESEARCHING A CLASSIC

At Bayer HealthCare's product development center in Morristown, New Jersey, USA, Ute Lex operates a robot system for high-pressure liquid chromatography. This works fully automatically around the clock to determine how much of which substances is contained in products like Aspirin™.

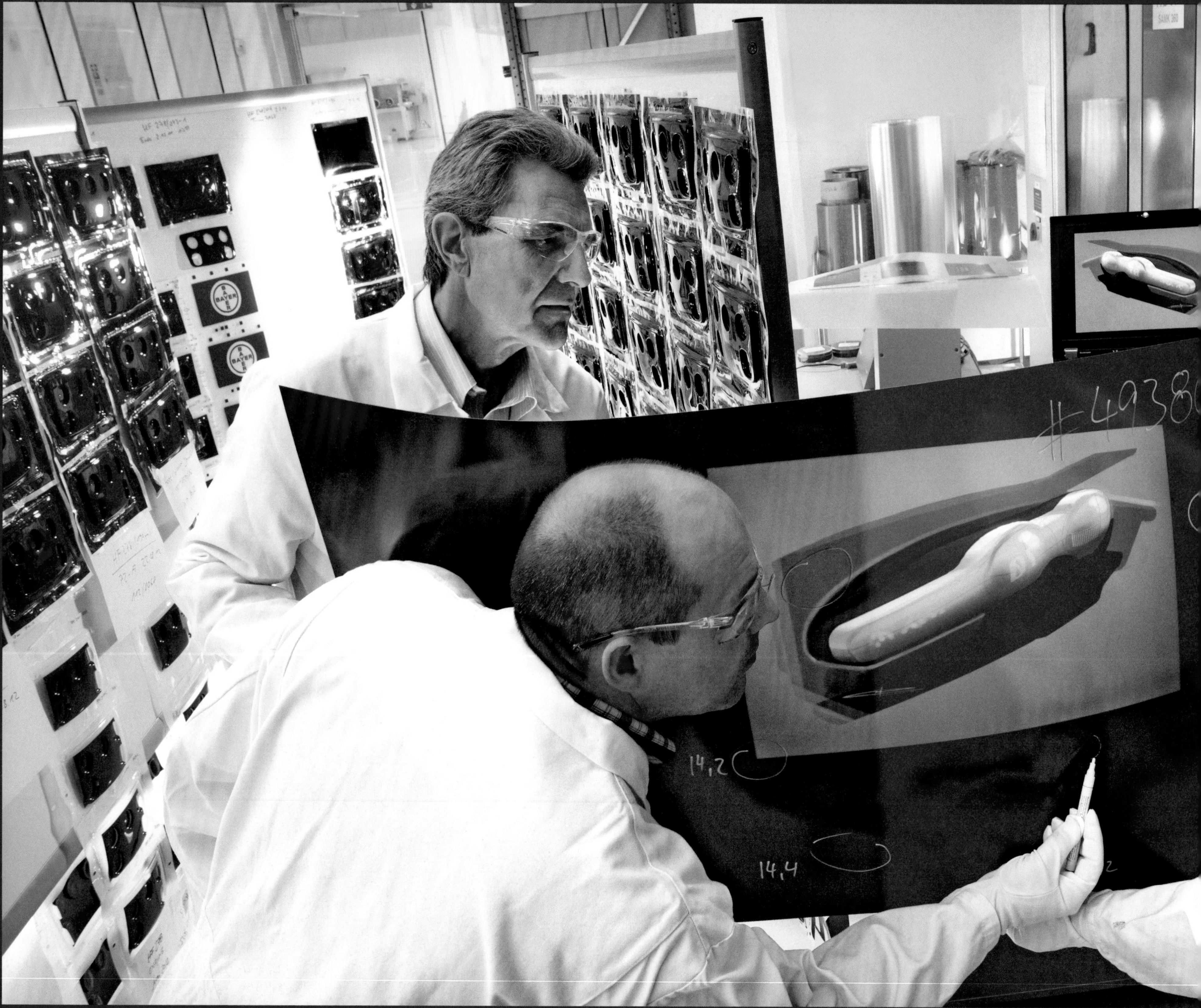
BAYER
BAYER
#4938
14,2
14,4

FILMS
VERSATILE, EFFICIENT, INNOVATIVE

Bayer MaterialScience film experts Roland Künzel (front left), Konstantin Leonhardt (right) and Manfred Lindner experiment with a black panel film for back projection at the Technical Competence Center in Leverkusen.

AN EXTRA LAYER OF SECURITY

New security elements for identity cards and documents are tested.

Find out more about the versatile films from Bayer MaterialScience starting on page 190.

Helen Free, the grande dame of the U.S. in vitro diagnostics industry, enjoys reading an eBook in the bar across the street from her home.

39

Helen Free

Rapid test for diabetes

1949

Helen Free's innovations include Acetest™ (1949), Ictotest™ (1953) and Clinistix™ (1956) – all rapid tests for diabetes. She also worked on the development of Uristix™, Ketostix™ and Multistix™, which have been in use for decades as well.

COFFEE WITH A LEGEND

Lucky coincidences shaped Helen Free's life as a researcher – that's how she sees it herself. Other people think she's a living legend. The mother of a large family received her greatest honor from the hands of the U.S. President.

T**he proudest moment** of my career was in the Golden Room at the White House. President Barack Obama placed the National Medal of Technology and Innovation around my neck. My children were applauding in the audience – it wasn't easy getting seats for all nine of them – and it was a totally wonderful feeling. I never expected such an honor so many years after my retirement. I got my first major award at the age of 44 and many have followed since then. My invention and I were even the subject of a question on the TV quiz show Jeopardy (but the contestant gave the wrong answer). I wish my late husband Al could still have experienced all this.

Al and I were together for more than half a century. We had a large family and worked together in research. The result: six children (Al had three from an earlier marriage), a lot of joy and a rapid test for diabetes that came on the market as Clinistix™ in 1956 and is still setting standards today. Al was the love of my life. He was my boss when I started working at Miles Laboratories (now Bayer, see the story on page 313) and we got to know each other. We were a great team.

My mother died of influenza when I was six years old. I actually wanted to be a teacher like my role model Miss Johnson, who taught English at our village school in Poland, Ohio. After I graduated high school, I studied English and Latin. But in December 1941, everything changed following the attack on Pearl Harbor. At that time, young women were encouraged to get involved in science because a lot of men were recruited into the army. The dorm mother of the student hall where I lived asked me: "Helen, you'll do chemistry, won't you?" She wasn't the kind of woman you said no to. It was probably the best decision I ever made.

"I drove some of our children to school in a red Studebaker."

When I look back at my life, I often talk about serendipity, lucky coincidence or fate. I'm an optimistic person. I'm convinced that everything is possible if you put your mind to it and work hard. I enjoyed chemistry and learned fast. In 1944, before the war ended, I finished my degree and got a job at Miles Laboratories, which was known for the invention of Alka-Seltzer™. I also applied to the Carnegie Institute in Pittsburgh. Their acceptance came two weeks after I had accepted the position at Miles but I stuck with my decision and moved to Elkhart, Indiana. However, I wasn't very happy after a few months because I was bored with the monotonous testing and quality control work in the lab. I wanted to go into development so I made my request and was interviewed by Al Free, head of the research group. I didn't just find a new job but also the love of my life. We married in 1947.

I'm often asked how I managed to balance my busy work schedule with the daily life of a large family. To be honest, I don't know. We just did it. Was I or am I a role model for women? I wouldn't go that far. I did my work. Our days started early and we took the children to their various schools. Al drove the older children to high school in his Hudson convertible. I took the younger children to elementary school in my red Studebaker convertible. During the week, we had help in the house. Summers in particular were harmonious at our home on the St. Joseph River, where the children liked to swim. Al and I sometimes went to the bar across the street. This is now called the "Miles Lab" and is run by a great-great-grandson of the company's founder. There are a lot of historic photos on the walls which remind me of the old times. I still like going there to read an eBook.

Helen Murray Free

Helen Murray Free was born in 1923 and grew up in rural Ohio. She retired officially in 1982 but continued to work for the company as a consultant until 2008. Helen Free has served as President of the American Association for Clinical Chemistry and the American Chemical Society. She has been inducted into the National Inventors Hall of Fame and the American Chemical Society named a prize in her honor. With 17 grandchildren, Helen Free today travels a lot to visit with her family. She lives in Elkhart, Indiana, USA.

Diabetes: figures and facts

Number of people with diabetes worldwide, current and forecast

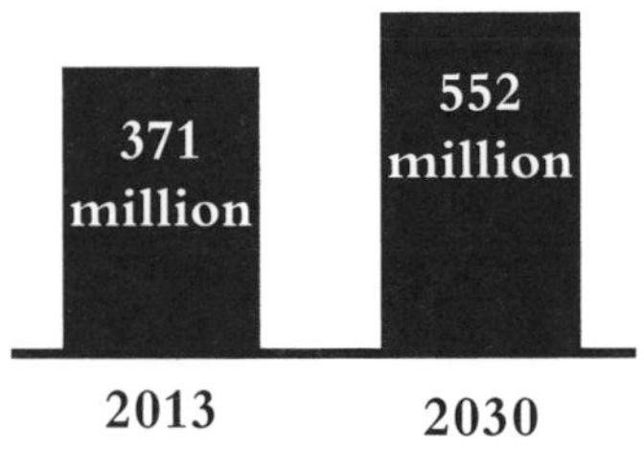

International Diabetes Foundation, IDF Diabetes Atlas

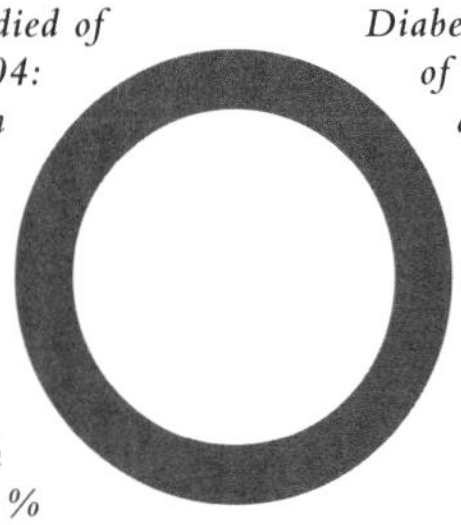

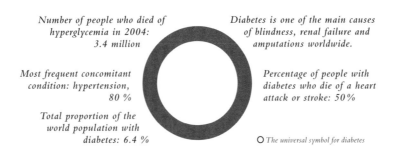

Number of people who died of hyperglycemia in 2004: 3.4 million

Most frequent concomitant condition: hypertension, 80 %

Total proportion of the world population with diabetes: 6.4 %

Diabetes is one of the main causes of blindness, renal failure and amputations worldwide.

Percentage of people with diabetes who die of a heart attack or stroke: 50 %

O *The universal symbol for diabetes*

WHO

Global spread of diabetes*, 2011

(% of the population)

* people aged 20–79

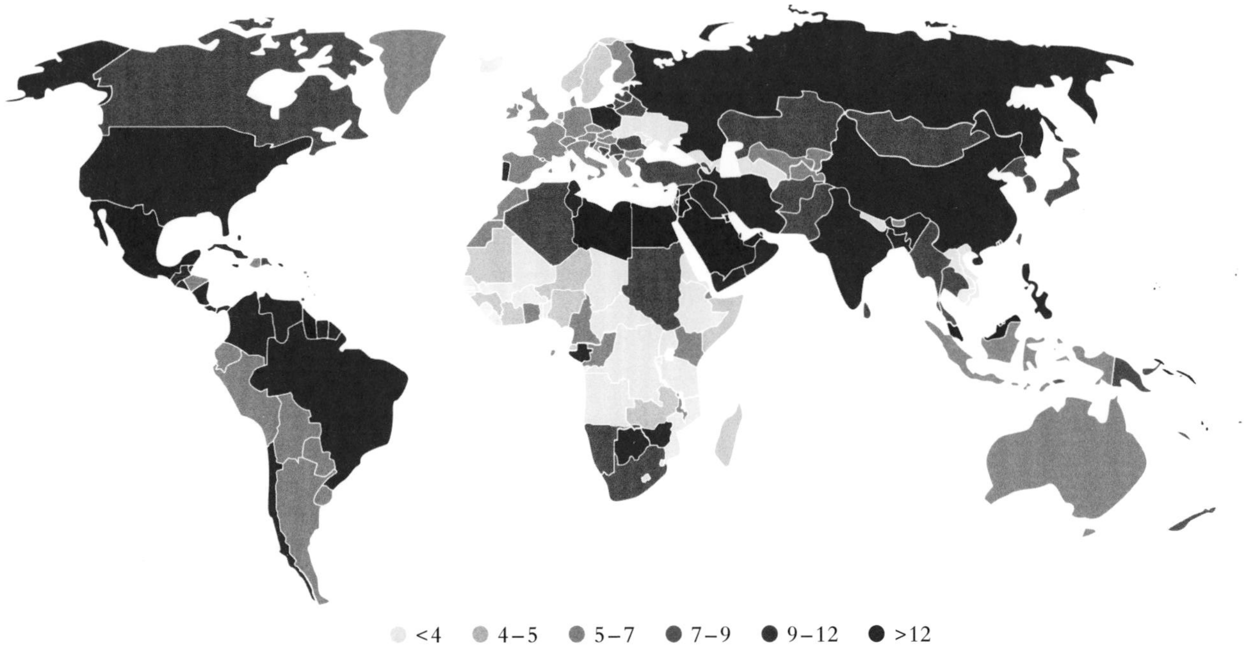

International Diabetes Foundation

Half
of all people with diabetes
don't know
they have the disease.

International Diabetes Foundation

30 MIN

of exercise each day significantly reduces the risk of type 2 diabetes.

WHO

The three most common types of diabetes:

Type 1 Reduced insulin production (congenital)

Type 2 Low insulin sensitivity; 90 % of all cases worldwide

Type 3 Gestational diabetes

WHO

Diabetes was the first non-infectious disease classified by the United Nations as a global threat to mankind.

UN

Innovative measuring devices

ONE DROP OF BLOOD IS ENOUGH

Diabetes mellitus is one of the main lifestyle diseases of the modern world. In Germany alone, seven million people have diabetes. The disease is increasingly a public health issue. Many people don't even realize they have diabetes because it doesn't hurt. However, the long-term damage can be dramatic. According to the International Diabetes Federation, there were 371 million people with diabetes worldwide in 2012. This figure is forecast to increase to 552 million in 2030.

40
Contour™
2003

Very high blood glucose levels can trigger a life-threatening diabetic coma. Fluctuations in blood glucose levels can only be detected by regular measurement, making it easier for people with diabetes to adjust their diet, daily routine and medication accordingly. Later effects can be prevented. Self-monitoring also makes it possible to reliably identify high or low blood glucose levels. Measuring their blood glucose level is therefore a daily routine for people with diabetes. Bayer has developed the Contour™ family of blood glucose monitoring systems for this purpose. First approved in 2003, they require just 0.6 microliters (0.0006 milliliters) of blood to analyze the blood glucose level and display the result in five seconds. The Diabetes Care business unit also markets devices with a USB connection for displaying the thousands of values they can store on a computer.

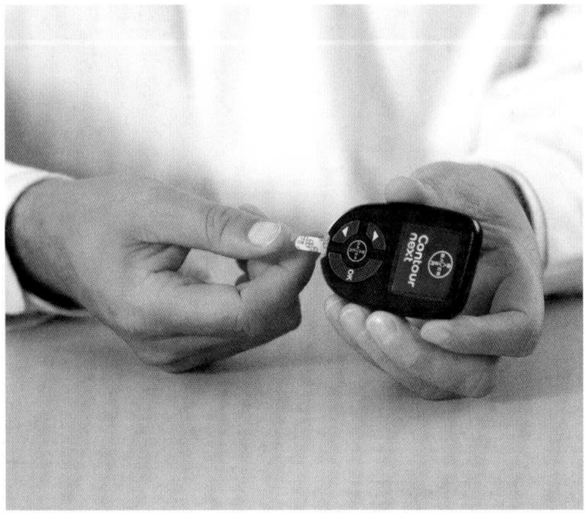

The Contour™ Next displays the user's current blood glucose level.

From bread rolls to active ingredient

THE BREAKFAST IDEA

Ideas are like surprise guests: they just turn up. Walter Puls, in charge of a pharmaceutical research team at Bayer, was enjoying his breakfast one day. Exactly what happened, he wondered, when he ate a bread roll? He thought about the enzymes that process carbohydrates on their way through the digestive organs. The date was October 25, 1968. For some years, Bayer had been searching for a product to effectively control diabetes. When, a short time later, bacteria of the genus Actinoplanes were discovered, Puls and his team made the crucial breakthrough. These bacteria are the basis for the biotechnological production of acarbose.

41
Glucobay™
1986

Acarbose significantly delays the breakdown of carbohydrates in the small intestine and the absorption of glucose and other simple sugars (monosaccharides) by the blood. As a result, blood glucose levels increase more slowly after a meal. The researchers had found the missing piece to a puzzle which began with an idea at breakfast. This was the foundation for the antidiabetes drug Glucobay™, which was first registered in 1986.

Active ingredient production: at the Wuppertal site, chemical production technician Christine Käseberg monitors the production of acarbose, an oral antidiabetes drug.

An American who loves soccer: Angelo Petrillo watched his first game during a stay in England – and now also enjoys visiting the BayArena stadium in Leverkusen.

THE NEXT GENERATION

Angelo Petrillo

Morristown, New Jersey, USA

Bayer HealthCare

ON THE BALL

Trust and respect are important, says project manager Angelo Petrillo. He likes the internationality of his job – and became a great soccer fan through his work.

My job as project manager is to ensure that everyone in my team does the tasks they are assigned. The team is made up of people from many departments – from R&D through to marketing, sales and licensing. I like problems. Problems are there to be solved. I often have to be a psychologist, have to listen, and sometimes have to close my ears if someone lets off steam. It's all about the common cause. Trust and respect are important. My father and my grandfather labored in a steel mill. I come from a working class family and that's shaped who I am.

One key to innovation is diversity, the range of cultures and ethnicities, internationality. I'm proud to be a part of this global Bayer community. During a long stay in England, I learned to love soccer. I became a fan of London club Arsenal – and whenever the opportunity arises I watch Bayer Leverkusen play at the BayArena stadium. The atmosphere is simply fantastic. I also learn from the coaches. I observe exactly how they lead their team. There are parallels with my job.

Angelo Petrillo

Angelo Petrillo was born in 1967 and grew up in Reading, Pennsylvania, USA. He studied chemistry at Lock Haven University, Pennsylvania, and at Rutgers, the State University of New Jersey, in New Brunswick. Angelo Petrillo is Director Global Project Management Analgesics for Bayer HealthCare, Consumer Care, in Morristown, New Jersey. He lives with his partner and three daughters in Phillipsburg, New Jersey.

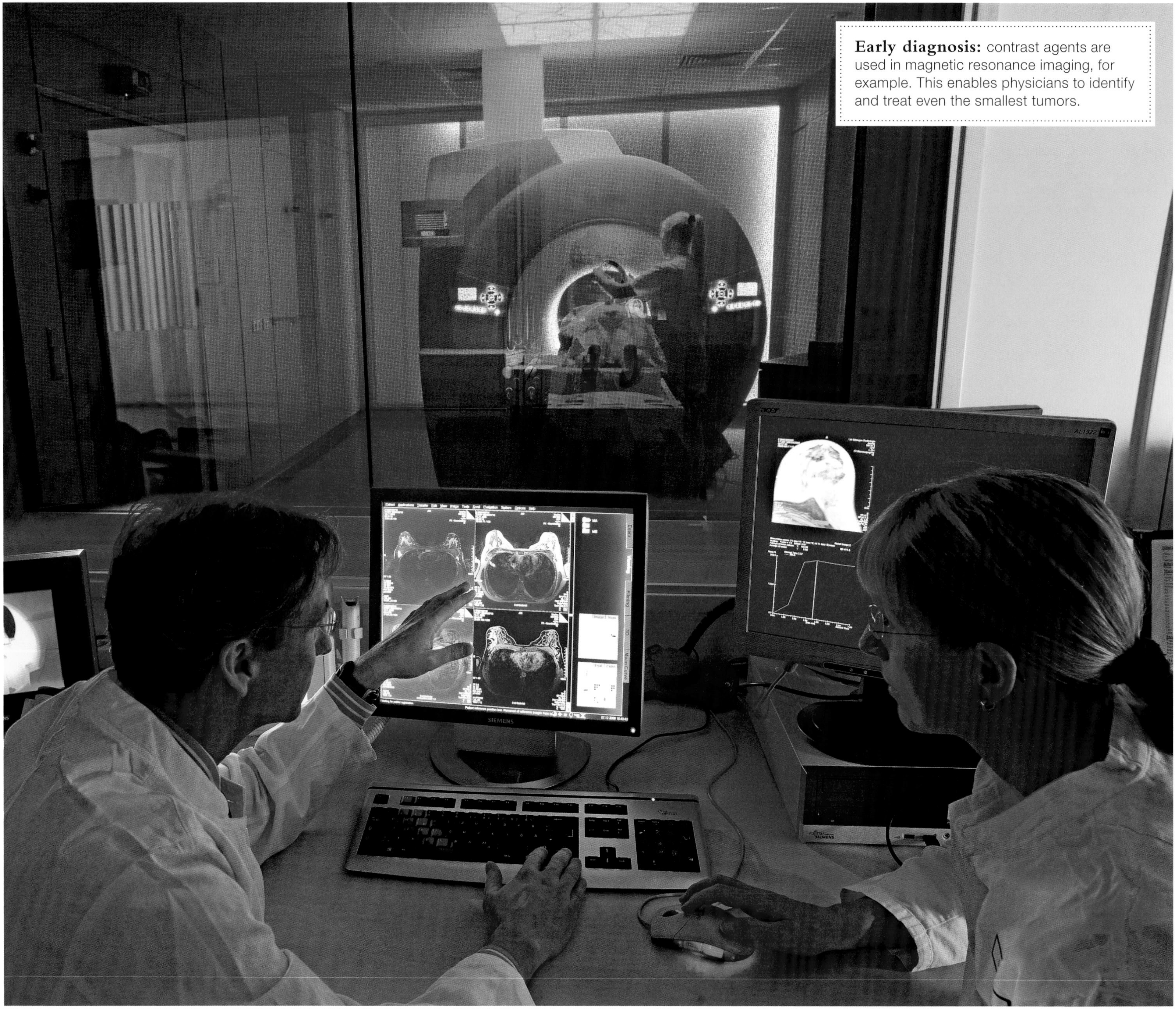

Early diagnosis: contrast agents are used in magnetic resonance imaging, for example. This enables physicians to identify and treat even the smallest tumors.

Innovative contrast agents and infusion devices

MEDICAL INSIGHTS

The invention of the X-ray machine in 1895 made it possible to look into the human body without surgical intervention for the first time, marking the beginning of medical imaging. Doctors now have many ways of checking the condition of organs and bones, and can do so with impressive accuracy. The products from Bayer HealthCare's Radiology & Interventional (R & I) business unit play an important role here.

42
Primovist™
2004

Bayer markets three contrast agents for magnetic resonance imaging (MRI). Primovist™, approved in 2004, was developed to be actively transported to healthy liver cells where it then accumulates. Doctors can then diagnose metastases in the liver even if they are only a few millimeters in size. In 1988, Bayer launched Magnevist™, the world's first MRI contrast agent, and in 2012, E.U. regulatory authorities granted its successor product Gadovist™ approval for MRI scanning of all body parts.

The added benefit of this new development is that the active ingredient molecules, thanks to their higher signal strength, produce particularly detailed images and only a relatively small amount of contrast agent is needed. Magnevist™ and Gadovist™ are non-cell specific, which means they spread through the body via the bloodstream. They enhance the contrast wherever differences in the flow of blood through tissue are visible, which may be a sign of a tumor. MRI can also be used to detect disease-related processes such as early-stage stroke and nerve lesions in multiple sclerosis. MRI images give doctors valuable information that enables them to initiate treatment earlier. Computed tomography (CT) is another diagnostic procedure widely used by cardiologists, orthopedists and oncologists. The most successful innovation in this field is Ultravist™, launched in 1985. The main component of this contrast agent is iodine, which has relatively large atoms and therefore weakens the X-rays. As a result, the points where it accumulates are brighter in CT images.

Bayer also markets programmable, automated injection equipment such as the Medrad Stellant™ system, which delivers high-precision contrast agent injections. The product range also includes infusion systems.

Therapeutic devices as an alternative to drugs

Drug products are vital to maintaining bloodflow in people suffering from certain conditions. Aspirin™ Cardio, for example, prevents blood platelet aggregation. Other products such as Xarelto™ inhibit the coagulation process in high-risk patients. If drug therapy cannot achieve the desired results, therapeutic devices are an alternative.

When doctors discover a blood clot that must be removed without delay, they frequently use AngioJet™, a system that guides a catheter through the vein until it encounters the thrombus, which it then pulverizes. Jetstream™ is a family of novel products for removing deposits from blood vessel walls. Each catheter is equipped with a two-millimeter cutting blade that pares away plaques at a speed of 70,000 revolutions per minute. The deposits are then removed from the bloodstream via a suction port.

Northern Rhodesia (Zambia), 1922: expedition member Dr. Walter Fischer examines the inhabitants of a village. He feels their necks to see whether their lymph nodes are swollen – a typical symptom of early-stage sleeping sickness.

In the "Heart of Darkness"

AN EXPEDITION INTO THE REALM OF SLEEPING SICKNESS

Mpika, Northern Rhodesia (Zambia), 1922. An expedition had been struggling through the jungle for months. The men were suffering from heat, and a lack of sleep and water. Professor Friedrich Karl Kleine, a highly respected doctor from Berlin who specialized in tropical medicine, had already covered hundreds of kilometers with his team. They wanted to free Africa from sleeping sickness, the scourge of the tropics, which kills millions and is a danger to travelers. Trypanosomiasis is carried by the tsetse fly. Its bite is hardly noticeable, but has devastating effects. Victims suffer fever and quickly lose weight. Their nerves and mental condition are devastated, their body spasms and limbs are paralyzed. A prolonged period of illness is followed by death.

Hope came from Elberfeld where, in 1916, Bayer employees Oscar Dressel and Richard Kothe developed a substance that worked in animals. Wilhelm Roehl, who directed the tests as head of the Chemotherapeutic Laboratory, was fascinated and approached Bayer's Managing Director, Carl Duisberg, to propose an expedition to Africa. Under the leadership of Professor Kleine, the group left Cape Town with 30 kilograms of the new drug "Bayer 205" in its baggage. It set up camp in the village of Ndombo, where Kleine wanted to treat fatally sick local inhabitants. Oral administration proved unsuccessful. However, when he diluted the substance in clean rainwater and injected it, the effect was dramatic: the symptoms eased within a few days. Some of the expedition members were reminded of the "miracle cures" related in the Bible. Kleine sent an enthusiastic report back to Leverkusen, stating that "Bayer 205 is the best substance we have to treat trypanosomiasis in humans." On January 6, 1923 it was registered with the Imperial Patents Office under the name Germanin™.

43

Germanin™

1923

Field research: a member of the expedition uses a microscope to conduct investigations.

In the meantime, Kleine had new problems to face, which he pondered on the veranda of the house he had had built. He needed to persuade patients to continue taking the substance for longer. Many of them were going back to their outlying villages as soon as their condition started to improve, and then they fell ill again. News of the medicine spread further afield. Hordes of patients made the pilgrimage to Kleine's house, and long queues formed outside his improvised consulting room. An item brought from Leverkusen came in handy here. Carl Duisberg had given the expedition a gramophone and those who were waiting passed the time listening to classical music.

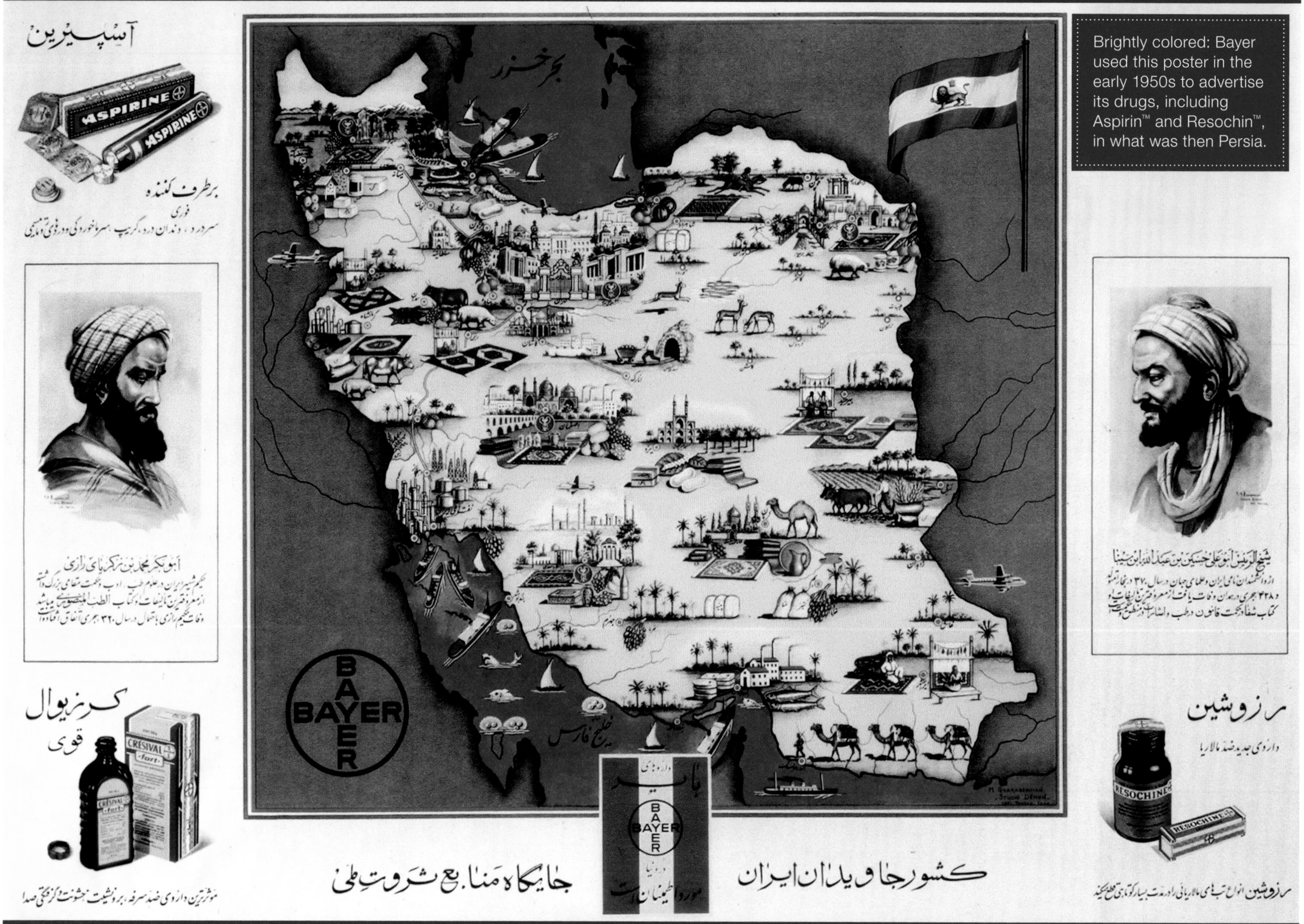

Brightly colored: Bayer used this poster in the early 1950s to advertise its drugs, including Aspirin™ and Resochin™, in what was then Persia.

Fighting bilharziasis

PROTECTION AGAINST THE CURSE OF THE GREAT RIVER

"El Fayoum" was a joint Egyptian-German project in which Bayer participated. It was named after an oasis where tests were carried out on substances aimed at eradicating the intermediate host of bilharziasis – a species of freshwater snail.

The Nile, also known as the "great river" or simply "the river," is sacred to the Egyptians. Every year it floods in late summer, irrigating vast tracts of land. It is this that has enabled people to survive in this drought-stricken region for thousands of years. But the river is also the source of deadly diseases – from the dawn of civilization to the present day.

A text written at the time of the Pharaohs tells of a plague that caused "violent stomach pain, heart palpitations, heartache and pain in the sides." This disease, "sent by the god of death," was incurable and fatal. Mummies from that era have been found to contain the worms that carry bilharziasis. The disease is prevalent near shallow waters, and where hygiene conditions are poor. It always follows the same course. In the river, the worms enter the human body through the skin and lay eggs which are eliminated by the body, usually back into the same water the worms came from.

44

Miracil

1949

Here the larvae emerge and infest freshwater snails, inside which they continue to develop and then re-infest humans. It is at this stage that the disease breaks out, causing skin rash, fever, and growths in the bladder and intestines. The disease can be fatal if not treated. Millions of Egyptians have the condition, and around a third of the world population is at risk – that third which has no access to clean water. Dr. Walter Kikuth, head of the Chemotherapeutic Laboratory in Elberfeld from 1929, was extremely concerned about this threat. He had already been involved in developing Plasmochin, an effective anti-malarial. He started testing countless substances to find a way of combating blood flukes, the worms that transmit bilharziasis. During the Second World War, Kikuth made a breakthrough in the laboratory. Hans Mauss was the "chemical inventor" who had discovered the effect of the new substance in 1938. It was given orally and was highly effective in controlling those forms of bilharziasis that affect the bladder, intestines and other organs. As it kills miracidia, the embryos that develop from the deadly worm eggs, it was given the name Miracil.

Miracil could not be tested until the end of the war. Trials took place in Northern Rhodesia (now Zambia), Egypt and the Congo and the new product was brought to market in 1949. Later, praziquantel (Biltricide™) was developed – a very significant and widely used active ingredient. Kikuth came a little closer to his goal of conquering tropical diseases.

Pioneering work in the fight against leprosy

HOPE FOR THE SHUNNED

45

Antileprol

1908

A **carriage had** been hooked up to the express train from Berlin to Bucharest. During long stops it was shunted into a siding and closely guarded. When a railway official approached, a small window was opened and an orderly was handed a tray of food. The empty plates were later destroyed and burned under supervision. All these precautions were taken because of one man, who was fatally ill. David Eisenmann was a leper being deported to his homeland under quarantine. Leprosy, the biblical plague, was regarded as a controlled disease by the early 20th century. That was why the Romanian patient's journey in 1907 attracted so much attention. The small number of leprosy sufferers still in Germany were kept in secure homes, and had no hope of a normal life, let alone a cure. The only 'remedy' for leprosy was a substance that had been obtained in India since antiquity but was not very effective. It had nasty side-effects and tasted revolting.

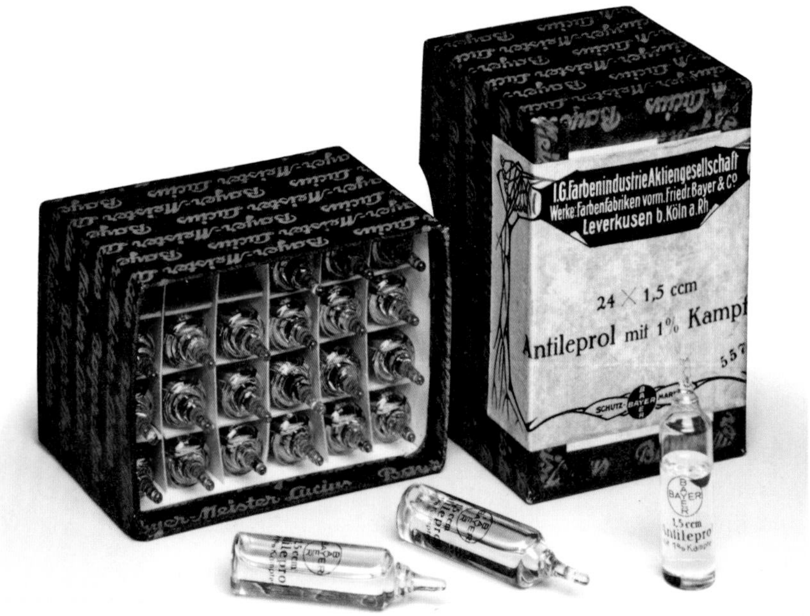

A pack of Antileprol, probably from around 1926

***There was no cure.
Not yet.***

Patients are helpless in the face of the disease. Their skin becomes pale and numb; lumps and swellings form. As sensation is lost in the affected parts of the body, countless small injuries lead to decay and disfigurement throughout the body. Tissue death results from a lack of blood to the patients' hands and feet. In the same year that the leprosy carriage passed through Germany, a chemist in Elberfeld named Ludwig Taub started to investigate the Indian drug – the oil obtained from the nuts of the rare chaulmoogra tree. Esterification of the oleic acid resulted in a preparation that was easier to tolerate, and Antileprol was launched in 1908. It acted on the mycobacteria that trigger leprosy. Although not strong enough to control the disease worldwide, Antileprol put leprosy treatment on a new course. As a result, the disease would eventually be almost entirely eradicated.

Malaria research

RESEARCH IN A WORKSHOP

The search for a cure for malaria had been going on for centuries – without success. Desperate patients in Europe endured Turkish baths and gastric lavage. They swallowed a concoction made of wormwood and brandy with a sprinkling of crushed iron nails. But one thing was known: the bark of the quina tree, brought back by missionaries from South America, reduced the fever.

46
Plasmochin
1927

In Elberfeld in the early 1920s, Wilhelm Roehl, who had been working for Bayer for many years and was involved in the development of Germanin™ to treat African sleeping sickness, had set up a laboratory in a former plumber's workshop. He was testing substances on canaries that had been infected with malaria. In 1924, he managed to control the pathogens using a substance that would later become known as Plasmochin. The new substance killed the pathogens before they were fully developed, was better tolerated than quinine and 30 times more effective. Trials were conducted in Italy and Spain, and soon there was no longer any doubt that Roehl had discovered the first synthetic drug to treat malaria. It came to market in 1927, just three years after it was discovered.

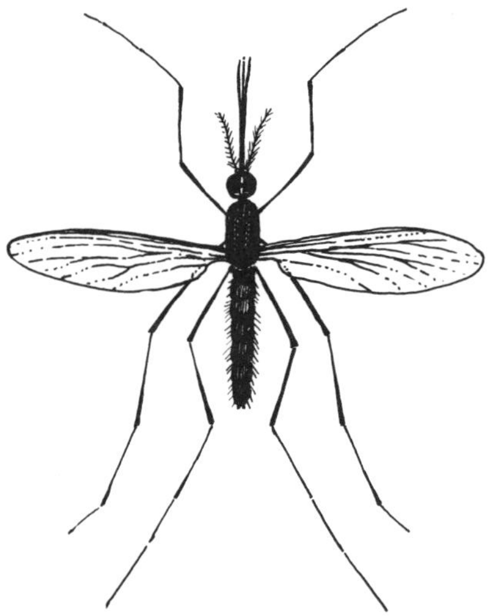

The malaria-carrying mosquito: the scourge of the tropics

Insect breeding

THE MOSQUITOES OF ELBERFELD

Elberfeld in the early 1930s: Dr. Walter Kikuth, a specialist in tropical medicine and head of Bayer's Chemotherapeutic Laboratory, had thousands of mosquitoes shipped in from abroad. This was done under the strictest security conditions because the insects carried the malaria pathogen.

47
Resochin™
1937

Kikuth was looking for a substance to control the disease which had been devastating entire regions for over 5,000 years, killing emperors, popes and pharaohs. It is most common in tropical swamp regions and this is where it gets its name, which literally means "bad air." Doctors had been powerless for centuries. The pathogen, which is transmitted by mosquitoes, was first discovered in the 19th century. This led the chemists in Elberfeld to their breakthrough. By 1932 they had developed Plasmochin and Atebrin, two products that were far more effective than quinine. But they had nasty side-effects, and so Kikuth continued his search. He used the mosquitoes from his breeding program to infect small animals with the disease. After testing 12,000 substances he eventually found a true wonder drug: chloroquine. This was synthesized by Hans Andersag, Stefan Breitner and Heinrich Jung in 1934 and registered as Resochin™ in 1937.

Effective against Chagas disease

A GIFT FROM THE HEART

The bugs come at night, creeping through gaps in walls and doors, especially in the slums of South America. As they sleep, people are infected by the bug's feces which contain trypanosomes. These parasites colonize the heart and nervous system, causing the insidious condition known as Chagas disease. Sufferers initially have few symptoms apart from a high fever, but this is when the parasites are reproducing and destroying body cells. After this acute phase the disease becomes chronic and gradually weakens the heart muscle, often going undetected for years. A long phase of illness begins, leading to death if no treatment is given. In the late 1960s, the World Health Organization (WHO) reported that at least seven million people in South America were suffering from Chagas disease. This was when nifurtimox was first synthesized by Bayer. The treatment principle of this substance in Chagas disease is the formation of free radicals by the parasites which are toxic for them. The drug came onto the market as Lampit™ in 1970. It is still the only product in the world to contain this substance. Bayer has been supporting WHO in its fight against Chagas disease with regular provision of Lampit™ tablets since 2004.

48
Lampit™
1970

Able to smile again: a girl from Honduras with Chagas disease (at front)

Medicinal fibers

PROTECTED BY LIFENET

Just one bite can destroy a life, but a net is enough to protect it effectively against the Anopheles mosquito. In Africa, one child dies of malaria every 30 seconds. The disease affects more than 225 million people worldwide. Hope comes from Bayer CropScience, which has developed a mosquito net that provides longer protection against bites than its predecessors: LifeNet™.

Unlike conventional nets, which often tear after just a few months, it is made from polypropylene, a plastic that is first spun into fine threads for this purpose. Working with Bayer Technology Services, developers were able to incorporate an insecticide into the fibers that greatly enhances the net's protective function. Patented in 2008, LifeNet™ exceeds the strict stability and durability requirements set by WHO. Bayer plans to use the product as its contribution to the U.N. millennium goal of reducing new malaria cases from 2015.

49
LifeNet™
2008

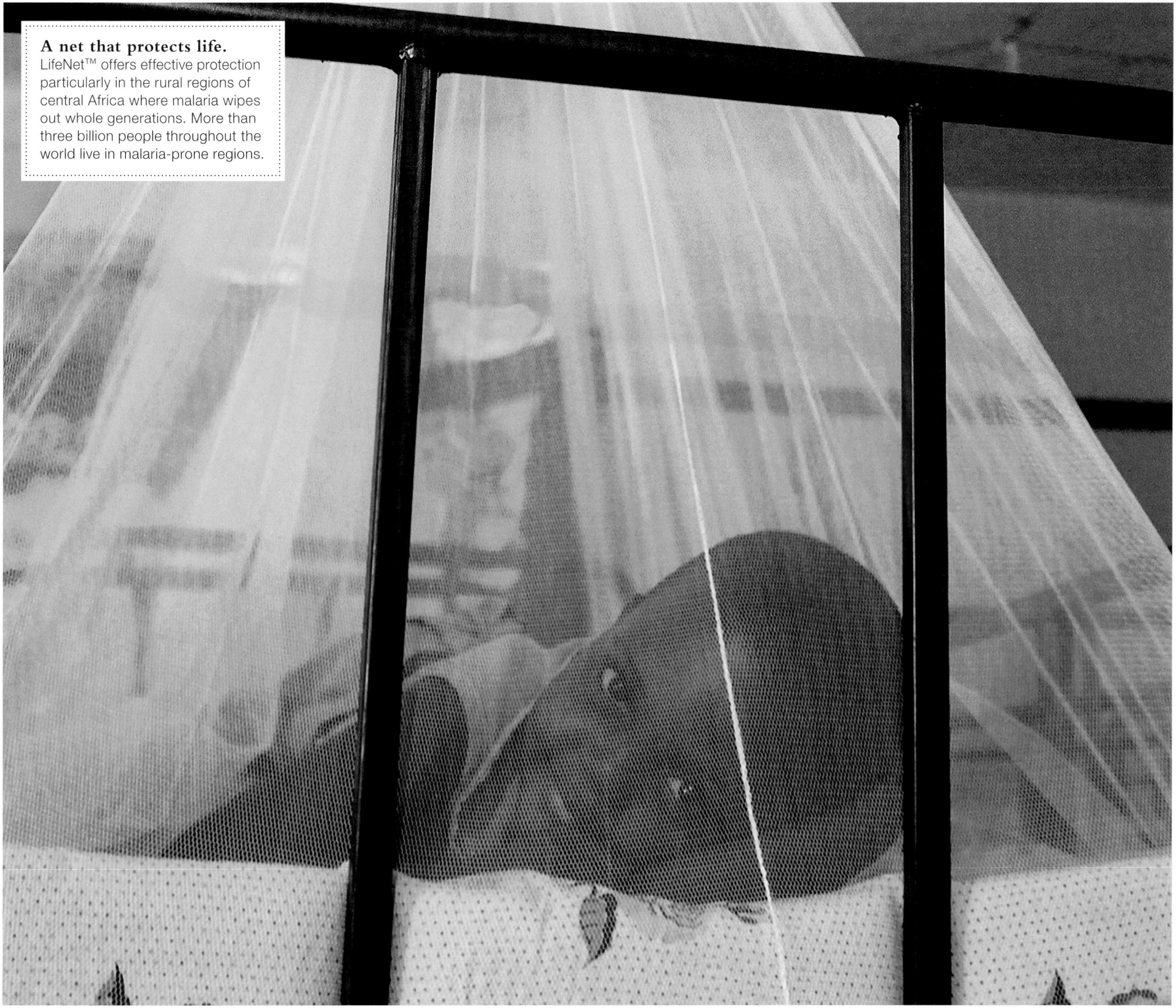

A net that protects life.
LifeNet™ offers effective protection particularly in the rural regions of central Africa where malaria wipes out whole generations. More than three billion people throughout the world live in malaria-prone regions.

Karl Heinz Büchel is a well-known philatelist. His home also houses a collection of objets d'art he acquired on his travels. Always close by: wire-haired dachshund Don.

50

Karl Heinz Büchel

Clotrimazole

1973

Clotrimazole, the first broad-spectrum antimycotic, was registered as Canesten™ in 1973 (see also page 142). The azoles prevent cell wall development in fungi by blocking the formation of an essential cell wall component. This makes the fungal cell unstable. Azoles have the same effect on fungal pathogens in both humans and plants and are therefore also the basis for successful crop protection products.

A PASSIONATE CHEMIST

Karl Heinz Büchel wasn't just a researcher. He was also a member of Bayer's Board of Management. Here he explains the five main factors in innovation – and how a childhood game with firebombs shaped his life.

I **was a** chemist and inventor with all my heart and soul but as the Management Board member responsible for innovation at Bayer and a budget of billions for almost two decades I also got to know the other side of a desk. On the basis of this experience I can say that innovation is always a team success and the interaction between many disciplines – starting with the chemist. But he alone can do little with his discovery because industrial research is far too complex.

The next stage of product development is efficacy testing. Competent testers are needed to determine the properties of a new active ingredient, for example. The toxicologists make sure the substance is safe and the expertise of the lawyers is crucial to securing the patent. Production experts develop an economical manufacturing process and the business managers devise the sales concept as the basis for commercial success. Today, no-one can do without a snappy marketing concept.

You shouldn't try cutting costs in the chemical synthesis stage at the start of the innovation process. The chemists who discover new substances are the key figures and the least expensive link in the product development chain. There are five main factors in innovation: intellect, patience, money, luck and legislation. The latter is doubly important today because the maze of regulations and bans, for example those concerning genetic engineering, means we are at risk of losing touch completely – especially in Germany.

Researchers need room to maneuver. As a researcher, I had a specific field of activity within my subject area. As a research manager, I covered a wide area and couldn't always apply the same thoroughness I was used to as a scientist. But both functions required intuition. And I enjoyed both functions.

"Innovation needs space. You can't command or prescribe it."

It was evident from an early age that I was fascinated with chemistry. I liked sitting in front of the coal stove in the kitchen and watching how the fire turned the stone-hard briquettes into powder. I grew up in Beuel across the Rhine from Bonn during the war years. My mother and I spent a lot of time in the bunker on Limperische Strasse. In the fall of 1944, a bomb came down right next to it. The explosion was incredible, the light went out and the air was filled with cement dust but the steel-reinforced concrete held out. I remember nights when the sirens wailed and we ran to the bunker in our pyjamas and slippers. I can still taste the sausage broth we fetched in milk cans from Ferres the butcher in Kaiserstrasse and brought to the bunker so we survived.

After the war, we children collected ears of grain from the fields and beechnuts from the woods or we poked round the potato fields after the harvest in the hope of still finding something edible. Our fun was setting off unexploded firebombs and other munitions. You had to look for a certain marking which indicated the presence of an explosive device. We would then ignite the hexagonal sticks by hitting them with a stone. The heat produced was enormous and we war children had no idea how dangerous our hobby was. We were very rarely scared, having survived the nights in the bunker.

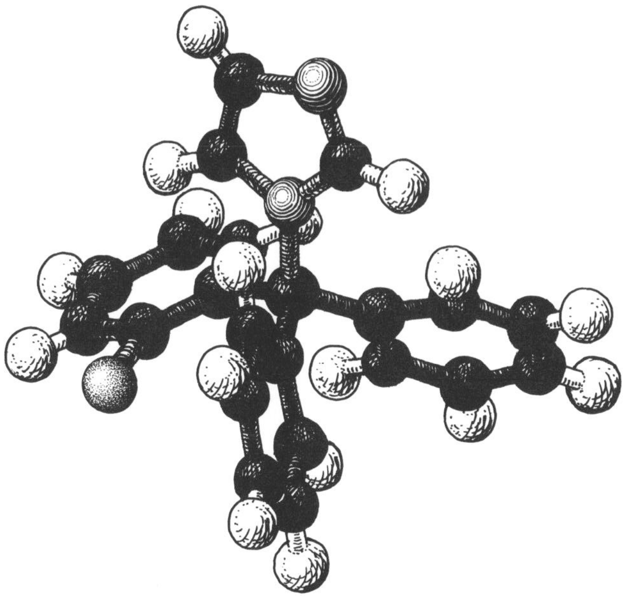

Spherical model of clotrimazole

There are things from these years which shape you. I can't throw food away and I've always had a tendency to take risks. That's probably also why my career path was unusual. After school and university – which I financed by playing in a swing band – I found a job in research at Royal Dutch Shell. I worked in the United States, England and

Bonn, Germany, but realized during the first oil crisis in 1966 that there was no future there for chemists so I applied to Bayer. As a "Shell refugee," things weren't easy for me at the start. My direct and emotional way of dealing with people made it a little easier.

> *"I found being a retiree difficult at first. I liked my job so much that I enjoyed driving to headquarters every day."*

Some of the things on the list of tasks my supervisor gave me seemed quite provincial. I systematically ignored ideas like that and I wasn't one to hold my tongue. My early successes and inventions protected me. A few months after I started, I found a new class of active substances – the azoles, fungicides that help both humans and plants.

Five years after joining Bayer, I was made Head of Research in the Crop Protection Division. Four years later, I became Head of Central Research and a short time after that I was appointed to the Board of Management. It didn't hurt me that I occasionally caused a minor upset or that my non-conformist behavior became the stuff of legends.

I liked to praise people and encourage performance. And I liked to celebrate. That was part of it. I saw myself as a popular champion. It was always an advantage that as a Management Board member and the discoverer of clotrimazole and bifonazole I could reproduce all the substances a researcher had discovered and that no-one could fool me when it came to science. There's not really any other way to explain how I was able to stay in such an exposed position for almost two decades.

I once made the headlines in a private capacity when my dachshund Azzo got stuck down a foxhole. I was able to dig him out and rescue him after an eleven-day search. It was a big story in *Bild*, one of Germany's most popular yellow press newspapers.

My greatest Bayer moments were when we were contacted by patients who had been helped by our products. Chemistry that does something for people – that was always my dream. I found being a retiree difficult at first. Not because of the loss of power; that wasn't important to me. It was more because I found my job absolutely fascinating, although others might have perceived it as stressful. I liked my job so much that I enjoyed driving to headquarters every day. This passion gave me strength.

Karl Heinz Büchel

Professor Karl Heinz Büchel was born in 1931 in Beuel near Bonn, the son of a music teacher. He joined Bayer in 1966 and was appointed the Management Board member responsible for research in 1977. Karl Heinz Büchel likes music ("Every Büchel tortures some instrument"), hunts and is considered one of the great philatelists in the Rhineland. He holds three honorary doctorates, one of which he received in 1995 for his services to universities in eastern Germany following reunification. Karl Heinz Büchel is married and has two children. He lives with his family near Leverkusen, Germany.

The fungus stopper

THE UNIVERSAL CURE FOR AN UNPLEASANT COMPANION

They lurk in every swimming pool, every sauna, every hotel bathroom but also at home: fungal infections. Statistically speaking, one in five of us suffers from some form of athlete's foot. The problem is that these parasites are unaffected by their host's daily hygiene routines and spread readily to other areas of skin and mucous membranes. It's an unpleasant condition that nobody likes to talk about. For many years, each individual species of fungus had to be treated with its own specific product. But in the 1960s, chemist and later Bayer Management Board member Karl Heinz Büchel (his profile is on page 138) made an astonishing discovery: the active substance clotrimazole, which is effective against a wide range of fungal pathogens – a universal cure for fungal infections. The product came to market in 1973 under the name Canesten™. Soon after, it gained over-the-counter status as a result of its excellent tolerability.

51

Canesten™

1973

Thanks to its good tolerability, Canesten™ – this picture shows the production facility in Leverkusen in 1993 – was switched to over-the-counter status.

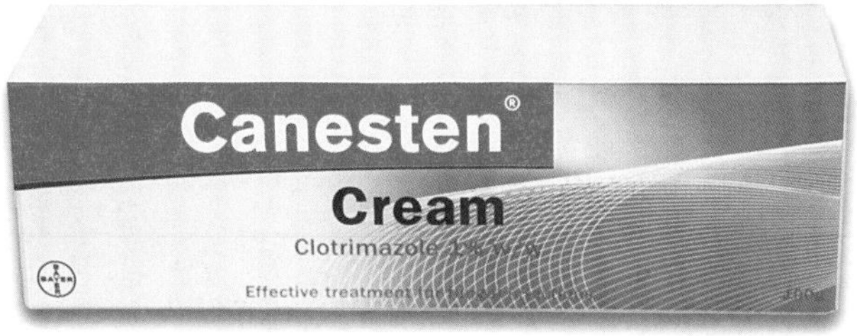

Universal treatment for fungal infections: Canesten™

The mechanisms of action of Canesten™ are complex. It inhibits the enzyme lanosterol demethylase, thus damaging the fungal cell membrane. It also binds phospholipids and natural substances and thereby intervenes in the cell structure of the fungus. Canesten™ allows users to effectively get rid of this unpleasant and tenacious condition. Today a whole family of products is available for special indications such as fungal nail infections, vaginal thrush and athlete's foot.

Bepanthen™: a versatile skin healer

THE OINTMENT THAT HAS HEALED SCRATCHES FOR GENERATIONS

Drugs that can be purchased without a prescription are known as over-the-counter (OTC) medicines. Aspirin™ is without doubt the most famous product in this segment. But there is another product that is fast becoming equally indispensable. Introduced by the Swiss company F. Hoffmann-La Roche AG in 1944 and acquired by Bayer in 2005, it has been providing gentle healing skincare for the whole family for more than 60 years. Its name: Bepanthen™.

Bepanthen™ is more than just an ointment. To young mothers with newborns, it's a powerful yet gentle ally in helping them protect against nappy (diaper) rash, which is now the best-selling indication for this remarkable skin healer. However, the success of Bepanthen™ has been fueled by a story of constant innovation, taking it from its beginnings in wound care to eye drops, eczema relief and now also stretchmark prevention – combining characteristic efficacy with a gentle touch.

52

Bepanthen™

1944

What makes Bepanthen™ remarkable as a skin healer is the active ingredient dexpanthenol, an alcohol analog of pantothenic acid, also known as vitamin B_5 – a key skin vitamin.

Vitamin B_5 was discovered by the U.S. nutritional biologist and biochemist Roger Williams in 1931. The name pantothenic acid is derived from the fact that the vitamin is present in almost all foodstuffs (the Greek word "pantos" meaning every or all). What's significant about vitamin B_5 are its beneficial effects on the skin and mucosa, delivering a restorative and regenerative effect and boosting dermal elasticity by increasing the synthesis of collagen. These special properties have recently been harnessed for the latest launch: a highly innovative scar treatment which helps reduce the appearance of raised and red scars. Thanks to the novel delivery system, it optimizes microcirculation to aid the healing process. Thanks to its remarkable healing properties combined with novel applications, this innovative and versatile skin healer is attracting new users around the globe.

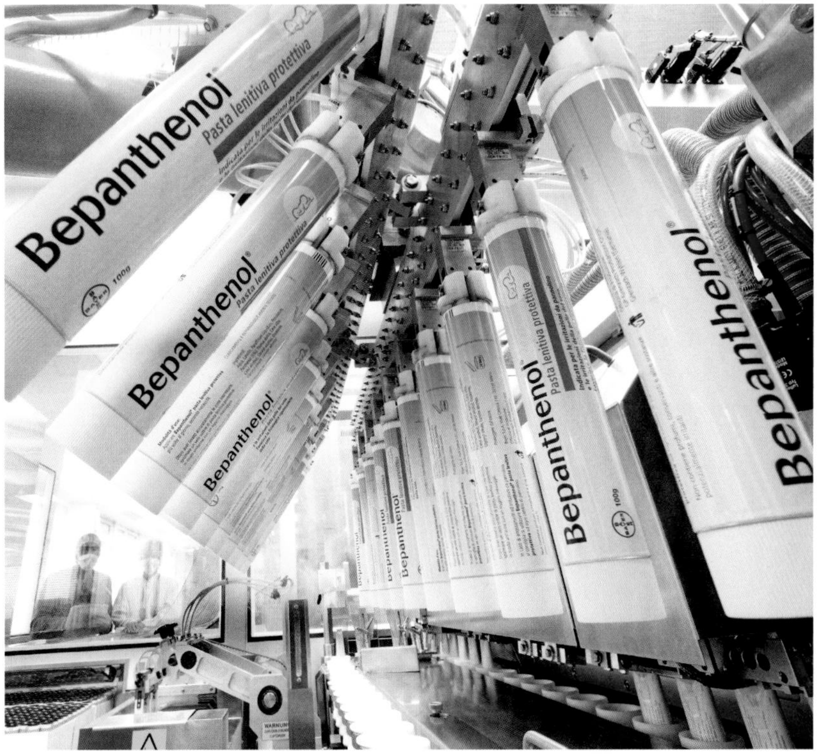

Bepanthenol™, a member of the Bepanthen™ product family, is automatically filled into tubes in a production facility in Grenzach, Germany. From there, it is shipped to many countries.

A researcher with a vintage hobby: Lothar Willms and friends own a small vineyard in the Moselle valley. He particularly enjoys helping with the harvest.

53

Lothar Willms

Safener technology

1971

Safener technology, which has been known since 1971, improves the selectivity of herbicides by exploiting minimal differences between the enzyme systems of weeds and crop plants.
The safener helps crop plants to break down the herbicide more quickly into harmless degradation products. Safeners are also used in products for cereals (see page 147).

MOLECULES AND GRAPEVINES

Lothar Willms comes from a wine-growing region. He remains true to this passion even now and enjoys helping with the harvest on the steep slopes. And while he's working, he can see whether the products of his regular job have passed the field test.

I **grew up** in Unkel, a small wine-growing town on the Rhine that claims to lie on the sunny side of the Siebengebirge hills. My grandfather had a vineyard. As a boy, I sometimes helped with the harvest and in the winery. No doubt what is now my hobby had its origins back then. In my free time, I'm a passionate winegrower. Not in the Rhineland now but in the Moselle valley, in the famous terraced vineyards at Winningen, which are among the steepest in the world. We have a small section, slightly more than half a hectare, that we share with friends. Harvest time in October is my favorite time. The vineyard has an incline of 45 degrees and work there is pretty hard – especially climbing up and down. The winemaker uses our grapes to produce a fine Riesling or Weißburgunder (Pinot Blanc). Our wines have even won several awards. I enjoy doing something with friends and being outdoors.

I got into chemistry because of a Christmas present. My parents gave me a chemistry kit for school students. They may perhaps have regretted this choice a little later because I made a lot of noise. I was fascinated by anything that sparked and flashed. At school, on the other hand, I got little encouragement. At 15, I began experimenting with fuels and was interested in rockets. I'd rather not say anything about the experiments and their collateral damage but my enthusiasm for the world of chemistry grew. I went to university in Bonn in 1971. This was the era of the "Außerparlamentarische Opposition" (extra-parliamentary opposition), of wild demonstrations which affected even the otherwise tranquil suburb of Poppelsdorf. Seven years later, I left the university with my doctorate.

From the several job offers I had, I chose a Frankfurt-based company and started out in crop protection research, synthesizing herbicides. Back then, there weren't many good products on the market.

> ***"The working environment has to be right. A glass of good wine with colleagues sometimes helps."***

Their environmental performance left a lot to be desired. After four years, I came up with my first active substance – amidosulfuron. This gently and effectively controls weeds such as goose grass, which at the time was a major problem for many farmers in Europe.

I quickly became a team leader and was then made responsible for agriculture in the central management department. I was no longer just a researcher but a research manager. Over the next few years I held various positions in research management, even moving to Paris for a time. Back in Frankfurt, I was part of the team that brought chemists and biologists closer together. Pragmatic interdisciplinary work in the laboratories, in the greenhouses and in the field yielded successes in the area of safener technology. This ensures that many active substances can be tolerated by crop plants and that only the target weeds are harmed. What always fascinates me particularly about this work is translating the chemical structure or structural information of a substance into a biological effect.

But I've also experienced what happens when a company loses its way. It was almost impossible to keep track of the number of times my employer merged with other companies or sold entire business lines. It was only when we finally landed in the Bayer fold that things calmed down again.

If innovation is to be possible, the working environment has to be right. Crucial features are freedom of thought, mutual trust and few regulations. You have to encourage, develop and reward your employees. Silo thinking, as I call it when a department beavers away on its own, shouldn't be allowed. I'm convinced that a glass of good wine with friends or colleagues also helps sometimes. If the wine is from your own vineyard, then so much the better.

Lothar Willms

Dr. Lothar Willms was born in Unkel in 1952. He has received various prizes, including the Otto Bayer Medal, for his research achievements. Lothar Willms is married and has one son. He lives near Koblenz, Germany.

Safeners to protect plants

THE PROBLEM OF THE SAME ANCESTORS

Atlantis – the name is a legend, a myth, the lost city mentioned in the writings of Greek philosopher Plato. It was a mysterious empire that was way ahead of its time in terms of technology and was said to have even controlled the weather before it sank into the ocean. For farmers around the world – especially those who grow wheat – the name is no longer just a reference from Greek mythology but a product from Bayer CropScience, a herbicide which protects their plants. In particular, it is effective against the dreaded black grass.

54

Atlantis™

2001

Crops and their weeds frequently have the same ancestors. Therefore, the goal for the researchers at Bayer CropScience is to develop herbicides that provide protection against weeds yet are well-tolerated by crops. For this reason, substances called safeners are added to herbicides. They increase the production of degrading enzymes in the plant that is being protected. These break down the active substance into harmless by-products.

Bayer's Atlantis™, which was introduced in 2001, is extremely effective against grasses. These are a major problem in modern agriculture and especially in wheat. It is estimated that more than 50 million hectares worldwide are affected by unwanted grasses which compete with crop plants for nutrients and water. These grasses can overrun entire crops, destroying harvests or at the very least reducing their quality. Atlantis™ has proved its capabilities in various regions and its effectiveness is not impacted by low temperatures. The unwanted grass stops growing after five to seven days and turns yellow. Its leaves wilt after ten to 14 days. After six weeks at most, the grass has been destroyed.

Over more than five years, Bayer's researchers tested and optimized Atlantis™ for flexible application in controlling weeds and grasses in cereal crops.

Bahar Miraghazadeh and Dr. Peter Chandler from the Commonwealth Scientific and Industrial Research Organisation (CSIRO) in Canberra, Australia, examine wheat plants.

Graham Holmwood's first trip from England to Germany was made in a Morris Minor like this. It's still his favorite car.

55

Graham Holmwood

Tebuconazole

1988

Tebuconazole, approved as Folicur™ in 1988, is a substance that is effective in controlling fungal diseases in many broad-acre crops including wheat, barley, rye, winter and summer oilseed rape, and in fruit and vegetables.

GENTLEMAN

A romantic journey brought Briton Graham Holmwood to Germany for the first time. Decades later, the inventor of fungicides now feels at home in the Rhineland – and misses only one very British institution.

I **came to** Germany for the first time out of love for a woman – to be precise, because of my school friend Johnny's unhappy relationship. He had lost his heart to a girl named Monika and because he still missed her years later, I decided to accompany him on his mission. Monika lived near Stuttgart and we came from Chelmsford, near London. In a Morris Minor, we took the ferry to Ostend and then traveled to southern Germany via Cologne. The middle of the Swinging Sixties was a wonderful time. Our trip wasn't very successful – Monika had another boyfriend – but I liked the country so much that, four years later, I applied for a post doc position at the University of Bonn while all my fellow students wanted to go to universities in the United States or Canada.

My father was a gentleman's outfitter who worked in London and then in Hull, Manchester and Glasgow before returning to London, advising his customers in matters of fashion and supplying them with tailor-made suits and bowler hats. I remember the delicate smell of sandalwood in the shop because this was used for the cores on which the bolts of cloth were wound. I spent a lot of time in the shop and liked watching the tailors as they worked. We lived for a while near the famous Old Trafford stadium and could hear from our garden when Manchester United scored a goal. We moved often. My parents always looked for a good school first and then for a house close by. They paid attention to our education. Science was my favorite subject right from the start. I jumped a year so I had to wait before I could go to university. I was awarded a scholarship from a glass company for my degree and got my PhD at the age of 24.

During the summer vacation, I worked as a trainee at their factory in Glasgow. I can think of one comparison to describe the working conditions there: Dante's Inferno. Flame throwers spat columns of fire, it was unbearably hot and the men at the furnaces – which were shrouded in the blue shimmer of sulfur dioxide – drank up to ten pints of beer to replace the fluids they lost. I learned a lot during this time. I understood how hard some people labor to earn a living.

"The sky was black from the smoke of coal fires."

When I look back on the years I spent in the north of the British Isles, I remember the black sky. People heated their homes with coal fires, smoke poured from the factory chimneys and smog often blanketed the city in the dark months, dense and heavy, like in the Edgar Wallace Mysteries. You could hardly see your hand in front of your face, your nostrils were rimmed with black soot and breathing was difficult.

In the early 1970s it was hard finding a job because the economy was in a bad way. I view it as luck that I found my way to Bayer after university. I had turned down another offer in England before I got confirmation because I liked the way Bayer replied to my application and I wanted to live here. Over the years, I've almost become a Rhinelander. Do I miss anything from the country of my birth? The coziness of an old pub.

I worked in both pharmaceuticals and crop protection research, developing fungicides. There is always an element of luck in a researcher's success and ability to innovate. I can say this with the experience of some 10,500 substances that were synthesized in my lab: you need to be in the right place at the right time with the right idea. One of my best days was when a development candidate of mine was used during a clinical study on a young skier who had broken her leg. The fracture was infected with a fungus that was spreading on the bone. My substance was the last hope before amputation – the infection disappeared within a few days and her leg was saved.

I'll never forget the day I got the news that a crop protection product from my lab had yielded extremely promising test results and a patent application was soon to be made. I experienced a deep joy and could have hugged everyone. The phone rang again a short time later. I was given the news that my father had died.

Graham Holmwood

Dr. Graham Holmwood was born in London in 1947, studied in Nottingham and Leeds, and joined Bayer in 1974. In the early 1980s, he synthesized tebuconazole, an important fungicide. He was awarded the Otto Bayer Medal for this achievement. Graham Holmwood has two adult children from his first marriage, who both live in Great Britain. He lives with his second wife in Hitdorf, Germany.

Second-generation fungicide

PLANTS NEED AN ANCHOR

Experts call it the anchoring effect. Strong and well-branched roots are crucial to the health of cereal crops. They act like an anchor, even during dry periods when water reserves in the soil start to run low. Launched in 1980, Baytan™ is a liquid seed dressing which protects plants against fungal diseases and promotes root growth.

56

Baytan™

1980

Following decades of development work and extensive testing, researchers at Bayer CropScience were able to build on this tradition with Baytan™ 2.

This combines three active substances that protect against the diseases and fungal infections which cause stress and inhibit plant growth. Triadimenol (also found in the original Baytan™) has been coupled with the fungicides prothioconazole and triazoxide. All three substances intervene in the synthesis of the fungus and disrupt cell membrane formation, causing the fungus to die.

Triple protection for plants

After germination, the active substances form a protective "halo" around the young plants – protecting them right from the start. This triple protection is effective against other pathogens. Triadimenol has a special role. It shortens and thickens the mesocotyl (the tissue between the seed and the first tillering node), making the plant more robust and less sensitive to the cold.

An Michiels of Bayer CropScience (left) and Ofer Haviv of Evogene examine young plants.

Father and son, two generations of Bayer researchers: Manfred (left) and Rolf Jautelat in the garden. Jautelat senior is an enthusiastic beekeeper.

57

Manfred Jautelat

Prothioconazole

2004

Prothioconazole is a fungicidal active substance from the innovative triazolinthione chemical class developed by Bayer CropScience. It is highly effective against, for example, all economically harmful fusarium species and thus reduces the content of hazardous mycotoxins (see also page 155). Prothioconazole was approved in 2004.

A FATHER AND SON THING

Manfred Jautelat and his son Rolf are both organic chemists. Jautelat senior worked in Central Research looking for fungicides, while Jautelat junior now researches medicines. A family conversation.

Mr. Jautelat, based on your experience as the senior of the two of you, what has changed in research?

MANFRED JAUTELAT: The ways of working, the methods are entirely different. We used to spend many hours in libraries. That is unthinkable today in the era of the Internet and high-speed data links. We used to dream of being able to access information at the touch of a few buttons!

ROLF JAUTELAT: That's true. While we're talking here in Leverkusen, I can use my phone to go online and track research findings or download publications. I can access my projects at any time around the clock. But you shouldn't be envious.

MANFRED JAUTELAT: Why not?

ROLF JAUTELAT: The image of pharmaceutical research has changed significantly in recent years and our room to maneuver is shrinking. The time pressure we now face is increasing and expectations are higher. You had more peace and quiet for your research.

What is still the same?

MANFRED JAUTELAT: I was discovering new molecules. That's what my son does, too. I was researching ways to control harmful fungi that can destroy harvests. My son is researching ways to fight cancer cells.

ROLF JAUTELAT: Yes, that aspect has great significance for me. I want to help people; that's important to me. It might sound a little strange in our very rational times but it's the reason I came to work for a pharmaceutical company.

But not at Bayer to start with?

ROLF JAUTELAT: No. I didn't want people saying: that's Jautelat's son. I wanted to make my own way, which is why I started out in medicinal chemistry at Schering in Berlin. I couldn't have guessed that Schering would one day be bought by Bayer.

What fascinates you about your job?

MANFRED JAUTELAT: All of life is chemistry, even if the term unfortunately has many negative connotations in the public perception. The complexity of life is created from just a few molecular building blocks – DNA, amino acids, fats and sugars. Every year, we manage to understand it a bit better.

Is chemistry still a topic of conversation at home?

MANFRED JAUTELAT: Oh yes. We meet up regularly and we both withdraw to my study. I may have retired but my son keeps me up to date. I still find chemistry exciting and continue to follow current developments.

How did you get involved in chemistry?

MANFRED JAUTELAT: I grew up in a rural area, on a farm in Schleswig-Holstein in northern Germany. When I saw that different plants grow at a different pace, I started wondering about how fertilizers work. That fascinated me and I wanted to understand it.

As a small boy, I fled East Prussia with my family in a horse-drawn wagon. At night, we could see the flashing of the heavy guns firing at the front. These images stayed with me for a long time. The fear of war and the tough post-war period greatly occupied my mind and influenced my career decisions. I hurried through my training and learned very hard. I wanted to finish as quickly as possible because a good qualification is a sound basis for the future.

ROLF JAUTELAT: I always enjoyed chemistry at school but somehow there was no real excitement in it. I signed on as a paratrooper in the German army. After two years in a rather physical occupation, I was glad to start studying. It's never bothered me that I was following in my father's footsteps. Chemistry is such a broad and diverse field so there's room for plenty of different characters.

What is elementary to innovation?

MANFRED JAUTELAT: Creativity and a lot of information.

ROLF JAUTELAT: The brains, the people, their enthusiasm. And despite all the technology, the intuition of researchers. Technical aids are no substitute for thought and thoroughness. That's something we can really learn from my father's time.

Manfred and Rolf Jautelat

Dr. Manfred Jautelat worked in Central Research in Leverkusen from 1968 to 2001. He was awarded the Otto Bayer Medal as a member of the team which discovered the fungicidal active substance prothioconazole.

His son Dr. Rolf Jautelat heads a medicinal chemistry department at the Aprath Research Center, which is investigating antibody / active substance conjugates for use as novel cancer drugs.

A risk to harvests and consumers

THE SEARCH FOR PROTECTION AGAINST TOXIC FUNGI

58

Prosaro™

2005

Fusarium fungi are considered to be one of the major unsolved problems in modern agriculture. These mold fungi mainly infest cereals and corn, particularly if it rains during the plants' flowering period. Fusarium fungi can produce potent fungal poisons called mycotoxins, which kill their host and destroy entire harvests. The financial damage to farmers caused by this fungus is currently estimated at more than US$1 billion every year in North America alone. Mycotoxins can enter food and animal feed via processed cereals. The Food and Agriculture Organization of the United Nations estimates that one quarter of the food produced worldwide in 2007 contained mycotoxins, mainly in wheat and corn. This can have dangerous consequences for consumers because mycotoxins can cause poisoning and nerve damage.

In the 1980s, Bayer CropScience was one of the leading players in the field of Fusarium research. The company discovered the cereal fungicide tebuconazole, which is contained in Folicur™ and in the late 1990s saved many North American wheat farmers from financial ruin. Starting at that time, Fusarium threatened fields in Europe as well. In 2004, Bayer's scientists came to the rescue with prothioconazole, an active substance that helps farmers comply with the European Union's stringent limits for mycotoxin contamination.

Healthy wheat

Prothioconazole was regarded as a quantum leap in fungicide technology. It led to the development of an extensive product range, beginning with Proline™ and Fandango™. These were subsequently joined by Input™ and then Prosaro™ (approved in 2005), which also became very quickly established and took market leadership positions. Yet even prothioconazole is unable to ensure full protection against Fusarium and mycotoxins. Depending on how close to the time of infection it is applied, the protection factor ranges from 60 to 90 percent.

That is why it is especially important to implement all possible measures to reduce mycotoxin contamination within the context of integrated crop protection. Alongside the use of fungicides, these measures include planting less sensitive varieties and working the soil in a way that destroys the residues of infected plants. To optimize the use of fungicides, Bayer has collaborated with an institute in Canada to develop the DONcast forecasting tool for Europe. On the basis of weather forecasts and parameters such as variety, soil type and previous crop, farmers receive information to help them decide on the optimal protection for their crops.

A coffee in the jungle: Ulrike Wachendorff-Neumann enjoys meeting with colleagues in the Tropicarium. This is probably Germany's most unusual company cafeteria – it is certainly the greenest.

59

Ulrike Wachendorff-Neumann

Bixafen

2010

Bixafen, approved in 2010, is a fungicide that belongs to the class of pyrazole carboxamides. It selectively targets the metabolism of a fungus, blocking a specific enzyme that is crucial to the respiration process inside the fungus cells. As a result, their energy production declines or stops altogether, and growth is inhibited. Bixafen is used in combination with prothioconazole (Aviator™ Xpro™) or tebuconazole (Zantara™) in cereal crops to control leaf blotch, brown rust and other major pathogenic fungi.

A REAL LADY SCIENTIST

Innovation is an important source of motivation for Ulrike Wachendorff-Neumann. Few other female scientists have been involved in so many patents. The biologist sometimes even gets creative in a place where cocoa and dates grow – in the jungle in the company's cafeteria.

Y**ou won't find** any articles about me in the archives, although after 30 years my name is on more than 2,000 patent applications. But that doesn't make me feel like an invisible scientist. Fame is not important to me. I enjoy my job, every single day. It was my decision and my wish to stay in research, even though I could have transferred to other areas of the company. I am driven by curiosity and powered by innovation. The feeling of being able to discover something new still excites me every time. And this hope is stronger than the problems we face. Problems are there to be solved. My team and I study how new substances act on fungal diseases in plants. We analyze their effectiveness and spectrum of activity in the laboratory and greenhouse. Then we look at the effect of selected preparations in field trials performed by our colleagues in Biological Development around the globe. Our objectives include protecting apple varieties, grapevines, tomatoes, potatoes, strawberries and mangoes. In summer I regularly join trials in southern France, Spain and Italy. In winter we concentrate on fruits in Asia, Brazil or South Africa. The impression you get in the field, where we look at the effect of each individual substance in fruit plantations, vineyards and vegetable fields, simply can't be conveyed by telephone or Skype. You have to experience it. I like being outdoors, because there you can sense how much our technicians love their work. Some of them actually have favorite substances. Those are the high points for me – similar to winning the Otto Bayer Medal.

I knew early on that I wanted to study biology. My father spent his entire career in crop protection and that sparked my curiosity. After I got my PhD, I looked around and Bayer seemed to be a company that knew exactly what it was doing. Hiring a woman as a laboratory manager was still unusual back then. But I never experienced any discrimination. Although one time right at the start, at a large meeting of researchers, one of the directors asked me: "Could you please serve everyone coffee?" One of my male colleagues took over.

> ***"Hiring a woman as a laboratory manager was still unusual back then. But I never experienced any discrimination."***

An electrician once asked me: "Are you really a scientist?" When I said yes, he responded: "You don't look like one." I took that as a compliment. Today, it's quite normal to find women in management positions in research as well.

If you want to foster innovation, you have to ensure freedom. You need a balance between experience and spontaneous curiosity, but also opportunities to just let your mind wander free from the pressures of everyday office life. At our research center in Monheim, we can enjoy that kind of freedom in the Tropicarium, a miniature jungle in our employee cafeteria. About 600 different useful plants from tropical and subtropical climate zones thrive under the glass dome.

> ***"Some real breakthrough ideas have been born in what is probably Germany's most unusual company cafeteria."***

Date palms grow alongside rice, sugar cane and fruit trees, Chinese cinnamon next to African mahogany and cocoa plants bearing fruit. High-intensity discharge lamps and automatic shade systems ensure the right amount of light year-round; electronically controlled humidifiers and misting nozzles regulate the moisture; and our gardeners are masters of their craft. It's like an oasis in what is probably Germany's most unusual company cafeteria. And it's where some real breakthrough ideas have been born – over a good cup of coffee with colleagues.

Ulrike Wachendorff-Neumann

Dr. Ulrike Wachendorff-Neumann was born in 1952, grew up in Bonn and studied biology. In 2010, she was awarded the Otto Bayer Medal as a member of the research team that developed bixafen. She is married and has one son.

The importance of seed

FEEDING THE WORLD

In 1950, the world's population numbered 2.5 billion people. In 2013, the figure is roughly seven billion. In 1980, 15 million people starved to death, 500 million were malnourished and 1.5 billion had an inadequate food supply. These figures would certainly have been higher if agricultural yields had not been hugely increased in the 20th century. Seed treatment played a crucial role in this development.

60

Uspulun

1914

Even in 2000 B.C., seeds were treated with various substances to disinfect the surface of the grain and protect it against disease pathogens. The ancient Egyptians, Greeks and Romans used olive residues, ash, onion juice or cypress sap, while farmers in the Middle Ages favored animal slurry and chlorides. From 1660 onwards, seeds were treated with salt water, copper and hot water. But all of these methods had little effect in the long term. Even the use of highly toxic arsenic was unsuccessful.

In the late 19th century, the efficacy of mercury compounds against fungi in cereals was discovered. Bayer played a leading role in the subsequent development of seed dressings. In 1914, Uspulun was introduced to the market as a liquid seed treatment. This was followed by the user-friendly Uspulun dry seed dressing and then, in 1929, by the dry seed dressing Ceresan, which was more effective and environmentally compatible. However, the search for more environmentally friendly products continued.

At the end of the 1970s, these pioneering seed dressings were replaced with a new generation of mercury-free products. Bayer again set standards, especially in 1980 with the systemic seed dressing Baytan™ (see page 151).

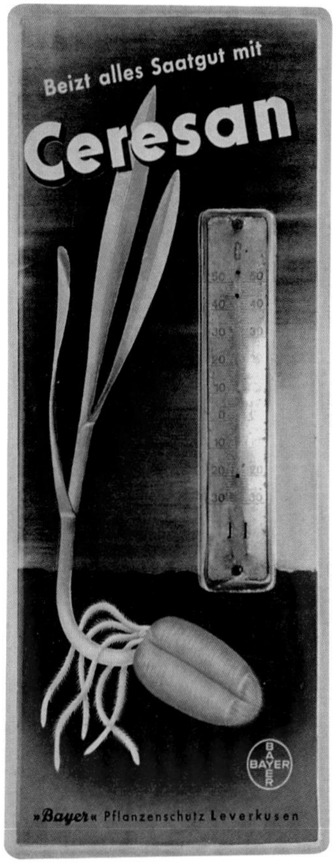

Above: a poster advertising Uspulun; right: a Ceresan advertisement, 1929

In retirement but still interested in the latest research: Wolfgang Krämer in the sunroom of his home.

61

Wolfgang Krämer

Triadimenol

1978

Triadimenol, approved in 1978 and sold as Baytan™, promotes healthy root growth, primarily by protecting seedlings and young plants against fungi and winter-kill. The product strengthens the mesocotyl and shortens this sensitive part of the plant, resulting in compact growth and good root development. This has a particularly positive effect on yield *(see also page 151).*

IN HIS FATHER'S FOOTSTEPS

Wolfgang Krämer was a small boy when his father died. He always knew that he wanted to be a chemist too. A sense of responsibility, persistence and an inner restlessness ensured that his dream came true. His initials "KWG" stand for a research career that resulted in many patents.

S**pring 1945, shortly** before the end of the war, at the Leuna-Werke. My father, a chemist, was on the way to Halle to get spare parts for his factory. There was an air raid. His foreman was killed outright and Father seriously injured. They operated, taking shrapnel out of his head, and at first it looked as if he was going to recover. But it turned out that the doctors had missed some grenade fragments. He suffered increasingly severe headaches and had trouble remembering the simplest things. He died in July 1945 when I was three years old. My mother didn't qualify for a war widow's pension and had to bring up my sister and me alone. After the currency reform she found a job as a telephonist in Schwäbisch Hall. She took me to Waldbach near Heilbronn, where I grew up with my aunt on a farm. We children helped in the fields, harvesting potatoes and picking cherries. It was a good time with no more hunger.

I can barely remember my father, but I wanted to be like him. I wanted to be a chemist. So I learned and experimented with substances I got at the drugstore. My favorite subjects at school, apart from chemistry, were the ancient languages of Latin and Greek. I paid my way through college – studying chemistry, of course – by working at an American bowling center, packing magazines and assembling irons in a factory.

My first job was at the Institute for Textile Chemistry at the Technical College of Stuttgart. I optimized synthetic leather and shirt fabrics. Later on, I studied business management at evening school. My childhood experiences had left a lasting impression. I was afraid of not having enough money.

> *"I was proud when I saw the first results obtained with my active substance in the field."*

In 1970 I joined the Crop Protection Department at Bayer. I did my research in a tiny laboratory and my office was previously a broom closet. My work focused on azoles, a new active substance class. Over the years I was involved in the submission of more than 250 patents, and my initials "KWG" – short for "Krämer, Wolfgang" – have a certain standing in the Bayer research community. I say you have to really get stuck into something, then you'll find a way. A good scientist is always critical and questions everything in order to find a solution. I felt an inner restlessness and was constantly on edge, which drove me to work from early morning until late at night. I had a responsibility – for the matter at hand but also towards the company and the employees whose jobs were safeguarded by discoveries. I experienced how close it can sometimes get when several companies are working on a product at the same time. When we submitted my first patent, the authorities informed us we were too late. A U.S. research team we were sort of racing had been a few days quicker. I cursed. That wasn't going to happen again. Responsibility is an important concept in my personal value system. A researcher needs to keep fine-tuning his internal motor. It's important that the atmosphere in the laboratory encourages people to communicate. "My" first product was Baytan™, a fungicide used as a seed dressing for cereals, particularly barley and oats. Baycor™, Sibutol™ and Impulse™ were also synthesized in my laboratory and brought to market. I was proud when I saw the first results obtained with Baytan™ in the field. "What's this devilishly good stuff you've come up with?" asked my supervisor. I think my father would have approved.

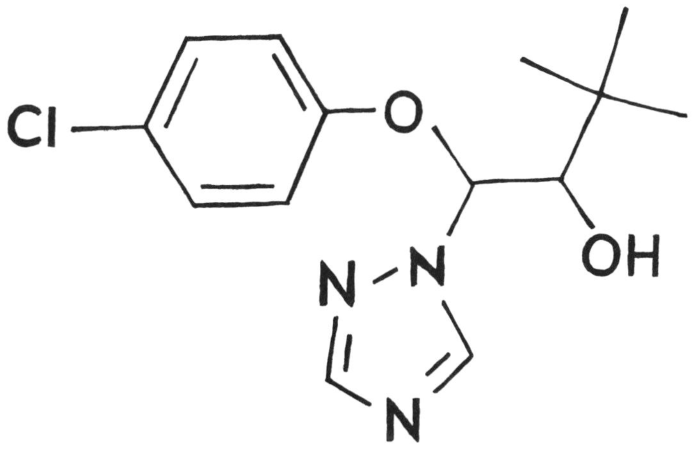

The chemical formula of triadimenol

Wolfgang Krämer

Dr. Wolfgang Krämer was born in Merseburg in 1942. He retired in 2005 after a career at Bayer. However, he has remained true to his field as co-editor of various books on crop protection research. Wolfgang Krämer received the Otto Bayer Medal in recognition of his research work. He is married and has two children. In his free time he enjoys sailing on the Ijsselmeer or in the Mediterranean. Wolfgang Krämer lives with his family in Burscheid, Germany.

Triple protection

POWER PACK AGAINST WEEDS

Wheat, corn and oilseed rape have a lot of enemies. Plants are not only threatened by hungry insects and fungal pathogens, but weeds can also stifle them before they have a chance to thrive. As soon as the first tender shoots emerge from the soil, they have to compete with up to 1,000 different types of weed. Without the early application of herbicides, farmers would be facing disaster.

One of the Bayer CropScience products with a proven and powerful impact on grasses and broadleaf weeds is Adengo™, first approved in 2008. It contains two active substances, each of which targets a different metabolic process in the same weeds. The first is isoxaflutol, which blocks an enzyme that plants need to manufacture the pigment carotene, which basically means that the weeds' leaves lose their sunscreen.

62
Adengo™
2008

The second component is thiencarbazone-methyl. This active substance, which was developed just a few years ago, blocks another enzyme that occurs only in plants and is responsible for the production of essential amino acids. These, in turn, produce various proteins which the plant needs to survive. To ensure that the crop plant can continue to thrive after application of Adengo™, the product contains a third active ingredient: cyprosulfamide. This is a safener which ensures that the herbicide concentration remains below the activity threshold in the crop plant and that the herbicide only kills the weeds.

Malmesbury, South Africa: farmer Neels Neethling (left) and his colleague Tol Kaptein check the quality of the wheat crop. South Africa is regarded as Africa's grain basket.

Dual antifungal strategy

EFFECTIVE AGAINST SURVIVAL EXPERTS

Fungi have probably been around for more than a billion years. They are among the oldest living organisms and have become outstanding survival experts. Fungal disease pathogens can thrive in nearly all climatic conditions. Sometimes a single spore is enough to infect an entire plant. Bayer CropScience researchers have adopted a dual strategy. They have combined prothioconazole (Prosaro™, see page 155) with the new substance bixafen to create a new-generation cereal fungicide: Aviator™ Xpro™, approved in 2010. The two substances intervene simultaneously in the respiration process and cell formation of the fungus.

63
Aviator™ Xpro™
2010

Novel herbicide combinations

OVERCOMING RESISTANCE

R**esistant weeds and** grasses can be a nightmare for farmers. They compete with soybeans, wheat and cotton for light and nutrients. In some cases, they cause serious harvest losses. A large number of these stubborn plants can no longer be controlled with many of the available herbicides. One of the reasons for this is a standard practice in arable farming. For many decades, farmers have been using herbicides with the same or similar mechanisms of action.

If a weed or grass is not destroyed by the herbicide, it can spread unimpeded – quickly and across large areas. The plants then pass on this resistance to their offspring. Palmer amaranth is a case in point. This plant, which is grown in many front gardens, is now also found in places where it isn't wanted – the soybean and cotton fields of North America, where it is spreading at a fast pace. The plants can grow to a height of three meters and produce up to one million seeds – a horror scenario for any farmer.

Research for healthy grain

Researchers at Bayer CropScience are now trying to solve the problem of herbicide-resistant weeds and devise novel crop protection products to control them. They are in a kind of race to protect crop plants and have developed Alion™, an innovative herbicide that has already been approved for use in the United States. It controls weeds in plantations growing citrus fruits, nuts and grapes. The product also adheres well to the plants it is meant to protect and is not washed off by the rain. This means it functions reliably for a long time so farmers don't need to apply as much.

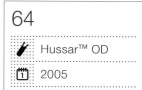

64

Hussar™ OD

2005

However, even if the success of this product speaks for itself, sustainable protection against weeds and grasses is about more than just new active substances. Farmers themselves can do a lot to prevent resistances developing on their fields. For example, they should use herbicides with different mechanisms of action in rotation and also employ crop rotation practices. Hussar™ OD, approved in 2005, is a proven herbicide used together with the additive Mero™ (Hussar™ OD PowerSet) in wheat, rye, triticale and summer barley. It can be alternated with the cereal herbicide Bacara™ Forte to effectively prevent the development of resistance in windgrass.

Diversity is the key to success for the future. Field practice shows that varying active substances and adopting integrated crop protection techniques such as crop rotation and crop management are essential. Diversity can no longer wait – it must be implemented now.

Inspecting wheat plants: the use of herbicides with the same mechanism of action means problems for wheat. Dr. Richard James of CSIRO and Richard Dickmann of Bayer CropScience (right) are researching new wheat varieties.

Marco Busch enjoys working with his hands, himself building the climbing frames in the garden for his children.

THE NEXT GENERATION

Marco Busch

Lyon, France

Bayer CropScience

A HANDS-ON GUY

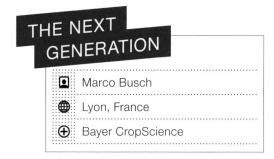

What exactly does a manager do in research? His role is something between ringmaster and conductor. To relieve stress, Marco Busch reaches into his toolbox.

T**o be successful** in research, you need to understand how chemistry works – the chemistry between employees. Where people work together, there is often friction. It's my job to coordinate all the different interests for the sake of the common cause. Sometimes, a person develops astonishingly well if he is given the right job to do or put in a team where he feels at ease. If someone asks me what my role is as head of department, then I answer: something between ringmaster and conductor.

I soon moved out of the laboratory and into management. I love the variety. The working day can be stressful and, to compensate, I like working with my hands and seeing what I've created at the end of the day. You can't imagine how many kitchens I've assembled for friends and family members. I built a climbing frame and playhouse in the garden for my two sons, both of whom are still small. It's a lot of fun for them – and even more for me.

Marco Busch

Dr. Marco Busch was born in Bremerhaven in 1972. Following his military service and a year working in a fish factory in his home city, he studied biotechnology in Braunschweig. After receiving his PhD, he first worked in research at Bayer before moving to various management positions. He now heads Biology Fungicides at Bayer CropScience in Lyon, France. Marco Busch is married and has two children.

A Frenchman loves a good cup of coffee:
Bernard Pélissier in downtown Lyon

65

Bernard Pélissier

Making soybeans herbicide-tolerant

1994

Bernard Pélissier helped to develop crop plants like soybeans that are tolerant to two herbicides – glyphosate and HPPD inhibitors. These herbicides control weeds without harming the soybean plants. Bernard Pélissier was a member of the team which developed the first herbicide-tolerant plants in Europe in 1994.

MONSIEUR AND THE TREE

At work in the lab, Bernard Pélissier looks for ways to strengthen plants. His free time is devoted to his own private forest. This is the story of a man who adds an entirely new dimension to the term "sustainability."

M**y personal passion** is my forest. I love to wander, hike and rest there, hunt for mushrooms or tidy up a bit. I trim the trees, many of them oaks, thin them out if they're too close together, and protect young saplings from hungry deer. The one thing I don't do is hunt; I don't like shooting animals. I just can't do this. Usually I'm out alone in my forest, which is about 70 hectares in size, near Bergerac in the Périgord region of France. I enjoy those days, even if some friends think I'm a little eccentric and teasingly call me "l'homme des bois" – the man from the forest. Sometimes I dream of how my forest will look in the distant future. In 50 years, say, or 100. I don't have children of my own but I'm caring for my forest on behalf of the next generations. I've designed one section so it can be made into a park. I've also planted some exotics like my Brazilian pine, an endangered species from South America. When I'm long gone, these trees will still be growing. I like that idea.

I inherited the forest from my family, from my mother. There's still an old farm house there. It doesn't have modern heating and the only way to heat it in winter is to light fires in all the fireplaces and stoves. It still takes two days before you can move around the house without a jacket. I enjoy this simple life, maybe because the contrast to my high-tech working environment could hardly be greater. My field is in vitro cultures, genetic transformation, all types of modern biotechnology. I conduct research to make plants more resistant to biotic stress factors. In the 1990s, I was part of a team of people who have been called pioneers because we were the first in Europe to succeed in making a plant that was resistant to herbicides. We then turned our attention to a new variety of soybean.

There are times in the lab when you need the kind of intuition you can't learn from books. Some ideas have occurred to me while I was out in my forest. One time, for instance, I noticed a certain fungus, which gave me the idea for solving a problem that had been on my mind for weeks. The forest is a great inspiration. The one thing my life in the forest and my work have in common is the passion I put into both. I've been interested in nature since I was a child. My spiritual father is the American philosopher and author Henry David Thoreau, whose essay "Walden" fascinated me. Thoreau describes his life in a cabin that he built for himself in 1845 near Walden Pond in the woods of Massachusetts so he could escape from industrialized mass society. I always wanted to know what was going on around me or how something worked. I also love life in the country. I like to climb on my Harley-Davidson (a Fat Boy – my second big passion) and ride across France to my forest. Every season in the forest is magnificent. Spring, when everything is growing. Fall, when the trees look like a giant paintbox. Winter, when it's silent and still. Summer is the only season I don't always like because it can get very hot. I'm outside from the first light of day to when darkness falls, with only a bit of food and a few bottles of water. I don't need more to be content and my everyday life is then far away. I love the scent of freshly cut wood and the steam rising off the trees after it's been raining. In the evening I treat myself to a home-cooked meal, perhaps with mushrooms I gathered myself. That's my idea of a perfect day.

A plant with many different uses: the soybean

Bernard Pélissier

Dr. Bernard Pélissier was born in Montpellier, France, in 1954. He originally wanted to be a chef but then studied biology at the University of Toulouse. Bernard Pélissier was a member of the team that developed Europe's first herbicide-resistant crop plant in 1994. He was also one of the researchers who received the 2008 Innovation Award from Bayer CropScience for a herbicide-resistant soybean variety. Bernard Pélissier lives in Lyon, France.

EverGol™ protects soybeans

STRONG BEANS

The world loves beans. On a global scale, soybeans are the most important oilseed. More than half of the world's vegetable oil is made from this legume. Soybean oil can be used to manufacture technical coatings and lubricants. It is even used to make bioplastics. And if the harvest isn't pressed to produce oil, it is processed into foods such as tofu, soya milk and soy sauce. Soybean products can be found in around one-third of all foods.

66

EverGol™

2012

But it's not just people who like soybeans. They are also very popular with fungi. Fungal spores already attack the seed, thus inhibiting the growth of young soybean plants. Their root growth is impaired, hindering the uptake of water and nutrients. As a result, the plants remain small. In the worst case, they then die. This has a significant impact on crop yields and quality. One such fungus is Rhizoctonia solani. It is found all over the world and infests many different plants, making it a nightmare for farmers. In U.S. soybean fields, it once destroyed almost half of the entire crop. It therefore makes sense to start the fight against this voracious fungus by using a seed dressing.

Seed dressing and seed treatment are factory-side processes used to gently apply a crop protection product to seed, thus ensuring a healthy start for the young plants. A further advantage of seed dressing is that less active substance is needed than when treating mature plants in the field. Bayer's EverGol™ family of seed dressings, launched in 2012, has a dual effect. It protects against the dangerous Rhizoctonia fungus and other important plant pests. It also gives the soybean plants a good start: treated plants grow faster and are better able to withstand dry conditions.

Researcher Dr. Bernard Pélissier checks whether a soybean plant has been successfully pollinated.

EverGol™ is available in combinations with various other active substances, each optimized for specific crops such as soybeans, corn, cereals and cotton. The active substances are put together in such a way that the seed dressing is effective against the main fungal diseases in the target crop – and ensures that plant growth shifts into a higher gear.

Aggressive soybean rust

A FUNGUS THREATENS HARVESTS AROUND THE WORLD

67

Prothioconazole

2004

Airborne danger: over the past decades, spores of Phakopsora pachyrhizi have been carried thousands of kilometers – even across oceans – from Japan, the fungus' country of origin, and spread over almost the entire planet by the wind. Soybean rust, the disease caused by the spores, leaves behind fields that look as if they have been burnt. It is one of the biggest threats to modern agriculture. Phakopsora pachyrhizi is an extremely aggressive fungus. It develops mainly in warm, humid conditions and primarily attacks soybeans. Spores accumulate on the underside of the leaves and cause pustules, initially gray and then orange-red to rust brown, on the upper surface. The leaves gradually turn yellow before falling off; the stem and pods may also undergo disease-related changes.

The whole process from infection to defoliation of the plant only takes a few weeks. Soybean rust can infect plants at any growth stage. Affected plants grow fewer pods and frequently produce underdeveloped beans or in some cases no beans at all. The result is harvest losses of up to 50 percent.

Soybean rust has only been regarded as one of the most important challenges in crop protection for about ten years. The fungal disease spread to the subtropical and tropical regions of Asia and Australia before reaching southern Africa and Hawaii, but the economic damage it caused there was relatively minor. That all changed in 2001, when soybean rust hit Brazil and Argentina, the world's second and third largest soybean producers. It has since also spread to the United States, which produces more than one-third of the global soybean harvest. The suspicion is that the spores of Phakopsora pachyrhizi were brought from Venezuela to the southern U.S. states such as Mississippi and Virginia by Hurricane Ivan.

The wildfire spread of soybean rust presented scientists with a massive problem. There was an urgent need for action, but they lacked the experience and the time to develop new active substances – a process that takes ten years on average. The scientists at Bayer CropScience remembered an active substance that had been highly effective on various types of rust when it had been approved some years previously: tebuconazole.

Studies by institutes such as the Brazilian agricultural authority Embrapa confirmed the efficacy of tebucanazole, marketed as Folicur™, against soybean rust. The fact that the United States granted Folicur™ and Stratego™ regulatory approval at relatively short notice in a special procedure in 2004 underscores the urgency of the problem.

According to the biologists, the active substance trifloxystrobin could also be used to effectively control the plant disease. As Phakopsora pachyrhizi is very aggressive, the switch was made to an active substance combination with trifloxystrobin (Nativo™). The most effective combination product was introduced in Brazil and the United States in 2011 – Fox™, containing prothioconazole and trifloxystrobin. Fox™ is now used by Embrapa as the market standard against which all other products are measured.

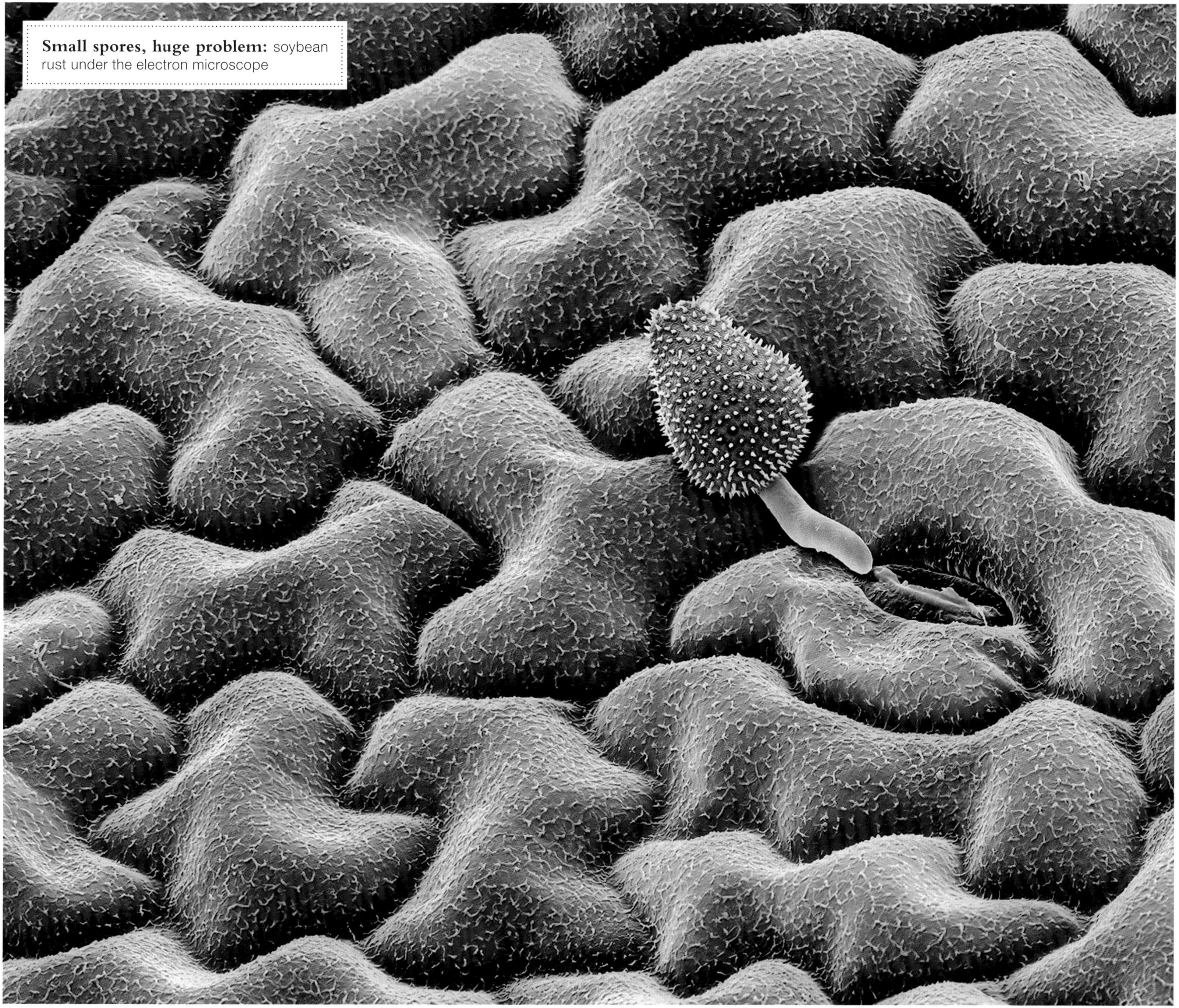

Small spores, huge problem: soybean rust under the electron microscope

Moths, caterpillars and co.

FIGHTING VORACIOUS OMNIVORES

Yellow-brown front wings, cream back wings, blackish with a dark spot. Wing span: 32 to 45 millimeters. Not very colorful, not very big. Heliocoverpa zea, the cotton bollworm, is no beauty among moths. Its significance is due to its activity as an insect pest. In the United States, it is one of the biggest threats to cotton fields, and its caterpillars – 3,000 of which are produced by each insect – also leave a trail of destruction in corn and vegetable crops.

In for it now: the cotton bollworm is a pest.

Of all the pests, caterpillars dominate the fields of the world. They are particularly prevalent in Asia due to the climate there. All the more reason for Bayer CropScience to search for a suitable active substance. These efforts resulted in flubendiamide, which was developed by Bayer in cooperation with Nihon Nohyaku Co. Ltd., Japan, and belongs to the chemical class of benzene dicarboxamides. Flubendiamide impairs muscle function in insects, causing them to stop eating immediately. The plant is spared from further attack.

68
Belt™
2007

Experts consider flubendiamide to be one of the major innovations in modern crop protection. Approved in 2007 and sold as Belt™, the active substance is used in cotton, corn, soybeans, rice, fruit, vegetables and nuts to control caterpillars of all types. It is characterized by its rapid, lasting effect and long-term rain resistance, an important factor especially in Asia. And it has yet another advantage: Belt™ also controls pests that are already resistant to some insecticides.

Tremendous damage: hungry caterpillars destroy entire crops.

LESS CROPLAND PER HEAD

The rapidly growing world population (billions) set against the available cropland per head (hectares) nearly 50 years ago, now and in 2050.

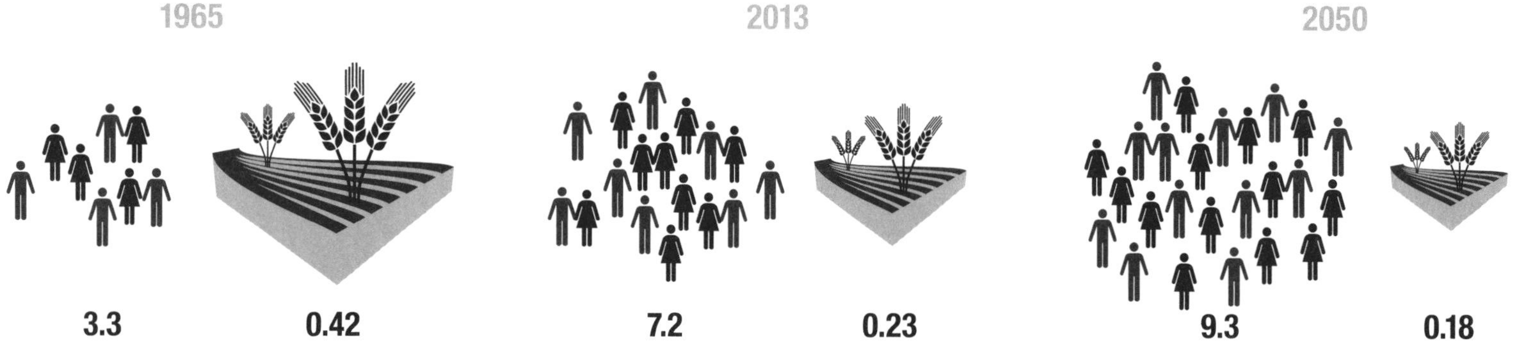

UN World Population Prospects (2010 Revision), FAO

INCREASING PRODUCTIVITY

A thousand years ago, a farmer reaped two grains for every grain he sowed. Today he harvests 50. In 30 years, he will have to increase the yield to 100 grains in order to meet growing demand.

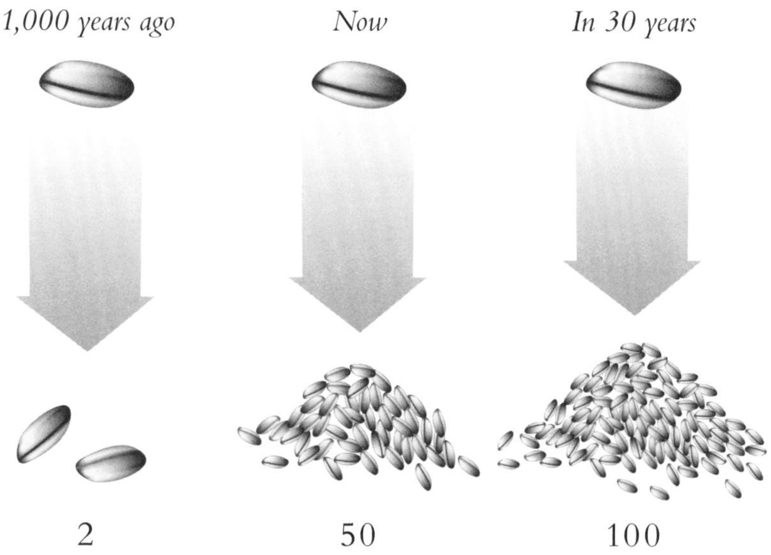

Bayer CropScience

*The five main producers of the five major crop plants around the world**

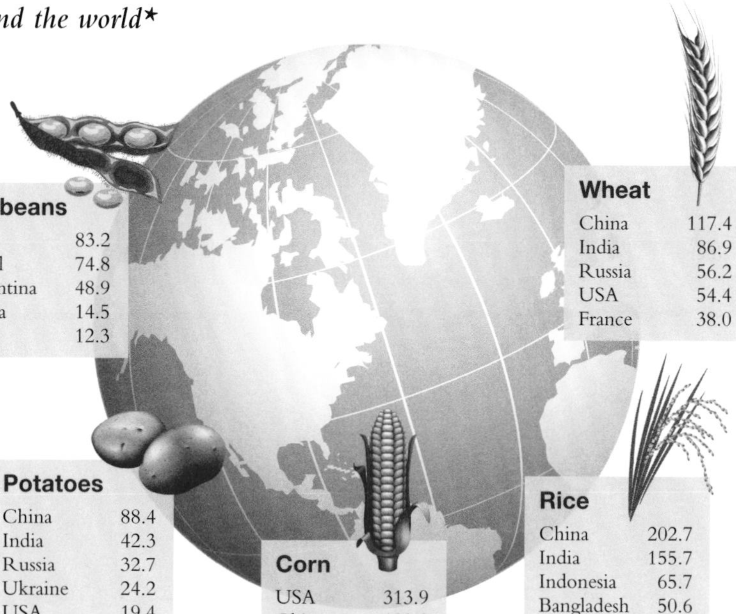

Soybeans

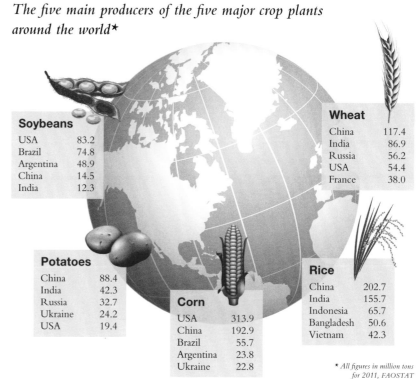

USA	83.2
Brazil	74.8
Argentina	48.9
China	14.5
India	12.3

Wheat

China	117.4
India	86.9
Russia	56.2
USA	54.4
France	38.0

Potatoes

China	88.4
India	42.3
Russia	32.7
Ukraine	24.2
USA	19.4

Corn

USA	313.9
China	192.9
Brazil	55.7
Argentina	23.8
Ukraine	22.8

Rice

China	202.7
India	155.7
Indonesia	65.7
Bangladesh	50.6
Vietnam	42.3

** All figures in million tons for 2011, FAOSTAT*

Lunch break in the Japanese Garden in Leverkusen: Bin Li enjoys moments of peace, right next to Bayer's main site.

THE NEXT GENERATION

Bin Li

Monheim, Germany

Bayer CropScience

THE STORIES OF WISE MEN

It wasn't athletes or actors but Einstein and Galileo who were the heroes of his childhood. Bin Li decided he wanted to be like them.

Researchers were the idols of my childhood. My father inspired my enthusiasm by often telling me the stories of wise men such as Jingrun Chen, a famous mathematician. I read anything I could find. I admire Albert Einstein, Galileo Galilei and Otto Bayer. Scientists have contributed the most to making the world a better place. I want to make my contribution as well. I want to become one of them. Today I work in strategic planning at Bayer CropScience. Previously, my function was at the interface between research and production. I was part of a team that mediated between researchers and production specialists in the construction of industrial plant. Now as then, I am responsible for ensuring our ability to innovate. I value sustainability and environmental protection in both my job and my private life. I often tell my small son about researchers. I want the story to continue.

Bin Li

Bin Li was born in 1973 in Yuncheng in central China. He joined Bayer following his studies in Hangzhou. The passionate swimmer is married and has a son. He lives with his family in Düsseldorf, Germany.

ASPIRIN – PROBABLY BAYER'S BEST-KNOWN INNOVATION AND THE PHARMACEUTICAL OF THE CENTURY

The pharmaceutical of the century: production of Aspirin™ tablets at the Bayer HealthCare facility in Morristown, New Jersey, USA

A fictional letter to the Bayer workforce

Dear Bayer family in 2013,

You may be surprised to get a letter from me – after all, I did die in Switzerland in 1946. I was already aware in my lifetime what a groundbreaking success my invention Aspirin was, but to be the pharmaceutical of the century? That my active ingredient would be carried to the moon in a rocket? That millions of people would take the product every day? All that was beyond my wildest dreams!

I was actually looking for something to treat rheumatism. At the time, only sodium salicylate provided any relief – but it had side-effects and tasted so vile that people could hardly bear to swallow it. That's why I was trying to make salicylic acid more tolerable. What was entry number 36433 in the Trade Mark Register of the Imperial Patents Office in Berlin became as familiar a name as Coca-Cola. Aspirin was regarded as a godsend by all classes of society.

It gives me great pleasure to see the Aspirin success story continuing today. Who knows what chapters will be written in the future. Perhaps Aspirin will be the first pharmaceutical product on Mars?

With my very best wishes,
Respectfully yours,

F. Hoffmann

ASPIRIN – MULTIPLE RECORD-BREAKER

It is believed to be the best-known painkiller in the world. It was one of the first pharmaceutical products to be compressed into tablet form. The active ingredient was on board Apollo 11 when it flew to the Moon. And it was a sensation when the largest Aspirin™ package in the world was created in Leverkusen. Stories of a superlative innovation.

69

Felix Hoffmann

Aspirin™

1899

Aspirin™, which was entered in the Trade Mark Register of the Imperial Patents Office on March 6, 1899, is the oldest synthetic drug product in the world that is still in use today.

T**he pharmaceutical product** that everybody knows. One of the best painkillers in the world. Synonymous with the relief of many everyday complaints. Myth and mystery in the history of medicine. Discovered in 1897, but eternally young. A billionfold tried and tested. The pharmaceutical of the century. Or to put it simply, in one word: Aspirin™.

Summer 1897, in the main laboratory in Elberfeld: Felix Hoffmann, a trained pharmacist and doctor of chemistry, a young man who had only recently joined the company, was experimenting with the acetylation of salicylic acid. He could have had no idea that he would be responsible for the discovery of one of the most innovative pharmaceutical products in history. An active substance that preoccupies science even today and still has plenty of surprises in store.

The structure of salicylic acid is relatively simple. The substance, which occurs in essential oils and plants, has been used for thousands of years for the relief of pain. The Egyptians, Greeks and Romans treated patients with infusions of willow bark or myrtle leaves. Plants containing salicylic acid were also known traditionally as remedies in Asia and North America. Herbalists in Central Europe mainly used Salix alba, the white willow, whose bark they used to boil up for their concoctions. Only when quinine, which is obtained from the bark of the cinchona tree, a native of

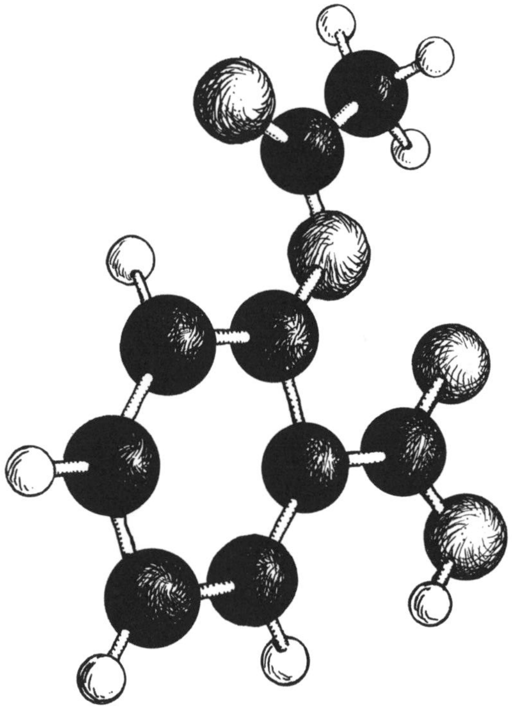

Structural model of acetylsalicylic acid, the active ingredient of Aspirin™

The active ingredient in Aspirin was with the first men on the Moon. It is also stocked in the on-board pharmacy of the International Space Station (ISS).

Apollo 11: a medicine flies to the Moon.

Aspirin™ was already being produced in tablet form around 1900, embossed with the Bayer Cross.

Peru, came into fashion did the curative powers of the willow fade into obscurity.

The come-back of salicylic acid started in 1806. Napoleon had suffered a crushing defeat at Trafalgar and imposed an economic blockade on Great Britain. The import of quinine into Europe came to a standstill and alternatives were needed. In 1828 Johann Andreas Buchner, a professor of pharmacy in Munich, succeeded in extracting willow bark with water, removing tannins and other impurities, and concentrating it by evaporation. He called the yellowish substance salicin. A year later, the French pharmacist Pierre Joseph Leroux converted salicin to crystalline form; in 1838 the Italian chemist Raffaelle Piria used it to produce salicylic acid. It took until 1853 for the Strasbourg chemist Charles Frédéric Gerhardt to chemically alter this acid by acetylation, but the result was not a pure – and therefore stable – form.

In 1859 the Marburg chemistry professor Hermann Kolbe succeeded in synthesizing salicylic acid, and in 1869 Karl-Johann Kraut was able to produce it chemically in crystalline, but still not pure form. Five years later, Kolbe's student Friedrich von Heyden produced salicylic acid industrially for the first time in Radebeul near Dresden. The price was one tenth of that of the natural substance and demand was correspondingly high. Salicylic acid was prescribed for rheumatism and headaches. However, it tasted revolting and had significant side-effects including vomiting and irritation of the mucosa in the mouth and stomach.

This was the status of research when Hoffmann started his experiments. On August 10, 1897 he succeeded for the first time in producing a form of acetylsalicylic

A masterpiece in miniature: close-up of one stage in the production of Aspirin™ Effect, which is sold as granules that can be taken without water

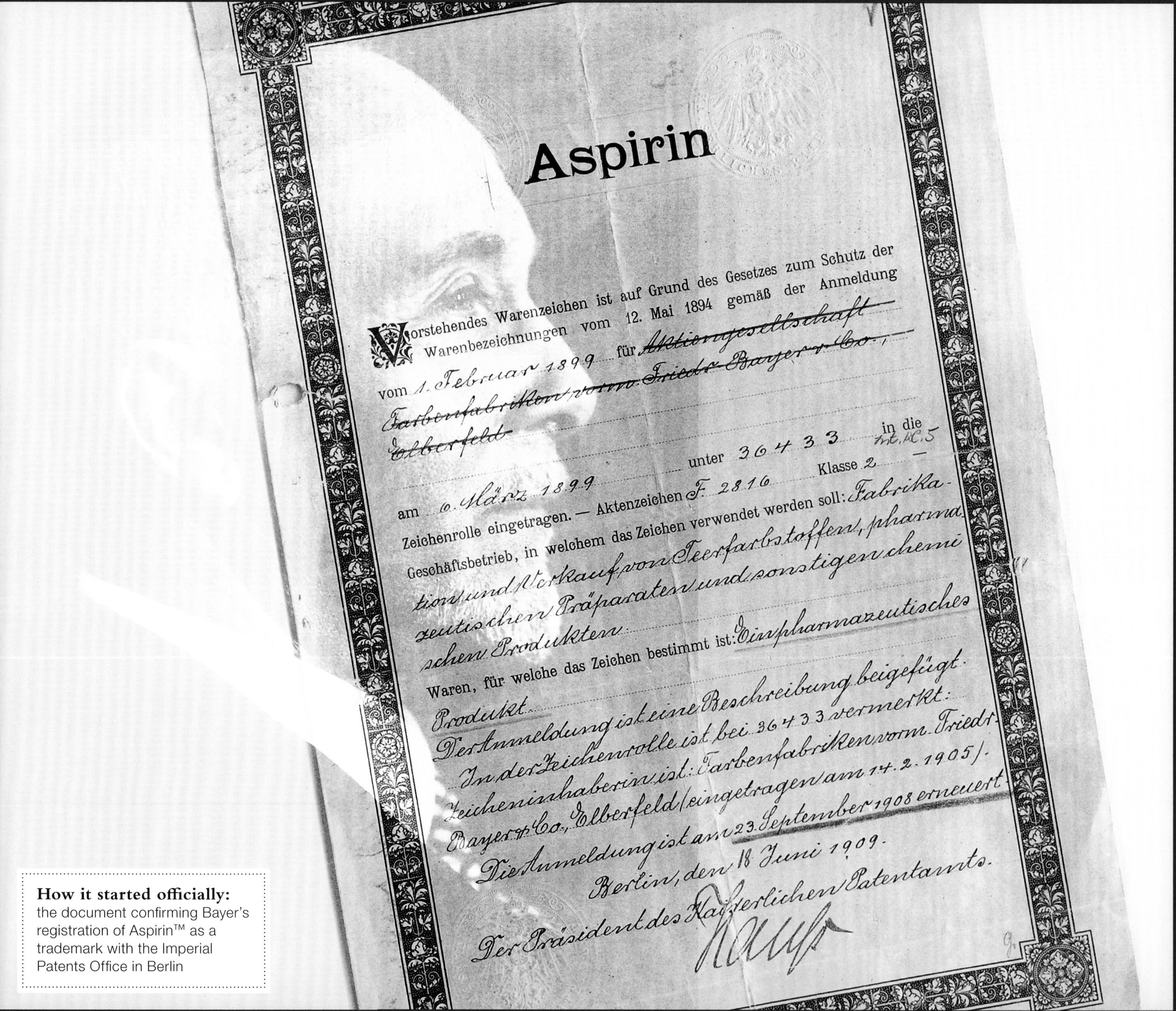

Aspirin

Vorstehendes Warenzeichen ist auf Grund des Gesetzes zum Schutz der Warenbezeichnungen vom 12. Mai 1894 gemäß der Anmeldung vom 1. Februar 1899 für ~~Aktiengesellschaft Farbenfabriken vorm. Friedr. Bayer & Co., Elberfeld~~ am 6. März 1899 unter 36433 in die Zeichenrolle eingetragen. — Aktenzeichen F. 2816 Klasse 2 —

Geschäftsbetrieb, in welchem das Zeichen verwendet werden soll: Fabrikation und Verkauf von Teerfarbstoffen, pharmazeutischen Präparaten und sonstigen chemischen Produkten.

Waren, für welche das Zeichen bestimmt ist: Ein pharmazeutisches Produkt.

Der Anmeldung ist eine Beschreibung beigefügt.

In der Zeichenrolle ist bei 36433 vermerkt: Zeicheninhaberin ist: Farbenfabriken vorm. Friedr. Bayer & Co., Elberfeld (eingetragen am 14.2.1905).

Die Anmeldung ist am 23. September 1908 erneuert.

Berlin, den 18 Juni 1909.

Der Präsident des Kaiserlichen Patentamts.

How it started officially:
the document confirming Bayer's registration of Aspirin™ as a trademark with the Imperial Patents Office in Berlin

acid which no longer contained any free salicylic acid or other by-products. It was chemically completely pure and therefore stable. In 1898, Hoffmann applied to patent the process for manufacturing this highly pure form of acetylsalicylic acid in, for example, Germany and the United States. The U.S. patent was issued in 1900. Aspirin™ went on sale in Germany in 1899. The "A" stands for acetyl; "spir" is derived from spireic acid, which is obtained from meadowsweet (related to the willow) and is chemically identical to salicylic acid. It was the first pharmaceutical product to be sold all over the world and gained its legendary fame virtually overnight. Aspirin™ helps to alleviate inflammation and relieve pain; it is well-tolerated, comparatively inexpensive and does not need a prescription. By the end of the influenza epidemics of 1900 at the latest, it was a standard item in the medicine chest of nearly every home.

Delivery trucks advertising Aspirin™ outside Bayer's warehouse in the Netherlands, 1907

Aspirin was immediately a global success. And Bayer continues to write history with new innovations.

The 20th century was the age of Aspirin™. The famous Italian tenor Enrico Caruso swore by its efficacy, as did authors Franz Kafka and Thomas Mann, who mention it enthusiastically in their correspondence. Aspirin™ found its way into world literature, for example in "The Carpetbaggers" by Harold Robbins, "The Day of the Jackal" by Frederick Forsyth and "Farewell My Lovely" by Raymond Chandler. In "The Revolt of the Masses," Spanish philosopher José Ortega y Gasset even raised Aspirin™ to the status of a cultural asset: "Today, ordinary people lead an easier, more comfortable and safer life than the most rich and powerful of the past. What does the average person care if he is not richer than others, when the world is a rich place and has streets, railways, hotels, telegraphy, physical safety and

Aspirin to offer." The fascinating thing about the product which made the name Bayer famous throughout the world is that everyone has their own experience of how it works, but for a long time no-one knew exactly why. By 1902 there had already been an estimated 160 studies of Aspirin™ and acetylsalicylic acid. Thousands more followed. In 1966 the *New York Times* described the phenomenon with the words: "The wonder drug that nobody understands." Only in 1971 did John R. Vane discover that acetylsalicylic acid inhibits the body's own production and biosynthesis of certain prostaglandins that intensify pain, thereby providing pain relief. Vane was awarded the Nobel Prize for Medicine for his work in 1982. The U.S. National Academy of Sciences has found that no analgesic works better than acetylsalicylic acid. It has become the product of choice in clinical pain therapy.

In terms of reputation, Aspirin is to pharmaceuticals what Coca-Cola is to soft drinks and Ferrari is to automobiles.

All this would be a unique success story in itself, but there is more. U.S. researchers found that Aspirin™ inhibits the function of blood platelets which under certain circumstances clump together. To put it simply: not only can Aspirin™ relieve pain, it can also save lives. Aspirin™ can help to prevent heart attacks and ischemic strokes as well as recurrent events in patients at appropriate cardiovascular risk. The U.S. health authorities announced in 1985 that a daily dose reduces the risk of heart attack

1899

Around 1912

Around 1940

Packaging history: the active ingredient has remained the same but the presentation has always moved with the times.

Around 1950

in patients who have already had a heart attack by a fifth, and in the case of unstable angina, often the harbinger of an acute heart attack, by as much as 51 percent. Aspirin™ can also help to reduce the risk of thrombosis, and hence a life-threatening embolism, during heart operations such as bypass surgery or in diagnostic or therapeutic procedures with a cardiac catheter. In 1988, Australian epidemiologist Gabriel A. Kune suggested that the regular administration of Aspirin™ appeared to reduce the risk of colon cancer. Scientists are forecasting that Aspirin™ and acetylsalicylic acid still have a long life ahead of them. Nobel Prize winner Vane called it "a story which ... will certainly continue in many more exciting chapters." Charles Barry, Medical Director of NASA, said during the Moon landing of Apollo 11: "Aspirin will be used as a standard pharmaceutical for all eternity." In terms of reputation, Aspirin™ is to pharmaceuticals what Coca-Cola is to soft drinks, Ferrari to automobiles or Chanel No. 5 to perfumes. With Aspirin™, Bayer has also repeatedly set new standards with innovations: in 1971 with the first effervescent tablet containing Aspirin™ and vitamin C; in 1992 with the first chewable Aspirin™tablet which can be taken without water; in 2000 with Aspirin™ Migräne, the first OTC analgesic approved for the treatment of migraine headache; in 2003 with Aspirin™ Effect in the form of granules. Bayer produces 100 billion Aspirin™ tablets alone each year.

Aspirin was the first pharmaceutical to go around the world.

A pharmaceutical product for the world: this advertisement from the Bayer Archive features the popular Chinese film actress Ruan Lingyu (not dated, probably from the late 1920s).

Around 1972

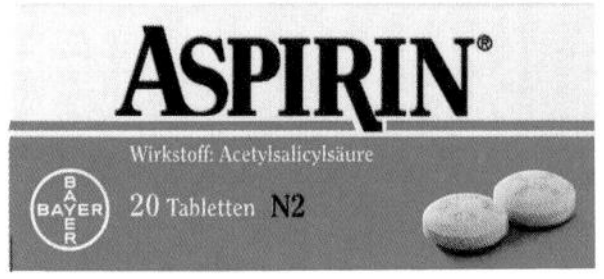

Around 1997

Since 2008

The first tablet

COUNTERFEITING GANGS STOPPED

When Aspirin™ first came onto the market, it was sold in powder form. Like nearly all pharmaceuticals around the end of the 19th century, the powder was filled into bottles or paper sachets. This turned into an enormous problem for Bayer. A range of derivatives soon became available which were also based on acetylsalicylic acid but did not sell so well. Distributors and pharmacists started to adulterate Aspirin™ or to sell other products under the trusted, registered brand name.

70

Tablet pressing

1904

In 1904, only five years after it was launched, Bayer responded with a measure that was revolutionary for the time. Aspirin™ was the first significant pharmaceutical to be pressed into tablets and embossed with the company logo, the Bayer Cross. This not only made things difficult for the counterfeiters, it also reduced production costs and the selling price by half. Moreover, the tablet made it easier for the consumer to take the exact dose.

Even with these innovations, Bayer was not able to entirely prevent the illegal trade. Secret factories sprang up which produced counterfeit pills en masse. Bayer was left with no alternative other than to threaten legal action against pharmacists who knowingly sold counterfeit products and to warn consumers of the risks. How serious these could be is demonstrated by a demand made by the delegates to the congress of the Norwegian Pharmaceutical Society in 1926 for trade in counterfeit Aspirin™ to be punishable by life imprisonment.

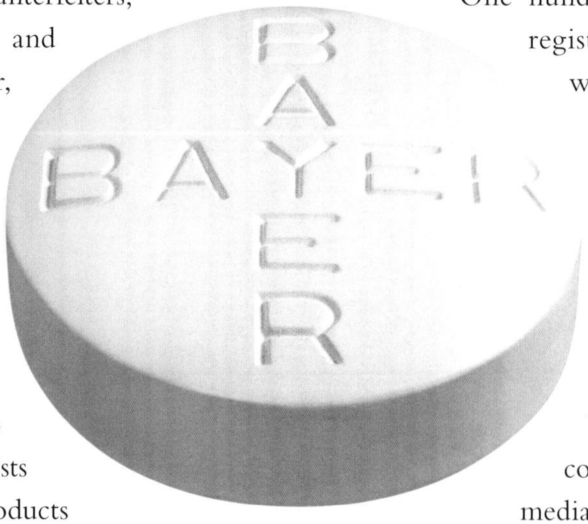

The original Aspirin™ tablet

World record in Leverkusen

HEADQUARTERS TURNED INTO A BOX

Leverkusen, March 6, 1999. Fifty industrial climbers moved in on Bayer's former corporate headquarters. Their mission was to swathe the 122-meter high, 65-meter long and 19-meter wide administrative building in 22,500 square meters of fabric. The result could even be seen from the viewing platform of Cologne cathedral.

71

Aspirin™ high-rise building

1999

One hundred years after the trademark was registered, the climbers created the world's biggest Aspirin™ pack. More than 40,000 guests experienced the spectacle from close up and hundreds of thousands more followed it on the Internet. As a footnote to this, Aspirin™ gained three more entries in the Guinness Book of Records, to add to the many that had gone before. Over 250 journalists from 29 countries ensured unprecedented global media coverage.

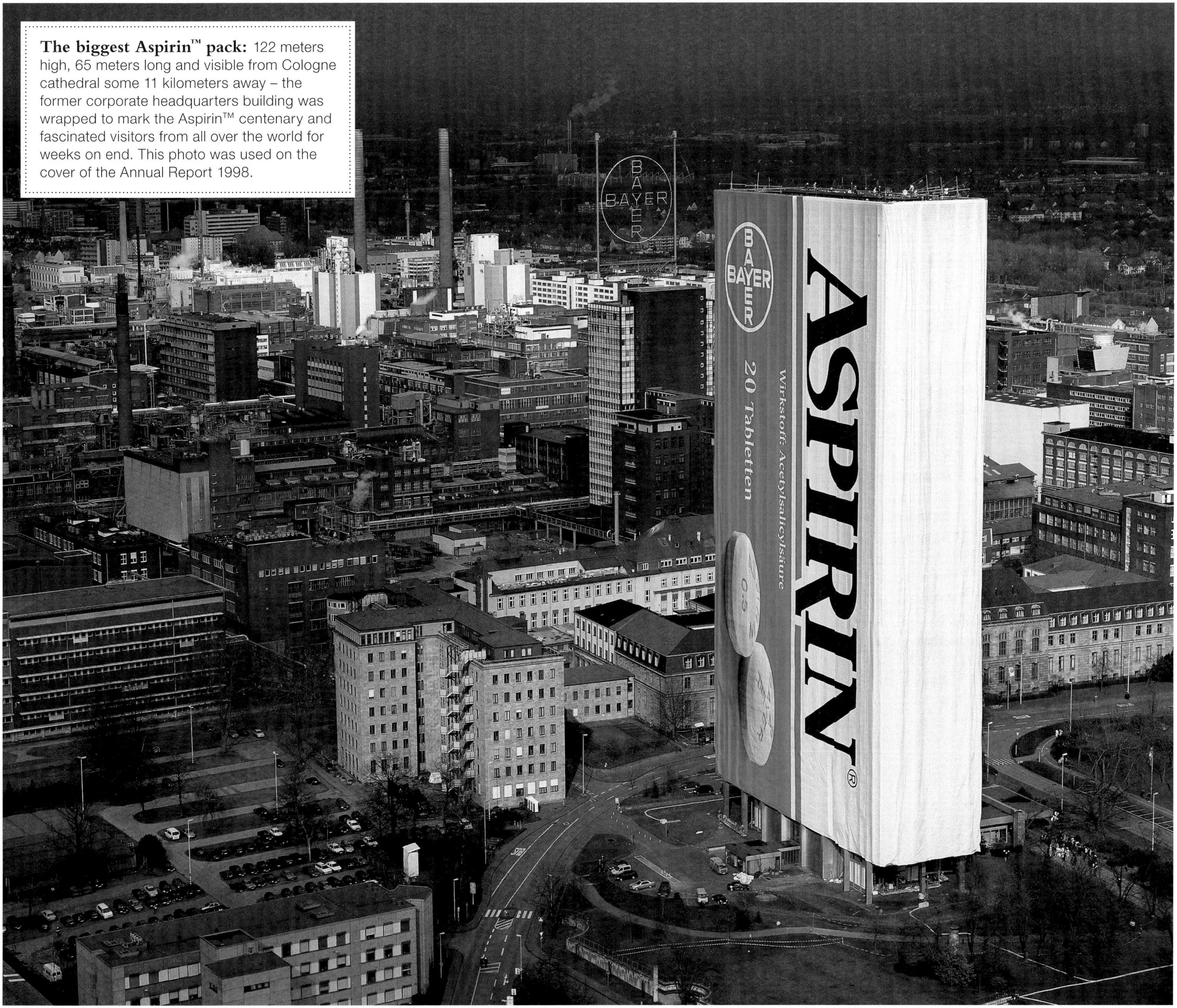

The biggest Aspirin™ pack: 122 meters high, 65 meters long and visible from Cologne cathedral some 11 kilometers away – the former corporate headquarters building was wrapped to mark the Aspirin™ centenary and fascinated visitors from all over the world for weeks on end. This photo was used on the cover of the Annual Report 1998.

A down-to-earth Frankonian:
Marc Claudius Schrinner is glad he listened
to some well-meant advice.

THE NEXT GENERATION

Marc Claudius Schrinner

Shanghai, China

Bayer MaterialScience

THE IDEA FROM THE FIXING BATH

Marc Claudius Schrinner discovered his career goal in his school's darkroom.

I **actually wanted** to be a photographer but the owner of a studio in our neighborhood in Nuremberg advised me against it. "Too uncertain," he said, "Don't do it." I decided not to make my hobby my career after all. Instead, I turned to another great interest. My first contact with chemical substances was in our school's darkroom (I still develop my photos myself) and the transformation of substances fascinated me.

I became a chemist. My doctoral thesis on nanotechnology was awarded the Bavarian Culture Prize and was the subject of an article in *Science* magazine. Between my degree and doctoral thesis I traveled around Australia and New Zealand. With my camera, of course. My present job is just as fascinating. I observe my environment and, whether I'm riding the subway or shopping with my wife, I'm constantly wondering: how can we make people's lives easier?

Marc Claudius Schrinner

Dr. Marc Claudius Schrinner was born in Nuremberg in 1980 and describes himself as being attached to his home city in Germany. In his spare time he enjoys hiking. Marc Claudius Schrinner moved to Shanghai, China, at the start of 2013.

DD coating systems protect the Deutsche Bahn's high-speed trains, for example. They are also used in aircraft construction.

Innovative coatings

TWO COMPONENTS FOR PLANES, TRAINS AND AUTOMOBILES

Germany after the Second World War. Large volumes of coatings were needed to protect the surviving buildings, furniture, machinery and vehicles from corrosion. But these materials were in short supply. Searching for new solutions, chemists looked at polyurethanes, a discovery whose uses are not restricted to plastics and foams. They can also be used to produce two-component coatings. The polyisocyanate (hardener) and polyol (mill base) components are stored separately. The coating does not harden until after they are mixed, although the drying time can be varied for individual applications.

It took off with jets.

The polyisocyanates and polyols for coatings marketed by Bayer at this time were named Desmodur™ and Desmophen™, respectively. Their many possible combinations were referred to as DD coating systems. The commercial breakthrough came in 1961 when the first lightfast Desmodur™ N grade was patented. The properties of the DD coating systems were an innovation. They dried even at room temperature to produce a cured coating film that is resistant to chemicals, abrasion and impact, has good gloss retention and is color-stable. From that point on, U.S. aircraft manufacturer Boeing used polyurethane coatings based on Desmodur™ N for its jets. Deutsche Bundesbahn followed in 1968, and the French state railway soon after. Demand grew rapidly.

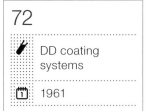

72

DD coating systems

1961

Today, products from the Desmodur™ N range are the world's leading crosslinkers for lightfast, two-component polyurethane coatings. The aircraft industry still values their resistance to high levels of UV radiation, extreme variations in temperature, de-icing agents and kerosene. They are the best option in shipbuilding because of their resistance to seawater. DD coating systems are the first choice for automotive OEM and repair coatings. Waterborne variants resulted from work to develop environmentally compatible coating systems – these are now used on trains.

Renewable raw materials

MANY PROBLEMS CAN BE SOLVED BY GOING BACK TO NATURE

The largest raw materials factory of the future would fit in the palm of your hand. At least in theory. A handful of soil contains around four million microorganisms, and that means billions of new genes. With the help of biocatalysts, they could be used to create countless new organic substances. Applying such biosynthetic processes to extract large quantities of raw materials and conserve or even replace dwindling resources like oil is one of the scientific community's most exciting visions. This idea of using tiny natural "biofactories" is not really new. It is how alcohol is produced. And penicillin, which was discovered by chance on a moldy bacterial culture in 1928. Factor VIII, a blood-clotting agent for hemophiliacs, is synthesized using the principle of industrial fermentation. In fact, many microorganisms seem destined for use in the chemical industry thanks to their unusual properties and capabilities. They can survive even boiling acid, radioactive rays, immense pressure or the lowest of temperatures. They will never be exhausted and never stop production, not even for a second. There will be an enormous surge of innovation if we succeed in creating completely new substances from microbes and enzymes. A study prepared on behalf of the OECD forecasts that just under 40 percent of value creation in the chemical industry will be generated by biotech processes by 2030.

73
Biofactories
1928

Bayer scientists Dr. Gesa Behnken (left) and Dr. Lutz Brassat testing a new polyurethane insulating panel in a cornfield

It's all about sustainability.

Bayer already uses sugar and oils as raw materials for polyurethane components. Among other things, these are used in thermal insulation for buildings. They also play a part in the development of lightweight construction concepts for the cars of the future. In the spirit of sustainable business policy, the focus in the future will not only be on replacing oil (currently still the source of 90 percent of all chemical products), but also on climate-friendly production processes for these natural starting materials. For example, rather than using food-grade corn to produce plastics with the aid of bacteria, the biofactories of the future could achieve the same thing using wood and other vegetable waste.

Special polycarbonate films

THE WORLD IN FILM

Films help foil counterfeiters; they make our roads safer; and they have fans among interior designers – just some of their many potential applications. Known since 2008 as functional films, the special polycarbonate films developed at Bayer MaterialScience are highly versatile. They deflect light, display 3D images and are resistant to scratching and UV light.

74
Functional films
2008

Their uses include consumer electronics, for example. In modern flat-screen TVs with LED backlighting, the ultrathin films scatter and intensify the light produced by the diodes. Organic light-emitting diodes (OLEDs) are considered to be the lights of the future, facilitating entirely new lighting concepts. The light extraction films made from Bayer MaterialScience's polycarbonate increase the light yield by 40 to 60 percent.

Three other Makrofol™ films go unnoticed in many everyday products. Makrofol™ ID is used for ID cards, vehicle registration papers and passports. The film must withstand long use, be heat-resistant and flexible, and allow the integration of various security features to prevent document manipulation. Makrofol™ DE is an unfilled transparent film used in the speedometers of cars. Experts estimate that more than half of all new vehicles now incorporate Bayer's high-quality films. Makrofol™ HF is a coated film that is resistant to scratching and chemicals, making it ideal for the surfaces of heating and ventilation control displays and other dashboard components. The resulting surfaces have a deep gloss finish (piano effect) that doesn't show every little scratch, ensuring a high-quality ambience in vehicle cockpits.

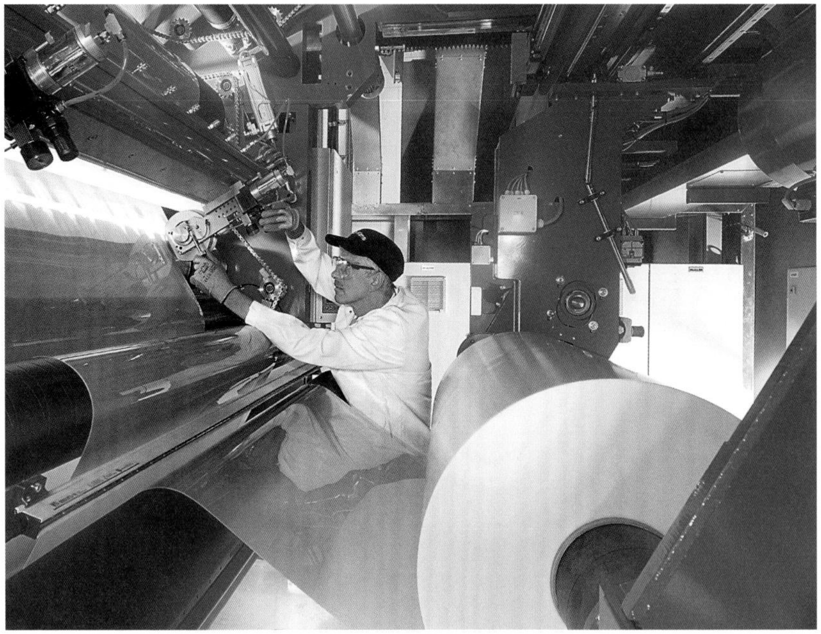

At the Dormagen site, Bayer employee Olaf Kellermann checks the settings on a film winder.

Bayer's high-tech films are also used to combat trademark piracy, with volume holograms made from Bayfol™ HX enhancing packaging security.

We are working on the optimization of our film portfolio at our technology centers in Pittsburgh, United States; Map Ta Phut, Thailand; and Bomlitz and Leverkusen, Germany. The entire production process can be simulated at these facilities. And we are collaborating with our customers to develop new film systems tailored to future markets and applications.

The ViviTouch™ effect

FUN REVOLUTION IN THE WORLD OF COMPUTER GAMES

The reaction is almost always the same – a little shock, amazement and finally a smile, followed by a spontaneous outbreak of a whole new kind of gaming fever. The ViviTouch™ effect has fascinated computer gamers since it was first introduced at trade fairs in 2011. Thanks to components developed by Bayer, games on smartphones, iPods, tablet computers and consoles can not only be heard and seen, but also felt in almost lifelike quality – a novel experience for users that is referred to as high-definition (HD) haptics.

Instead of simple vibrations that merely simulate motion, gamers can feel every movement just by touching the display, touchpad or controller. They experience the rolling of digital pin balls or the impact of a virtual arrow on the target as intensively as if the games were reality. With some 400 million gamers worldwide and a market for computer games that has long surpassed the film industry in terms of sales, it is a concept for the future.

Innovation for the entertainment industry – ViviTouch™

In the future, ViviTouch™ will also change audiovisual perception and how people experience music and movies. Headphones incorporating this new technology provide much more intense, live listening, but at a safe volume setting. Music, game and movie sounds become physically tangible. ViviTouch™ technology does not influence the sound waves themselves, but functions through direct contact with the scalp and transmission of the sound to the skull. Test users compared the feeling to the surround sound experience during a live concert.

75
ViviTouch™
2011

The technology developed by Bayer MaterialScience is based on electroactive polymers (EAP). These plastics are able to change shape when a voltage is applied and thus transform electrical energy directly into motion. Due to the way they work, they are often also referred to as "artificial muscles." To make tactile feedback actuators, electrodes are applied by coating on both sides of an EAP film. They are similar in structure to a plate capacitor. If a voltage is applied to the electrodes, they attract one another, exerting pressure on the non-conductive film in between, which expands over its whole surface. Once the voltage is turned off, the film returns to its original shape. Controlled motions with response times in the millisecond range are the result, which can be used to simulate haptic effects.

To date, the potential of this technology platform has not been exploited to any great extent. Bayer's researchers are looking at applications for these electroactive polymers outside the area of entertainment electronics.

CHAPTER

3

WILLPOWER

“

ALL RESEARCHERS MUST HAVE
A TALENT FOR SELF-MOTIVATION,
OTHERWISE THEY WON’T LAST
IN THIS JOB.

”

REINER FISCHER, MONHEIM, GERMANY

Page 256

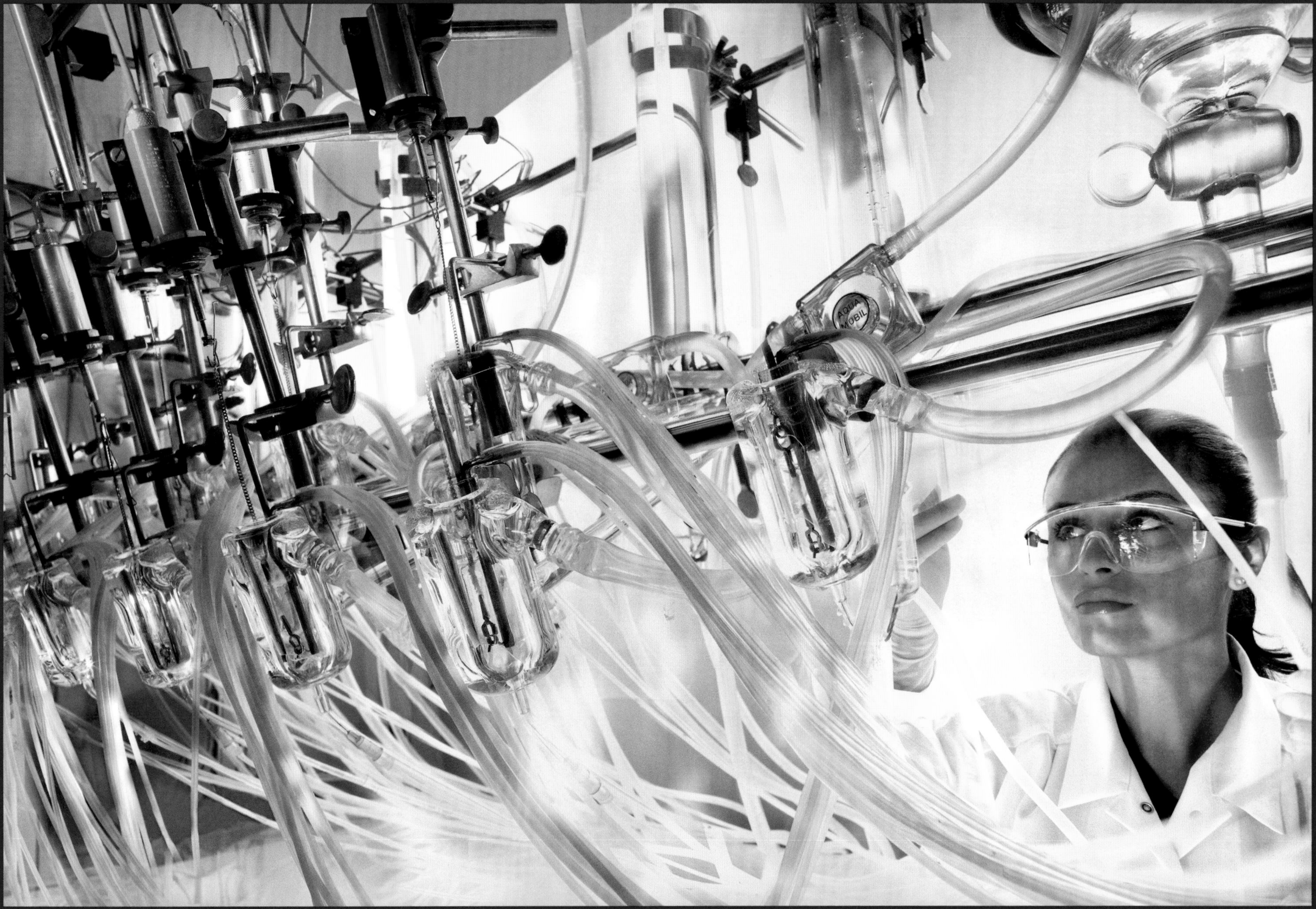

CARDIOVASCULAR DISEASE
THE TRANSPARENT MAN

In a photo used in the Annual Report 2006, Dr. Astrid Brüns and Dr. Dirk Heimbach are shown with a model of the human body in the Health Care Exhibition Room at the Bayer Communication Center in Leverkusen, discussing the way innovative drug products work.

Read more about cardiovascular disease starting on page 208.

ERECTILE DYSFUNCTION
BREAKTHROUGH

A component of vardenafil, an active ingredient to treat erectile dysfunction, was developed at the Pharmaceuticals Research Center in Wuppertal in the 1990s.

Read more starting on page 222.

NS 45.40

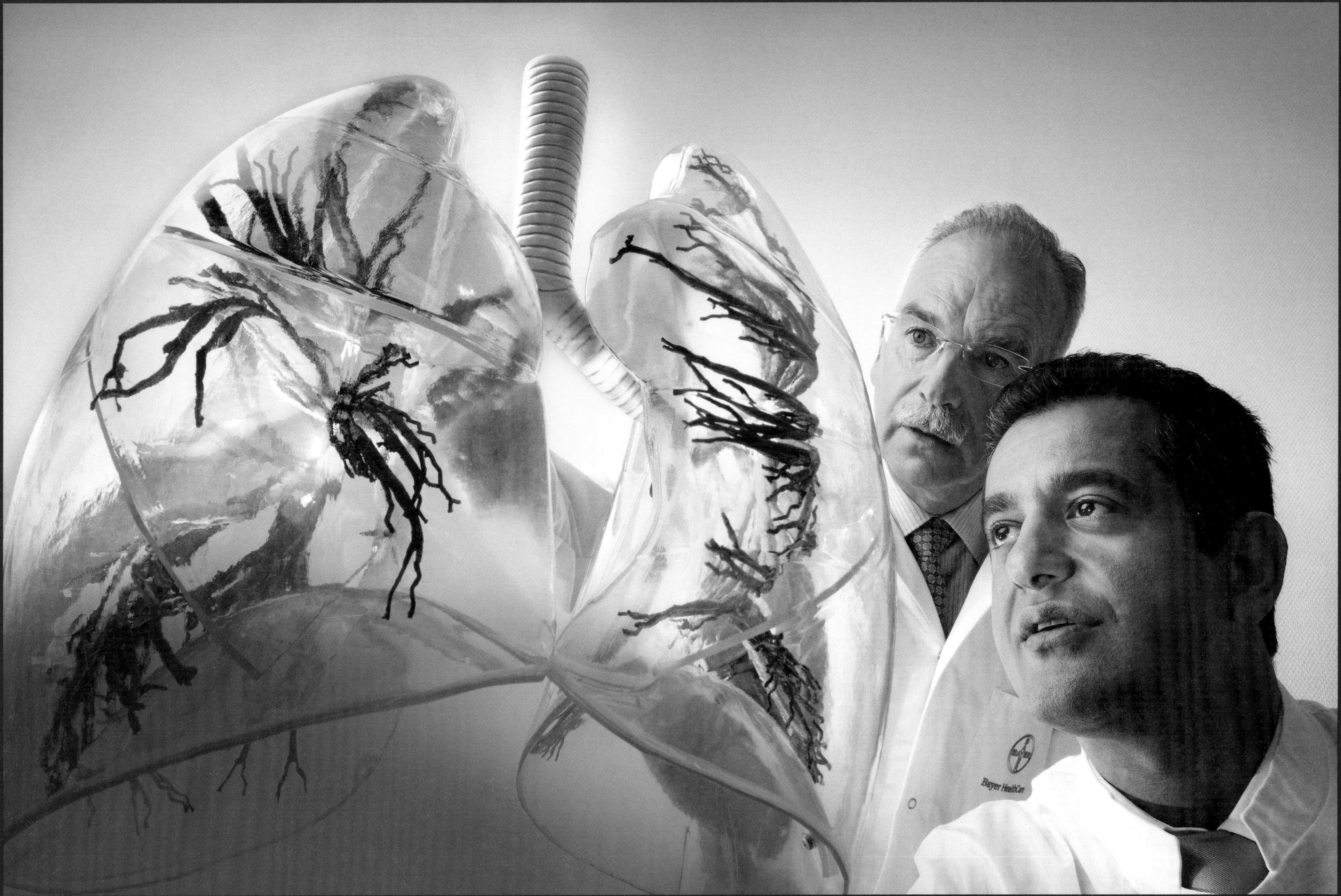

CARDIOVASCULAR DISEASE
OUTSTANDING RESEARCH

Bayer HealthCare scientist Dr. Susanne Röhrig at the Aprath Research Center: she contributed to the development of rivaroxaban (Xarelto™), an anticoagulant drug. This product has already received many awards, including the 2009 German Future Prize for innovation and technology from the German President.

THE LUNG
TREATING HYPERTENSION

Their field of research is the insidious disease pulmonary hypertension: Bayer scientist Dr. Johannes-Peter Stasch and Prof. Hossein Ardeschir Ghofrani (front) from Gießen University Hospital. The model shows the structure of a lung.

Read more about cardiovascular disease starting on page 208.

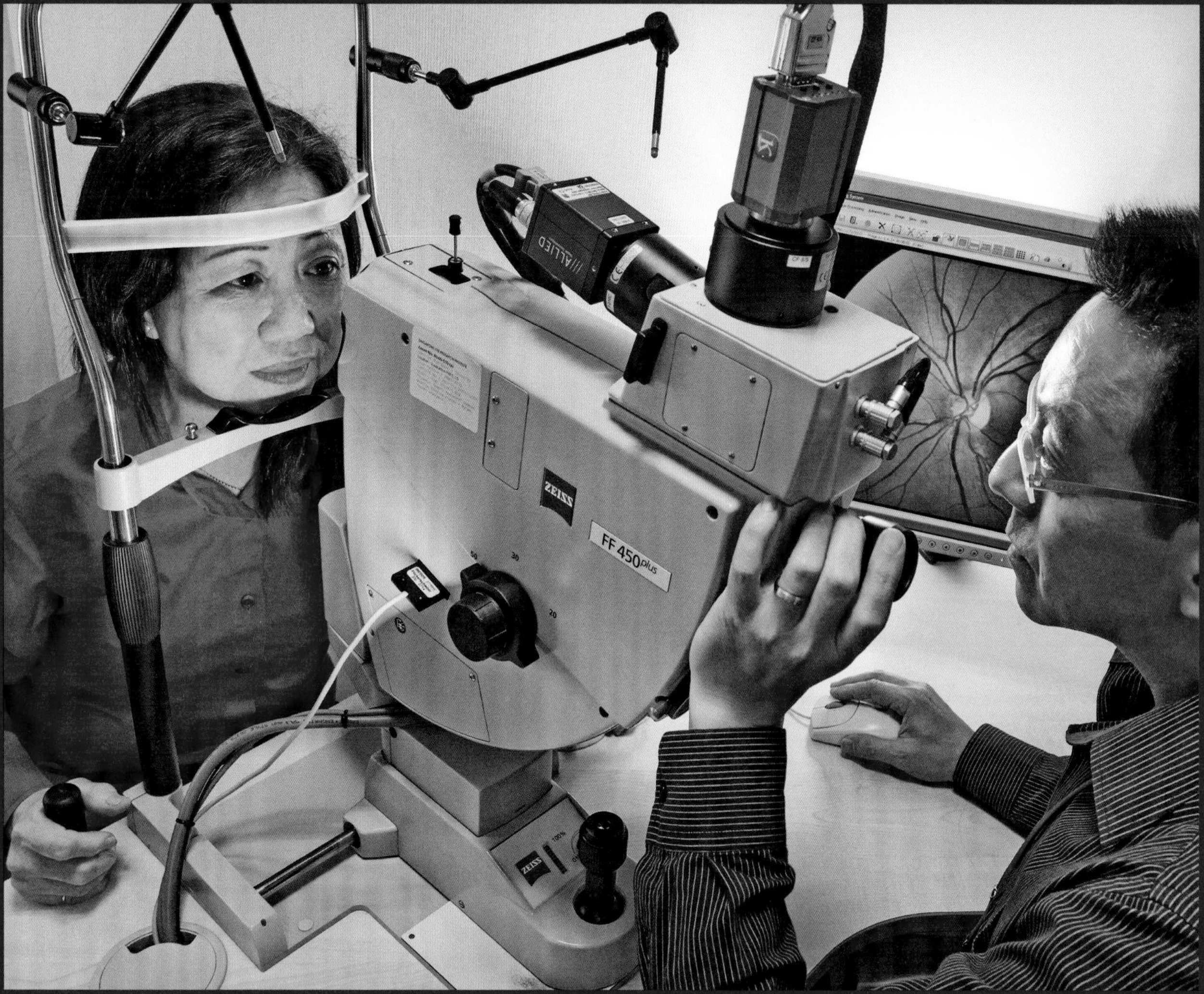

EYLEA
VISION IN OLD AGE

Examining the retina: age-related macular degeneration is a dangerous condition which robs many elderly people of their vision. Working with a partner, Bayer HealthCare has developed an active ingredient to stop this disease: VEGF Trap-Eye.

Find out more about vision in old age starting on page 225.

MULTIPLE SCLEROSIS
IDENTIFYING SUCCESSES

Bayer employees Sandra Patkovic and Dr. Jürgen Heubach assess the results of tests in multiple sclerosis patients treated with Betaferon™/Betaseron™.

Read more starting on page 226.

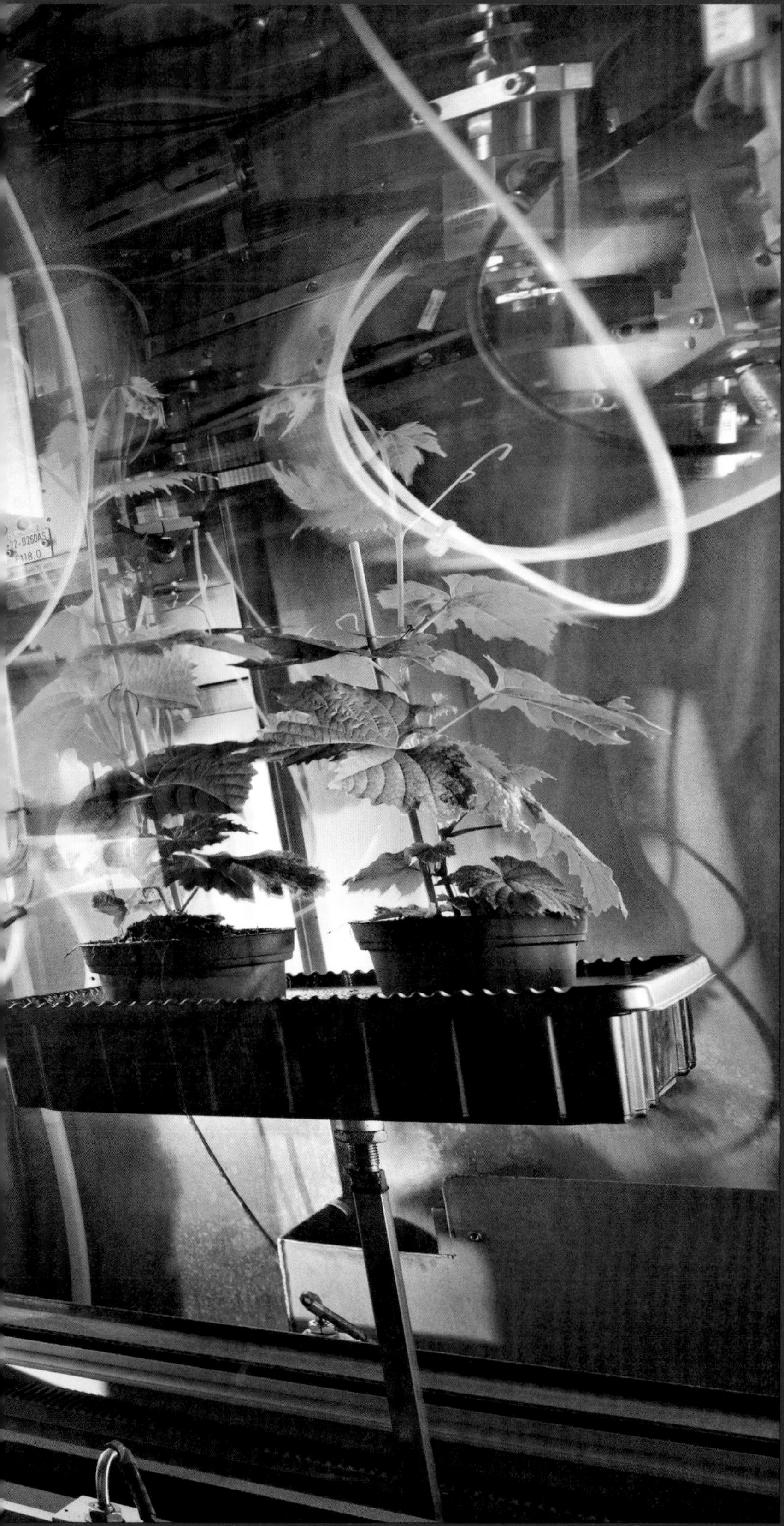

FRUIT AND VEGETABLES
TENDER YOUNG PLANTS

Bayer CropScience researcher Dr. Andreas Görtz examines young vines after a robot sprayer has applied a new active substance.

HIGH-TECH IN THE LAB
NEW VEGETABLE VARIETIES

Paul Buddiger and Fiona Knubben-Schot use fully automated gene analysis and molecular markers to investigate plant samples. The results aid the targeted development of new vegetable varieties.

Find out what Bayer scientists are doing to ensure healthy fruit and vegetables starting on page 250.

NEW HARVEST
TASTY BANANAS

At the Grupo Calinda plantation in Costa Rica, Bayer employee Rigoberto Estrada Brenes, plantation manager Ivan Sánchez Araya and Viviana Matarrita Ledezma assess freshly harvested bananas.

COTTON
HIGHER QUALITY WITH LESS WATER

Vivian Oliver and Gary Henniger from Bayer CropScience assess cotton plants at the research center in Lubbock, Texas, USA. The researchers are working to improve the quality and yield of cotton crops and to breed plants which need less water.

Read more starting on page 230.

Bayer

Elisabeth Perzborn is still in demand as an expert. In her free time, she enjoys a round of golf.

76

Elisabeth Perzborn

Rivaroxaban

2008

Rivaroxaban (Xarelto™) has been on the market since 2008 and is used to prevent thromboembolism. The active ingredient inhibits a specific enzyme (factor Xa) involved in the blood coagulation process, which prevents another coagulation factor (prothrombin) from being converted into its active form (thrombin). This stops blood clots from forming. *(See also the profile of Alexander Straub on page 212.)*

A PIONEER

Elisabeth Perzborn's persistence and stubbornness paved the way for young female researchers. Today, she holds the German Future Prize.

I **have a** toy jumbo jet on my desk. It was a gift from the member of our Board of Management responsible for research – given with a smile but with a serious message as well. You could have bought several real jumbos with the billions of euros it cost over the years to develop our medicine Xarelto™, which contains the active ingredient rivaroxaban. Yet I never lost any sleep over this. We researchers are used to bearing a lot of responsibility.

I was one of the first female laboratory managers in pharmaceutical research. It's something I'm rather proud of because at the time it was so unusual that I like to think of myself as a kind of pioneer. I grew up in the years of Germany's economic miracle – Adenauer, Erhard's clouds of cigar smoke and Freddy Quinn's schmaltzy songs, the Volkswagen Beetle, sentimental *Heimat* films and clearly defined roles: the husband went out to work, the wife stayed home and looked after the children. If a woman did work, then she had a job that was compatible with childrearing. But I didn't want to be a teacher or a dental nurse, and that really worried my aunts. "Child, what on earth do you want, then? Look at Marlies! Why do you want to do a high-school diploma and then even study? Do an apprenticeship and save for your dowry – that'll be more use to you as a woman," they kept on saying. My father took a different view. "She should have a good education and then she can stand on her own two feet," he growled. My parents (sadly my mother died early) and brothers always supported me. They were the ones who gave me my interest in science. We often used to ramble through the forests of the Bergisches Land, looking at nature and asking many questions that we couldn't answer at the time.

"When I saw the data, I knew we'd done it. Then I drove home and cooked dinner for my children."

It was with some defiance that I went to college. I remember one professor's opening address: "Ladies, I advise you to do the teaching qualification – that way you can combine a job with having a family. Is there anyone here who wants to do a full degree?" Sadly, very few hands went up. I was shocked at this narrow-mindedness and thought: "Biology teacher? No, there's got to be another way." And there was. Today I have a family, two grown-up children who are both just writing their doctoral theses. And I hold the German Future Prize, awarded by the German President in recognition of outstanding achievements in technology and innovation.

I felt comfortable as part of the company right from the very first day. Block 500 at the Aprath Research Center in Wuppertal became my professional home. It's where my career started in the 1970s and it's where it ended as well. I perceived the working environment as being innovation-friendly, successfully achieving the balance between self-directed work and a framework of rules that are necessary so everything doesn't spin out of control. Things that inhibit innovation: interminable discussions on too many committees, the hectic pace of everyday life. I was given the task of discovering active ingredients to treat cardiovascular diseases. We started looking for a substance to inhibit coagulation factor Xa in 1998, and the breakthrough came already in April 2000. It was a Friday afternoon. My colleague Susanne Röhrig had synthesized BAY 59-7939. The laboratory sent up some promising data, and as I checked them I knew: "We've done it!" Shortly afterwards I drove home and cooked dinner for my children. I've sometimes been asked in jest whether women make better researchers. There's no sensible answer to that question, but I always made sure that the working atmosphere in my team was good.

When I retired, there was a nameplate on my office door that said "Mother Xarelto," in reference to the drug containing our active ingredient.

Elisabeth Perzborn

Dr. Elisabeth Perzborn was born in Opladen (a district of Leverkusen) in 1948. She did her PhD in Aachen and joined Bayer in 1979. She officially retired in 2012, but still likes traveling in support of Xarelto™ and is a frequent visitor to Block 500. She enjoys golf, skiing and gardening. Elisabeth Perzborn was awarded the Otto Bayer Medal and the 2009 German Future Prize for innovation and technology from the German President for her role in the development of Xarelto™. She lives in Wuppertal, Germany.

The adult heart beats...*

4,000
times per hour

35 million
times per year

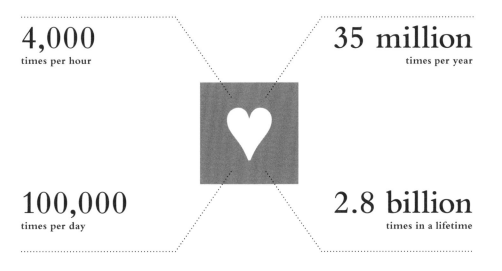

100,000
times per day

2.8 billion
times in a lifetime

** The figures are rounded and based on an average heart rate of between 66.6 and 69.4 beats per minute.*

Cardiovascular disease is more prevalent in Europe and the USA than in the developing countries. Asian populations with a low-fat, high-protein diet are at less risk.

WHO

40% of adults over the age of 25 suffer from hypertension.

WHO

Proportion of the population in Africa that suffers from hypertension: 46%

Number of people in Germany who undergo hospital treatment for heart disease each year: 2.7 million

Destatis

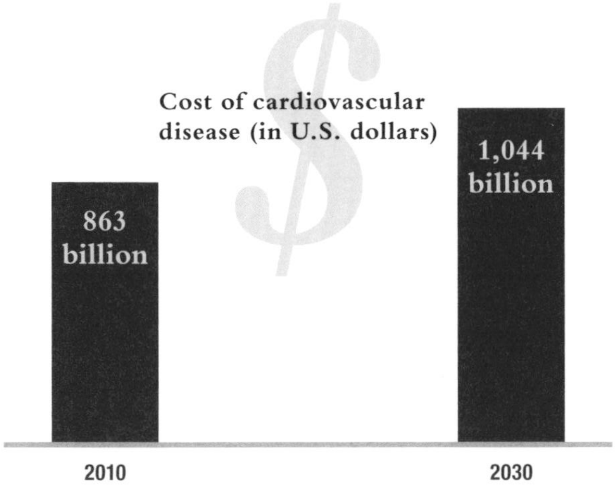

World Economic Forum

17.3 million

people die from cardiovascular disease each year (2008)

23.3 million

people are predicted to die from cardiovascular disease in 2030

WHO

Main causes of death worldwide:
1 Cardiovascular disease **2** Infectious diseases
3 Cancer **4** Respiratory disease
5 Accidents

WHO

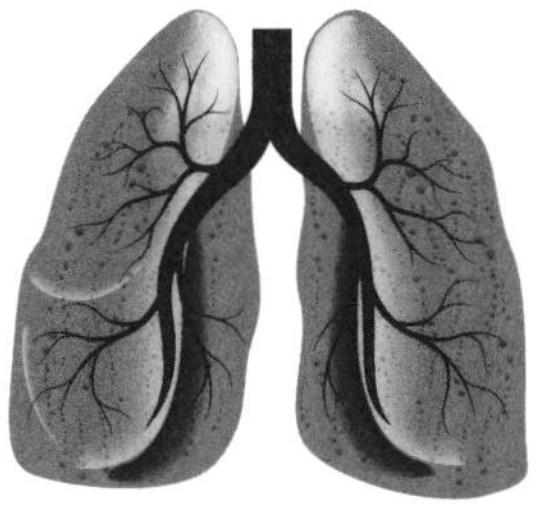

Respiratory rate of a baby:
30
Respiratory rate of an adult:
13
Tidal volume of an adult:
0.5 l

Mean observed values

Alexander Straub has an unusual hobby:
he collects Tiffany lamps.

77

Alexander Straub

Xarelto™

2008

Xarelto™, authorized in 2008, is a direct factor Xa inhibitor in tablet form that is approved for indications such as the prevention of stroke in patients with atrial fibrillation. (See also the profile of Elisabeth Perzborn on page 208.)

ART NOUVEAU

Alexander Straub had his first successes as a chemist during his teenage years – in an inventor's competition. Looking back, he believes it's a miracle that his parents' house survived his experiments. However, Straub learned one thing early on: the sensuality of chemistry.

I**f friends ask** me what happens in a normal day as a researcher behind the fence at the research center, then I answer: failure, lots of failure. But not to worry. You need to see the good in that. I find that failure strengthens the character. Researchers must not lose their sense of humor and should never stop working hard. That's because there are also feelings of happiness that are indescribable. The library from which we select potential active ingredients contains around three million substances. Three million substances from which maybe 1,000 remain after initial tests with the target molecule. Then we have to find out which structures and molecular properties are the most suitable. If you make a mistake at this point, you may spend years going in the wrong direction. That can happen if you don't give up at an early stage – although no-one can say whether you might not be close to a breakthrough after all. Give up? Keep going? It's a tough one to call.

It can be hard for someone without a fundamentally cheerful approach to life. Even when you get close to finding a solution, the next questions pop up. Which synthesis routes should we use? How can we get a handle on efficacy, tolerability and solubility? In the case of riociguat, we needed 2,000 syntheses and for rivaroxaban around 700.

To be a researcher means combining the characteristics of a triathlete and a concert pianist – stamina and virtuosity.

> ***"Researchers ask why. We question things that are seemingly incontrovertible."***

Like other colleagues, I discovered my love of chemistry as a child when I was given a microscope that I used to examine pollen grains or onion skin. I built rockets and launched them; set fire to the living room furniture when an experiment with thermite got out of control; and made chlorine gas in my bedroom which bleached the green from the leaves of the pot plants. Looking back, I think it's almost a miracle that my parents' house is still standing. Both of them are artists and they observed my goings-on with a mixture of fascination and disbelief. I won a special prize in the European Union Contest for Young Scientists, disrupted chemistry class in school because I was bored, and applied to study chemistry in Stuttgart – the city of Swabian inventors – after completing my compulsory community service. With a scholarship from the Robert Bosch Foundation, I completed my studies "with distinction."

Ever since my experiments for a student research competition, I've always been driven to find solutions to complex problems – especially if these were at the interface between chemistry and other disciplines. You can't just gather experience in theory; you have to actually feel things as well. It's about the sensual experience – fascinating crystals, strange-smelling chemicals, exciting color stimuli. Laboratory equipment and old pharmacies always held an esthetic attraction for me. Industrial romanticism also makes my heart beat faster. When I was a process researcher at a plant in Dormagen, I enjoyed wandering around the site to experience the large production facilities, refineries, chimneys and reaction vessels at close quarters. For me, Wuppertal also radiates a slightly old-fashioned industrial romanticism. As the birthplace of Bayer, my second hometown played a key role during Germany's industrial revolution. To this day, my fascination remains unchanged. Researchers need to preserve their sense of curiosity, playfulness and naivety when exploring their surroundings. We ask why. We question things that are seemingly incontrovertible.

The best ideas come to me in the evening, when the laboratory is quiet. That's when innovations are created. I encourage my team to try things out, even if they seem far-fetched. It's always the successes that are publicized, never the failures. But who knows. Perhaps it was the right idea but we just got one detail wrong. Luck, chance, surprises and intuition can't be planned. Sometimes, it's precisely that moment of surprise that is needed in real inventions.

Alexander Straub

Dr. Alexander Straub was born in 1959 and is considered one of the leading researchers in the field of cardiovascular disease. He has twice been awarded the Otto Bayer Medal. To "blow away the cobwebs," he likes spending time outdoors and cycling with his family. He has a weakness for art nouveau design. Alexander Straub lives with his wife and son in Wuppertal, Germany.

Decades of work – years of success

WHEN A RESEARCHER'S LIFELONG DREAM BECOMES REALITY

It was an honorable assignment that Friedrich Bossert had been given, but unfortunately it also seemed to be next to impossible. He had been asked to find a drug to treat what is now the main cause of death worldwide – heart disease. The chemist had just turned 28 when he found a job at Bayer, and he suspected that his younger years would have long passed before he could achieve the objective he had been set. In Wuppertal, he got to work with his colleague Wulf Vater, who was just a little older. It was 1948. Over the following decades, the scientists worked on a project aimed at countering the downside of prosperity that had become apparent in the industrialized world by the mid-1960s: lack of exercise, obesity, stress. Factors that put a strain on the circulation system. Since infectious diseases could mostly be cured with antibiotics, most people were dying of heart failure, vascular occlusion or other circulatory disorders.

The inventors of Adalat™, Dr. Friedrich Bossert (left) and Dr. Wulf Vater, were also involved in the discovery of Nimotop™ (see page 216).

Scientists began the search for effective therapeutic options. Pacemakers had just been invented, bypass operations were still the exception and a plant-based remedy called Khellin that had an anticonvulsive effect was only mildly effective. Nonetheless, this was the starting point that Bossert and Vater chose for their work. They believed there must be a chemical way to prevent contraction of the vascular smooth muscle. At the Pharmacological Institute in Wuppertal, they tested thousands of substances until they finally discovered nifedipine. 19 years had passed since they began their research. But then they came up with a real innovation.

78

Adalat™

1974

When a muscle contracts, calcium migrates into its cells. However, if too much calcium flows into the vascular smooth muscle, it impairs the blood circulation and heart rhythm and increases the blood pressure. Nifedipine affects the blood vessels and regulates the inflow of calcium, which is why it is also referred to as a calcium antagonist. It causes dilation of the blood vessels, eliminating spasms, lowering the blood pressure and reducing the risk of myocardial infarction. In 1974, the product was launched on the market as Adalat™. Of course, heart diseases can only be relieved and not cured, as was the case with some infectious diseases. Nonetheless, thanks to their persistence, Bossert and Vater were able to help countless patients. Adalat™ remains one of the company's strongest-selling drug products to this day.

Boosting the blood supply to the brain cells

IMPROVING MEMORY IN OLD AGE

Sometimes, the lessons learned during the development of a new active ingredient lead right to the next innovation. That was what happened in the case of nimodipine, which was patented in 1979. This substance can improve the blood flow and supply of nutrients to the nerve cells in the brain, reducing memory loss and preventing mental impairment in most cases. The initial foundations for this discovery were laid by Bayer researchers years before it was filed for approval, when a team led by chemist Friedrich Bossert was developing the cardiovascular drug Adalat™ (this story can be found on page 215).

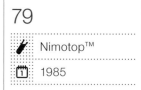

79

Nimotop™

1985

During his research work, Bossert wondered whether circulatory disorders of the brain and other parts of the body could be caused by the same problem – narrowed blood vessels that block the flow of blood and the supply of nutrients. But Adalat™, the drug product that he had synthesized together with his colleague Wulf Vater, brought him no closer to a solution.

The scientists didn't give up: Bossert and his colleagues tested countless substances until they finally achieved their objective. Nimodipine is able to pass through the blood-brain barrier and activate brain cells in a previously unimaginable way. It limits the inflow of calcium which causes cellular contraction and thus often leads to spasms. As a result, the cramped and narrowed blood vessels that block the supply to the brain cells in elderly patients are dilated again. More oxygen then reaches the brain, which can significantly improve patients' memory and attentiveness.

Nimotop™ was brought to market in 1985 and since then has helped to improve the quality of life in old age for many people.

Bayer scientists Jin Weihua (left) and Liu Guiging analyze active ingredients in Beijing, China.

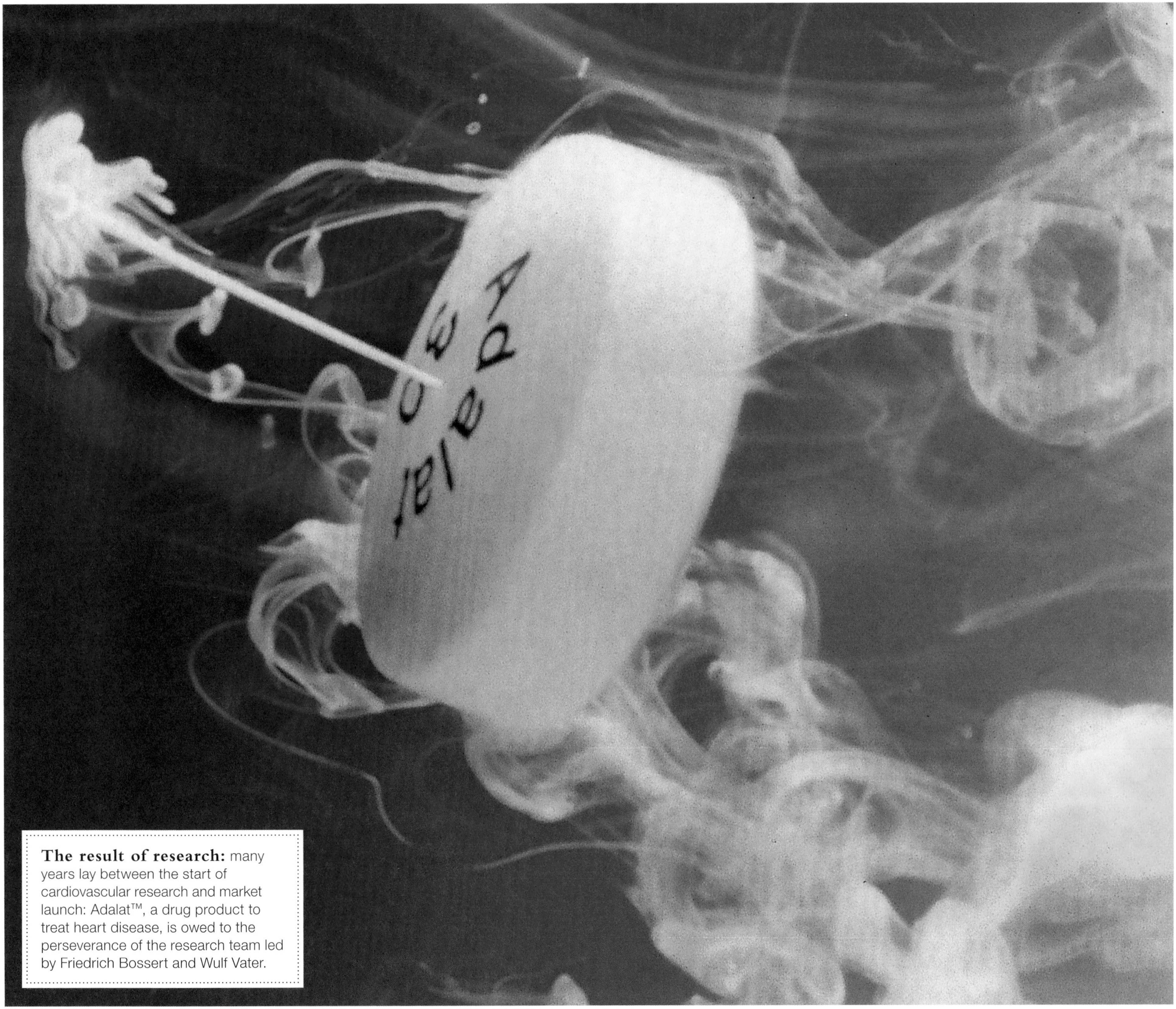

The result of research: many years lay between the start of cardiovascular research and market launch: Adalat™, a drug product to treat heart disease, is owed to the perseverance of the research team led by Friedrich Bossert and Wulf Vater.

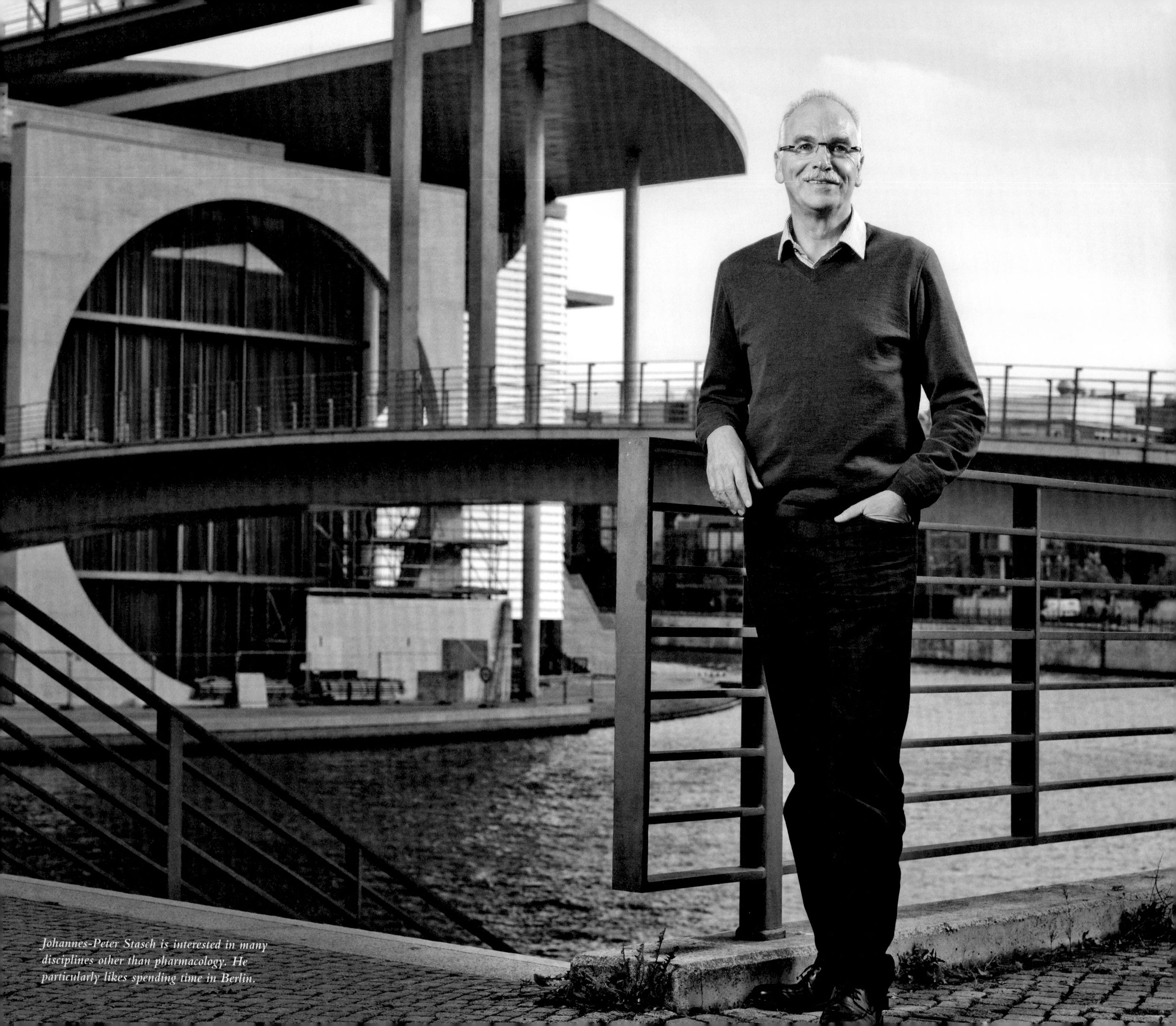

Johannes-Peter Stasch is interested in many disciplines other than pharmacology. He particularly likes spending time in Berlin.

80

Johannes-Peter Stasch

Riociguat

2008

Until now, there have been very few therapeutic options for treating pulmonary hypertension, a severe, progressive and life-threatening disease which causes increased pressure in the pulmonary arteries. Riociguat, in clinical development since 2008, is the first substance in a new class that directly stimulates the enzyme soluble guanylate cyclase (sGC). This reduces the pressure in the pulmonary arteries and significantly improves lung capacity in patients with advanced pulmonary disease.

FASCINATED BY BEAUTY

Johannes-Peter Stasch headed a team which found an active ingredient to treat pulmonary hypertension. A story about the capacity for suffering, the strength to accept alternative concepts, Heinrich Rombach and an uncle in Chicago.

I **like to** congratulate my employees when something goes wrong. If we draw the right conclusions from failure, then we learn the most in the long term. In a quarter-century of research work, I've gone down many wrong tracks but I've also found some right ones. There was one inspiring moment like those otherwise experienced perhaps only by explorers. One moment when the curtain lifts and allows us to glimpse the beauty of creation. That makes everything worthwhile.

I discovered the active substance class termed the sGC stimulators. An important pharmacological innovation to treat pulmonary hypertension, a life-threatening disease for which new medicines were being urgently sought.

On the wall of my office is a quote from the Italian poet and philosopher Dante given to me by colleagues after more than twenty-five years of joint research work: "Some wait for time to change. Others seize the moment and act." I followed a twisting path to reach this milestone. An uncle in Chicago got me involved in science by giving me ten dollars for a chemistry set. Back then, you could still make things which stank and banged. My fellow students and I were soon experimenting with gunpowder and turned our attention to rockets. I got supplies of chemicals from a friendly pharmacist who supported my enthusiasm. Once, while my parents were at church, there was a small fire in our cellar. My father, a railway official, viewed my experiments with a certain degree of skepticism but also trust. After graduating from high school, I refused to do military service – scandalous behavior at that time – and defended myself in court, right up to the highest instance. I harbor a certain skepticism towards authority. I then did community service.

"A researcher needs passion and a capacity for suffering. And the strength and belief to follow up on ideas."

I studied philosophy as well as chemistry. The thoughts of Heinrich Rombach and Klaus Hemmerle were always an inspiration to me. Chemistry alone? Too little for me. I think it's important to be active in various areas in parallel. These include my social commitment and my passion for nature, art and science. What pleases me is the extremely good atmosphere among my colleagues. I've made many friends, researchers who are more interested in what they are doing than in advancing their careers. The atmosphere among my colleagues at the Aprath Research Center is extremely positive. People you can trust, who display a high degree of integrity. Those are what I consider to be values.

You can't force success or chase it. Researchers seldom experience success. A physician heals a patient; a craftsman sees what he's created with his hands at the end of the day. By contrast, it may be that a researcher achieves no tangible results for years. It's a little like playing the lottery. I've always been helped by the thought that any discovery I made would improve the lives of thousands of people.

It's important to me to be independent of material things. In my experience, material things are not the most important things in life. There are a few other attitudes which have stood me well. It's dangerous when your job eats up your life.

If you get away from the careerist approach, there's a great deal more time for scientific work. Success then comes by itself. It's difficult to push through a genuine innovation. Nine out of ten people will always tell you why it won't work. You have to be able to deal with skeptics. Passion is also essential in our job, just like the capacity for suffering. A lot of people have good ideas. However, only a few people follow up on their ideas and have the strength and the belief to convince others of their value. Ultimately it's about making people look at familiar things with new eyes.

Johannes-Peter Stasch

Professor Johannes-Peter Stasch was born near Hamelin, Germany, in 1954. He studied in Hannover and Würzburg. Stasch holds a degree in chemistry and is a registered pharmacist. He obtained a PhD in science in 1983, qualified as a professor of pharmacology in 2003 and is professor for drug research at the University of Halle-Wittenberg. He has received numerous awards for his research achievements including the Otto Bayer Medal (2008). Johannes-Peter Stasch is married, has three children and lives in Solingen, Germany.

Insidious high pressure in the lungs

WHEN BLOOD VESSELS HARDEN

People with pulmonary hypertension often have similar symptoms to patients suffering from heart failure or lung disease: shortness of breath, palpitations, fatigue and sometimes even fainting spells. In people with pulmonary hypertension, the walls of the pulmonary arteries harden and thicken and the vessel lumina narrow. Soft blood vessels become like stiff tubes. On exertion – and possibly also at rest – not enough oxygen-rich blood gets into the bloodstream that supplies the body's major organs. In healthy patients, the blood vessels in the lungs are extremely elastic to compensate for the fact that the lungs have only one seventh as many veins as the systemic circulation yet have to handle the same quantity of blood. When the pressure in the lungs is persistently high, this flexibility is increasingly reduced. At first, the heart tries to compensate for the resulting oxygen deficiency by pumping harder. But if the condition is not diagnosed in good time, the heart will at some point fail.

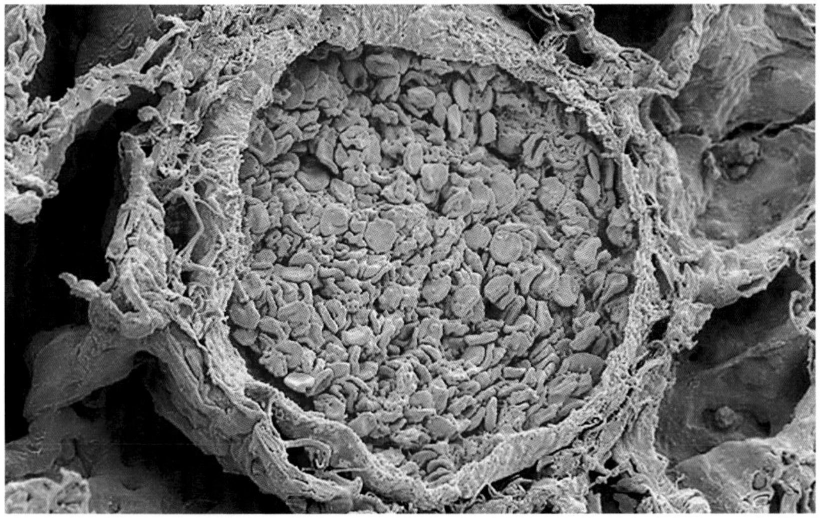

Electron micrograph of a pulmonary blood vessel – it is filled with red blood cells.

Worldwide around 15 people per million suffer from the disease, but the incidence may be higher. If the underlying cause of their symptoms could be identified at an early stage, they could be helped with medication. The rare occurrence of pulmonary hypertension means it may go undiagnosed or correct diagnosis may be delayed. While systemic hypertension can be easily detected with a blood pressure cuff and a stethoscope, the diagnosis of pulmonary hypertension requires insertion of a catheter into the pulmonary artery through a vein in the groin or neck. This is the only way to measure blood pressure in the lungs.

81

Ilomedin™

1990

This complicated diagnosis method is one reason why little attention was paid to pulmonary hypertension for a long time. However, the causes of the disease are now largely understood. They include genetic predisposition, HIV infection and liver cirrhosis. The pulmonary arteries become irritated, eventually narrowing and closing entirely. Medications to treat some variants of this disease have been available for about 15 years. One milestone in the development of active ingredients to treat pulmonary hypertension was the discovery of prostacyclin and its synthetic derivatives such as Ilomedin™ (active ingredient iloprost), which was approved in 1990. This substance is capable of at least delaying right heart failure, which is when the heart stops beating as a result of high blood pressure. Ilomedin™ dilates the narrowed pulmonary blood vessels, alleviating shortness of breath and easing strain on the heart.

A man with drive: Erwin Bischoff enjoys sports in his free time. One of his other passions is model flying.

82

Erwin Bischoff

Vardenafil

2002

Vardenafil, registered in 2002 and sold as Levitra™, is an active ingredient for the treatment of erectile dysfunction. It inhibits phosphodiesterase type 5 (PDE 5), the substance which causes an erection to subside.

RESEARCHING A TABOO SUBJECT

Friends tease him, colleagues are skeptical and there is a great deal of internal discussion. But Erwin Bischoff remains determined – and drives forward the development of an active ingredient to treat erectile dysfunction.

M**y colleague from** the Weizmann Institute, whom I met at a conference, was so enthusiastic that he couldn't stop talking about it. The subject was a substance which had a potent effect on the sexual organs of rodents. I'm a biologist and actually specialize in cardiovascular diseases. But I was interested in this stuff that had so impressed my colleague. Back in Wuppertal, I was able to convince my supervisors that it made sense to conduct some initial tests. We started out and ran into a problem: the mysterious substance didn't work. It didn't permeate the skin. But we didn't give up and kept going with our research. The results of the next tests were completely different to what we'd expected. We were on the right track with our PDE 5 inhibitors. The rabbits hopped round their cages in a state of permanent arousal. Further tests confirmed our observations with scientifically verifiable facts. The question was whether we should continue. One competitor already had an advantage of several years in researching an erectile dysfunction drug. We don't work at a university but in an industrial enterprise. As a rule, if you're second, you've lost the race. It wasn't even clear if Bayer actually wanted to enter the race anyway.

Within the company, our project was controversial and the subject of considerable discussion.

"You can research all you want," teased our critics, "that kind of thing isn't for Bayer." A product to treat erectile dysfunction somehow had a sleazy taint which didn't really fit in with our corporate philosophy or our clean and pure image. "That kind of thing" had never been on the company's agenda before. Within a very short time, news of what we were doing had spread round the research campus. Colleagues stopped me in the cafeteria or in the hallway and came up with plenty of funny remarks. There was a lot of teasing from friends as well and puns abounded. Many people obviously found the whole thing very funny. But erectile dysfunction is actually a serious problem that affects thousands of men and their partners.

"A debate started concerning the pros and cons, sense and potential."

Things then got serious for us. After extensive discussions, I was given permission to carry on with our research. It was the start of a very intensive experience. Within a very short time, our team managed to find the active ingredient BAY-389456, which was actually water-soluble. A real achievement by our chemists. This meant we could have offered the substance as both a tablet and a nasal spray. In rabbits, our success was convincing. I'll never forget November 13, 1997 – a Thursday. We were presenting our results and data to a large group – and a heated debate again started concerning the pros and cons, sense and potential of the product. The discussion also covered the form and even the color of the tablet. It was to be an oral presentation rather than a nasal spray - there was consensus on that point. At the end of the meeting, it was decided to take the substance forward into clinical trials.

"Our team was carried by euphoria whenever there was a problem or we came to a standstill."

A short time later, two renowned American urologists gave a neutral opinion that confirmed what we had already hoped. Our product worked! There were highs and lows in our work, but our team was carried by euphoria whenever there was a problem or we came to a standstill. Media reports were peppered with amusing puns.

In 2002, after exhaustive studies, the product was finally brought to market as Levitra™. It wasn't intended as a lifestyle product but as a medicine to be taken under strict supervision. We had to continue convincing people, including physicians. I found out that erectile dysfunction can still be a taboo subject.

Erwin Bischoff

Dr. Erwin Bischoff was born in Ravensburg in southern Germany in 1943. The father of three enjoys sailing, mountain-biking and tennis; he also flies model aircraft. Erwin Bischoff and his team were awarded the Otto Bayer Medal for the development of Levitra™. He lives with his family in Wuppertal, Germany.

Innovative active ingredient for eye diseases

HELPING GRANDPARENTS KEEP THEIR VISION

Grandma can no longer see her granddaughter's face or her smile. A dark blur is all that remains at the center of her visual field. The elderly lady is suffering from age-related macular degeneration (AMD), a severe disease of the retina. It is a condition that affects many senior citizens.

In the western industrialized nations, AMD is the most common cause of blindness in elderly people – it affects 15 percent of those aged 61 to 70, while the figure is four out of every ten people in the over-80s. AMD is caused by fatty waste products in the eye that, unlike in young people, are no longer transported away. These deposits accumulate and destroy the macula, a small area in the middle of the retina which has the highest density of visual cells. Here, information about brightness, contrast and colors are merged together to make a sharp, vivid image. The rest of the retina is largely capable of perceiving only silhouettes and light/dark contrasts. Doctors use the term "dry AMD" to describe a condition that develops gradually over a period of years.

83

Eylea™

2011

The course of "wet AMD" is far more rapid and aggressive. Here, pathological blood vessels form in the eye, secreting blood and fluids and causing the retina to swell. This can lead to an irreparable loss of vision within a few months. The formation of these blood vessels is regulated by a natural growth factor called vascular endothelial growth factor (VEGF). In other words, it is a completely organic process with catastrophic consequences.

Since 2007, Bayer HealthCare has been working together with U.S. company Regeneron to develop a drug product that can halt this disease. The product is based on an active ingredient developed by Regeneron called VEGF Trap-Eye, a soluble receptor-binding protein that blocks the formation of new, harmful blood vessels. Long-term studies have shown that VEGF Trap-Eye is effective against wet AMD in nine out of ten patients. It can also be used to treat other eye diseases. The drug product is injected into the vitreous body of the eye. In November 2011, a product marketed by Regeneron was granted regulatory approval in the United States. Bayer HealthCare began marketing the product in Europe and Asia in 2012.

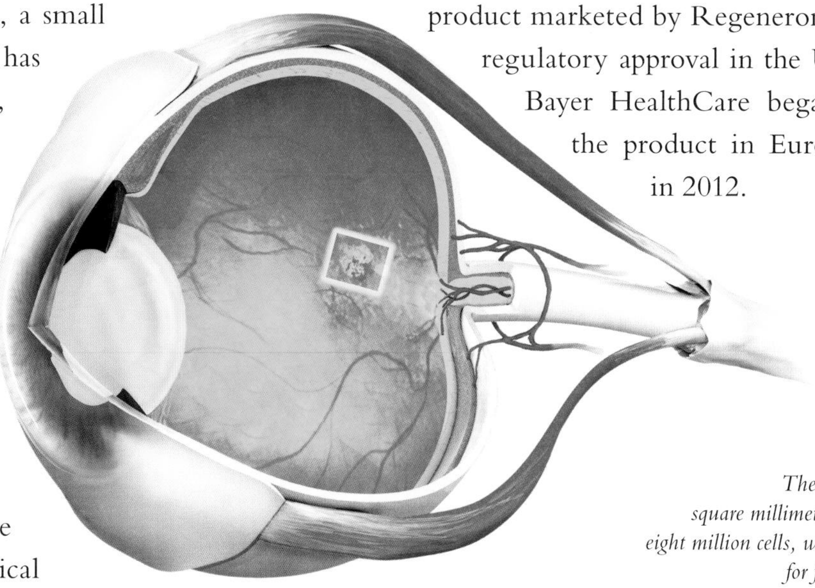

The macula is only one square millimeter in size but holds eight million cells, which are responsible for focused color vision.

Joachim-Friedrich Kapp is interested in history and architecture. He is especially fascinated by the classical buildings around Berlin's Gendarmenmarkt.

84

Joachim-Friedrich Kapp

Interferon beta

1995

Interferons are substances which occur naturally in the body. They transmit messages between the cells and therefore play an important role in the immune system. Interferons also participate in the destruction of microorganisms that cause inflammation. They suppress inflammation and cell proliferation (rapid cell growth), allowing tissue to recover. Interferon beta, approved in 1995, is important in the treatment of multiple sclerosis. It interferes selectively in the disrupted immune system processes. Thanks to its anti-inflammatory properties, it can significantly stabilize or slow the progression of the disease.

THE FIRST SERVANT OF RESEARCH

Driven by the desire to become a physician and help others, Joachim-Friedrich Kapp became a scientist. For decades he steered research and development departments and, thanks to his practical experience, was always able to put himself in the experts' position.

I**t was a** dramatic moment between life and death that prompted me to study medicine. It happened in 1924 and was often recounted in our family. My great-uncle, a surgeon, was doing his rounds and came to the bed of a patient whose condition worsened dramatically at that very moment. He recognized that she was suffering a pulmonary embolism and acted without hesitation. The patient was taken to the operating theater immediately and he operated without anesthetic – she was unconscious – to remove the clot from the pulmonary artery. She survived. The method was named the Trendelenburg operation after the surgeon Friedrich Trendelenburg. The immense courage and determination he showed inspired me. I knew what profession I intended to pursue. I wanted to become a doctor.

In the chaos of the war, I fled as a small boy with my mother from Neubrandenburg. Via rural Lower Saxony, we arrived in Essen, where my father found a job in the steel industry. I still remember the soot and dust that were omnipresent in the region during these years and hung like a veil over our housing division. If you sat outside to drink coffee in the afternoon, you would find specks of black in the milk or your coffee cup after just half an hour. My school grades were good enough for me to study medicine.

I moved to Hamburg and was lucky in several respects. First of all, at university, I met the woman who was to become my wife. Then I moved in as the sub-tenant of a well-known physician close to the student hall where she lived. I learned a lot from him and developed a friendship with his sons, which has lasted until today. During my time as a student, I was especially interested in immunology. I was also aware that, as a researcher, I would be able to help a very large number of people. More even than I could as a physician.

After receiving my physician's license, the question arose again: what now? Research at the university or in the pharmaceutical industry? As so often in life, it was chance that determined my path and led me to Schering. While reading the newspaper, I happened to notice the obituary for the Schering management board member responsible for research. I reached for the phone and had the company's switchboard put me through to his successor – to be honest, I didn't even know his name. Remarkable that direct access like this was still possible in 1974. I introduced myself and asked if they could use an immunologist. "Sounds interesting. Wait a moment, I'll put you through to our head of research," I heard. The line crackled and we spoke. My first and only application was successful. I got the job, started as a scientific employee, was soon made head of a section and about a year later head of department. That was the start of my career in research, which soon continued in management. I worked in the United States, heading large and small teams and the research departments of various companies. During those years, I used planes like other people use buses. My family and I returned to Berlin in 1991 and I went back to my first employer, where my responsibilities included strategy, research, development and strategic marketing for the business group.

Although I prefer to call myself a developer rather than a researcher, I always understood exactly what my colleagues in research were talking about. I could follow what they were saying in terms of the subject and I also knew how they ticked. I could think like them. It was a broad and fascinating task. Several projects were always running in parallel. The key to innovation: hard work. The fact that I was able to help was a source of personal satisfaction for me. Among the challenges was gauging which way a drug would go: an expensive flop or a blockbuster, as we now call money-making products. Some things don't work. Sometimes it's a fine line and we often take a risk. However, I always had the support of my boss, Günter Stock. That was the case with interferon beta, an active substance which slows the progression of the insidious autoimmune disease, multiple sclerosis. I was able to end my career on a high note.

Joachim-Friedrich Kapp

Dr. Joachim-Friedrich Kapp was born in Neubrandenburg, Germany, in 1942. Following his retirement, he received acclaim for his book about the life and achievements of the Prussian king Frederick II. He is married and has three children (all physicians). Joachim-Friedrich Kapp lives in Berlin, Germany.

Number of people with multiple sclerosis worldwide

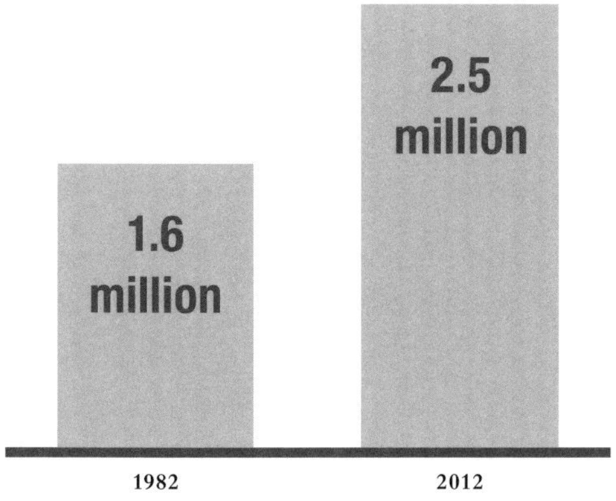

WHO

2,000,000

Number of years of health lost each year worldwide by people with multiple sclerosis (as at 2008)

WHO

Average life expectancy in industrial nations:

80 years

Life expectancy of people with multiple sclerosis in industrial nations:

76 years

WHO

Ten countries with the highest incidence of multiple sclerosis (per 100,000 inhabitants)

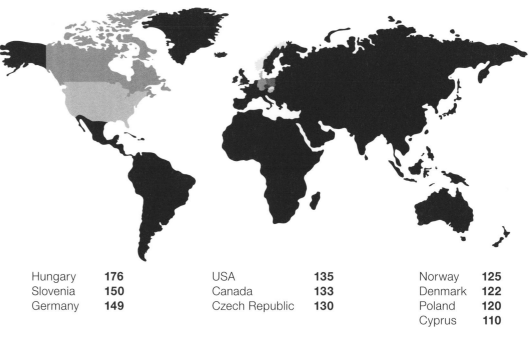

Hungary	176
Slovenia	150
Germany	149
USA	135
Canada	133
Czech Republic	130
Norway	125
Denmark	122
Poland	120
Cyprus	110

MS Atlas, WHO 2008

WHO

The different types of multiple sclerosis

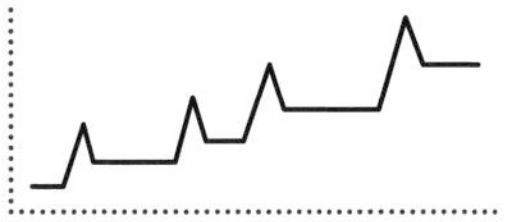

1 Relapsing-remitting multiple sclerosis: Well-defined attacks alternate with complete recovery from symptoms.

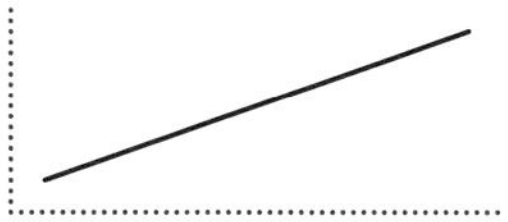

2 Primary progressive multiple sclerosis: Symptoms worsen continually with no well-defined attacks.

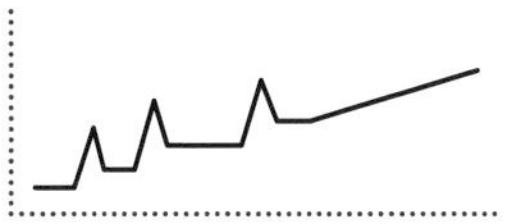

3 Secondary progressive multiple sclerosis: At the start, attacks and recovery alternate as in 1. Symptoms then worsen continually.

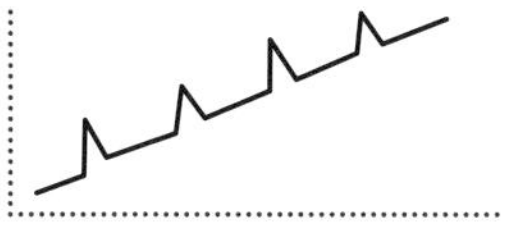

4 Progressive-relapsing multiple sclerosis: Symptoms worsen from the start, accompanied by well-defined attacks. It is the least common form of multiple sclerosis.

Jeroen Van Rie likes living near the old city of Ghent, which is known for its beauty.

85

Jeroen Van Rie

Insect-resistant plants

1989

Scientists at Bayer CropScience have been working since 1989 to optimize the photosynthesis of plants by modifying their DNA. They are also searching for proteins that make plants resistant to insect pests like moths and beetles.

FRIEND OF THE ENVIRONMENT

Jeroen Van Rie sees no contradiction between his love of nature and his job as a researcher at Bayer CropScience. In his free time, the Belgian enjoys adventure holidays – and feels most comfortable when man and nature are in harmony.

S**ome of my** friends are surprised that I'm a researcher at Bayer. "You're so green" is a comment I've heard more than once. I'm very close to nature and have been since my childhood. As a teenager, I was a member of a nature group that went on bird-watching trips to woods and to the marshlands near the Belgian coast. Today, I still like observing nature and birds in particular. I like many birds of prey because of their elegance and power, and our native owls because they seem to me to be particularly mysterious animals. I'm green at heart, that's true, but I don't see any contradiction between that and my work as a researcher at Bayer CropScience. Indeed, it's because I like nature that my private interests and my job fit together. Our task is important in a global context. While the amount of cropland is declining, a growing number of people need to be fed. I want to make a contribution – and protect nature at the same time.

Our laboratories and offices are on a site on the outskirts of Ghent, a Flemish city rich in history that is renowned for its picturesque old town, more than 250 kinds of beer and the charming stubbornness of its inhabitants. We try to make our operations as environmentally friendly as possible and minimize our CO_2 emissions. That's why we established a "Climate Change" working group. For example, we requested optimization of the temperature and humidity settings for the air conditioning system in our offices. We check the available options for more energy-efficient lighting. We motivate people to car-share or use a bicycle for their journey to work, rather than coming in their own cars. Everyone can do their bit, every day. We also organize vegetarian potluck events to encourage reflection about food habits. We aim to foster this awareness.

In the laboratory, we're working to improve the photosynthesis of plants – to boost their engines in a sense. And we want to make them resistant to insect pests. Not by applying an active substance to plants, but by genetically modifying their DNA. For us researchers, part of our work is the search – or even hunt – for the right protein.

"We're in a race that is difficult to win."

The plants then produce their own insecticidal protein to protect them against the larvae of a certain moth, for example. We're in a race that is difficult to win because insect pests like beetles and moths are able to adapt. That's evolution. Our challenge is to delay this adaptation by insect populations for as long as possible. On my first trip to Manhattan – not in New York but a small city in the Kansas corn belt – I found out why a certain moth species is resistant to a certain bacterial protein. That was a fairly groundbreaking discovery at the time and got me an article in the renowned magazine *Science*. In my free time, I enjoy long trips to far-flung corners of the world. I've journeyed in Ladakh, one of the most isolated parts of India, and traveled with friends in a 4WD truck in Mali and Mauretania. My most beautiful natural experience was in a kayak off the coast of Alaska. Our group was traveling for a whole week and we moved as if we were in a dream. The wild beauty of the landscape impressed me, as did the loneliness. I liked not seeing a house or road, not hearing a car for days on end.

"Living in harmony with nature is the most wonderful way of life as far as I'm concerned."

In Ladakh, when we came to a village during our trek, I was impressed by the harmony between the people and with the wilderness that surrounded them. They seemed to be living in isolation but they weren't isolated. Nothing works by itself. We're all part of one big whole – of that I'm convinced. Living in harmony with nature is the most wonderful way of life as far as I'm concerned.

Jeroen Van Rie

Dr. Jeroen Van Rie was born in Bruges, Belgium, in 1964. He loves being out and about in nature and dancing salsa. Jeroen Van Rie lives in a village close to Ghent, Belgium.

Cotton fibers

THE STUFF FABRICS ARE MADE OF

They must be thin and long, but also strong and tear-resistant, if they are to be made into premium yarns and fabrics. The demands imposed by the clothing industry on cotton fibers are complex, and for good reason. Sweaters, jeans, t-shirts and socks – people wear cotton from head to toe. When trouble hit the traditional cotton-growing regions in the United States – in a sense the motherland of jeans – Bayer was there to help. In the mid-1990s, the reputation of cotton farmers was hit by declining yields and poor quality.

86

FiberMax™

1998

In 1998, Bayer CropScience introduced FiberMax™ seed, a high-grade, long-fiber variety adapted to harsh climates that had already been successfully tested in Australia. This marked the start of a success story that has seen farmers steadily increase both yields and quality – and made FiberMax™ a premium label.

Tolerant and doubly resistant

PAMPERING A DIVA

Gossypium, as it is known to scientists, is the diva among the crop plants. As the crop develops, it needs plenty of sun and warmth. What's more, it is highly susceptible to insect pests, and it must compete with weeds for nutrients. If growing conditions are not ideal, the quality and quantity of the yield suffer. A shrub from the mallow family, cotton has therefore long been the focus of genetic modification. By altering the plant's DNA, researchers have already developed a number of high-yield and hardy varieties, the significance of which is growing rapidly. Climate change is making water ever scarcer in the major cotton-growing regions of China, India, the southern United States and Brazil. Furthermore, increasingly nutrient-poor soils likewise require new plant varieties. These are the challenges scientists are working on.

Ripe cotton bolls, open and ready for picking

87

TwinLink™

2011

One of the most outstanding results of research is TwinLink™ technology, which was authorized in the United States in 2011. It combines double the resistance to pest caterpillars with tolerance to herbicides.

The history of jeans

GOLD-DIGGERS, JAMES DEAN AND ATTITUDE

The fact that jeans had their beginnings during the Gold Rush era in San Francisco is just as well-known as the name of their inventor: Levi Strauss. Born in 1829 as Löb Strauss in Buttenheim, Germany, he emigrated as a teenager with his parents to America, and started selling dry goods and fabrics several years later during the emerging gold rush. Less well known is how the pants got their name. The trail leads to Italy.

The predecessors to Strauss's pants were from France, but the cotton fabric used to make them was produced in the Italian city of Genoa – "Gênes" in French, which became jeans in American slang. Searching for a hard-wearing material, Strauss initially hit upon canvas made from brown hemp, which was much more common at the time. Gold-diggers, cowboys and farmhands liked the new creation because of its durability. The idea of reinforcing the corners of the pockets with rivets to protect them from tearing came from a tailor named Jacob Davis. Because he did not have the money to apply for a patent himself, he turned to Levi Strauss. Together they had the novel idea patented on May 20, 1873.

From work pants to fashion object: jeans

Jeans have undergone numerous transformations in the course of their evolution. The canvas was soon replaced with an indigo blue cotton fabric called denim, and in the 1930s the suspenders were exchanged for a belt. By this time, the pants had long since become a common article of everyday clothing. Wearing jeans, pop culture rebels like Marlon Brando and James Dean styled themselves as individualists who made their own rules. The pants were not merely a piece of clothing, but the symbol of an attitude to life. Jeans became mainstream many years ago, and today are a standard item in the wardrobes of most people.

88

Stoneville™

2007

When it comes to the cotton that jeans are made of, Bayer CropScience is continually advancing development. Cotton remains an important crop. Some 1.5 million tons of cotton are processed each year just to make these ubiquitous pants. One of the world's leading seed brands is Stoneville™, developed by the long-standing Stoneville Pedigreed Seed Company, which was acquired by Bayer CropScience in 2007. In the case of FiberMax™ seed (see page 233), the product's success story has been accompanied by a further innovation. Thanks to a collaboration with a fashion manufacturer, jeans customers can now trace their pants from the cotton fields of Texas to the cotton mill to the store. One thing is certain – the history of jeans is far from over yet.

Valuable fibers: in their history, jeans have not only been a comfortable item of clothing, but also the symbol of an attitude. The cotton used to make the pants for the "American way of life" frequently comes from the USA. New TwinLink™ technology, designed to provide the plant with multiple protection, could make life easier for cotton farmers. The photo shows Jerry Mimms of Lubbock, Texas, with his crop in 2005.

CARL DUISBERG: A VISIONARY TAKES BAYER TO NEW HEIGHTS

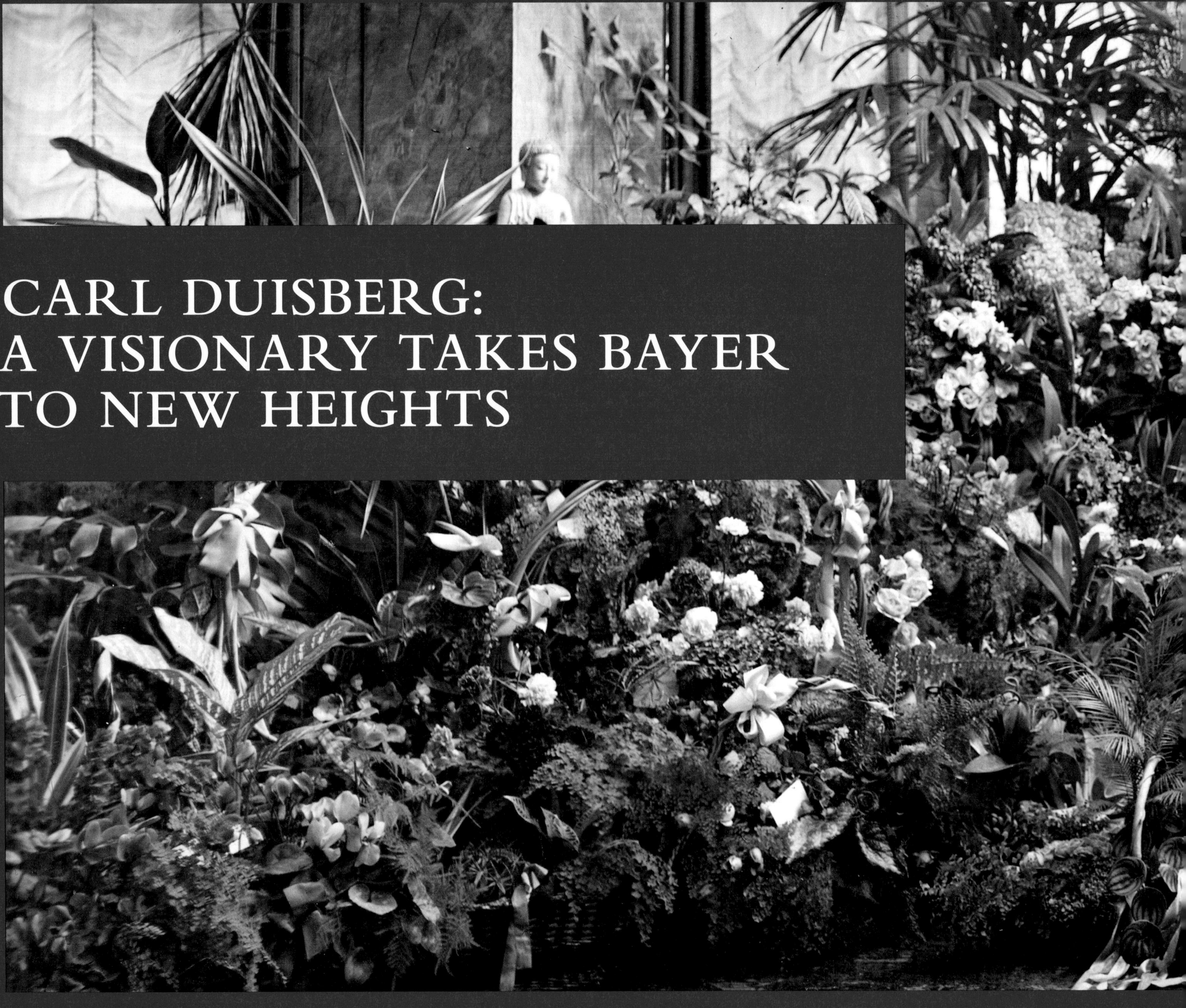

Carl Duisberg in 1931 surrounded by gifts delivered to his villa by well-wishers

An industrialist with a philanthropic streak: unlike some of his peers in corporate management, Carl Duisberg – shown here in his office in Building Q26 in 1921 – always considered social aspects to be of great importance.

A MAN WHO CHANGED THE WORLD

Few other personalities have had such a strong influence on Bayer's history as Carl Duisberg. Inventor, industrialist and a role model in everything he did – his biography reads like an adventure story.

89

Carl Duisberg

Leverkusen

1861 to 1935

Carl Duisberg was responsible for many innovations and inventions at Bayer. In product development, strategic planning, his revolutionary design for a chemical production site and social achievements, Duisberg was a visionary in many ways.

The boy is reading. His heart is thumping and his head is burning. He is gripped by longing and dreams of a world full of Bunsen burners, test tubes and flasks, accompanied by the smell of ammonia and sulfuric acid. He saved his pocket money for the book. And now he's got it: Justus von Liebig's "Familiar Letters on Chemistry."

The boy reads Liebig's introduction: "I hope I succeed with this first letter in strengthening the conviction that chemistry as an independent science is one of the most powerful means of achieving a higher intellectual culture, that its study is useful, not only in as much as it supports man's material interests but also because it provides insight into the wonder of creation." His decision is irrevocable. Chemist. Nothing would stop him from becoming a chemist.

Where else can one start to tell the story of this man whose life seems to have been one big adventure that took a decisive turn when he read a book about chemistry.

Carl Duisberg turned a dyestuffs company into an innovative chemical and pharmaceuticals enterprise. His invention of Benzopurpurine 4B saved the Farbenfabriken from insolvency. His memos concerning the first central laboratory in Elberfeld and the plans for the site in Leverkusen were revolutionary and the basis for Bayer's commercial rise. Duisberg recognized the potential of pharmaceuticals at an early stage. Without him, Aspirin™ possibly would not have become the pharmaceutical of the century and Bayer would not have become the global enterprise it is today. He was a brilliant chemist and a clever economist. He was

Carl Duisberg as a boy in 1868: he came from a simple but caring background.

He never forgot where he came from. He was kind and had a strong morality.

Duisberg and his lifetime achievement: walking round the Leverkusen site in 1933

an all-round talent capable of both scientific and economic thought, who studied the law and understood the effect of advertising. He was a visionary in everything he did. Yet he never forgot where he came from. He had a strong morality and was driven both by a sense of humanity and ambition in all his actions. His energy and tenacity were as legendary as his courtesy and conviviality.

Carl Duisberg was born on September 29, 1861 at Heckinghauser Strasse 58 in Barmen – now a district of Wuppertal. The family can be traced back to Evert Duisberg, a pastor and reformer in Hückeswagen. His descendants were merchants, landowners, councilmen, mayors, blacksmiths and farmers. Father Johann Carl Duisberg was an inkle weaver, like his father before him. He had two looms and employed a journeyman. His wife Wilhelmine (née Weskott) had a small farm. Duisberg senior wanted his son to become a weaver as well. But his mother realized that he would find no fulfillment in this. "That's my business so leave it to me. The boy has a good head. I know that best of all," she said.

Duisberg related: "My mother was a wonderful woman, simple and uncomplicated. She possessed an amazing energy and a particularly clear mind. She was a woman of the soil, in touch with nature. She stood with both feet firmly in reality." It was his mother who encouraged Carl's education – against his father's wishes. He went to middle school and then on to the high school for chemistry in Elberfeld in 1878. After that, he studied in Göttingen before obtaining his doctorate in Jena in 1882. He first worked as an assistant to his professor in Jena. To improve his chances of employment in industry, Duisberg served for a year in the First Bavarian Lifeguards in Munich. At the same time,

The Duisberg family goes for a drive, 1905.

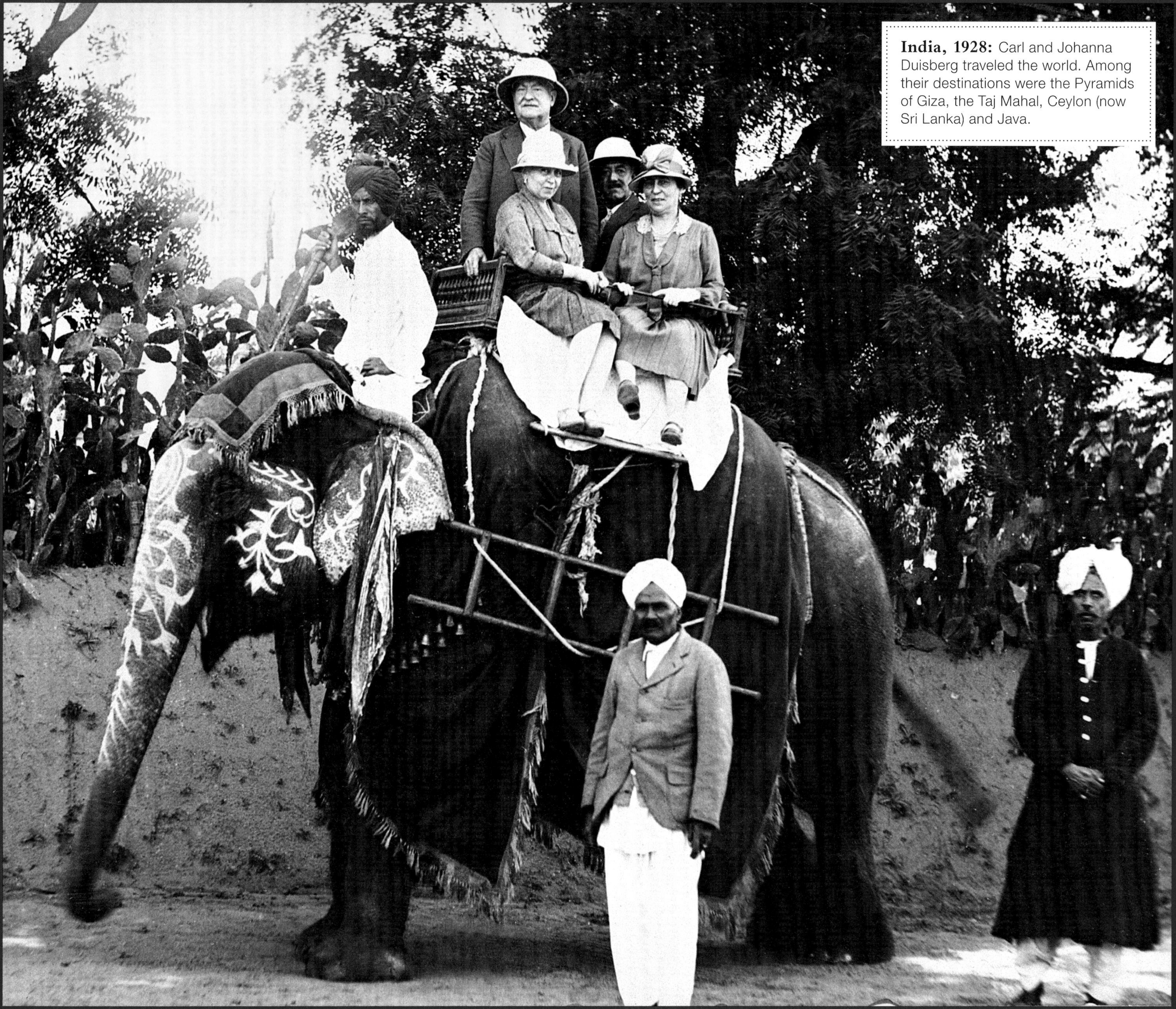

India, 1928: Carl and Johanna Duisberg traveled the world. Among their destinations were the Pyramids of Giza, the Taj Mahal, Ceylon (now Sri Lanka) and Java.

Carl Duisberg with his fellow students Carl Hauptmann (left) and Johannes Walter (right). The young chemist attracted attention at an early stage on account of his achievements.

he worked at a chemical institute in the city. Wilhelmine again intervened in her son's life. She wrote a letter to Mr. Weber, the man who had taught her and Friedrich Bayer, asking him to show it to a suitable person.

In fall 1883, an important visitor arrived at the Duisberg home. Carl Rumpff, Chairman of the Supervisory Board of Farbenfabriken vorm. Friedr. Bayer & Co., wanted to meet the young chemist. Rumpff then asked Duisberg to meet him a second time at his castle in Aprath. Duisberg was engaged for a probationary period and sent to the University of Strasbourg. Rumpff: "We have purchased patent number 25135 from Dr. Paul J. Meyer for making isatin. You are to test whether it is possible to transform isatin into indigo at a reasonable price." At that time, synthesizing this natural dyestuff was one of the major challenges in the chemical industry. Duisberg was unsuccessful but was able to show that the route Rumpff hoped for was not feasible. Duisberg was given a permanent position at Bayer on September 29, 1884. Shortly afterwards, he developed Benzopurpurine 4B, an acid-resistant red dyestuff which enabled Bayer to challenge the market leadership of Agfa's Congo red. It was the first of 26 chemical patents registered by Duisberg between 1885 and 1892.

"We do what we consider to be right and good in the interests of everyone."

The visit to Rumpff's castle in Aprath not only marked the start of Duisberg's career as a successful chemist. It was there that he met Rumpff's niece, who became his wife five years later. Johanna Seebohm was the calm and level-headed counterpole to the temperamental, ambitious and restless

A meeting of the dyestuffs commission in Versailles, France, in 1919. Standing from left: Carl von Weinberg, Eugen Frank, Carl Bosch. Duisberg is seated.

Duisberg, who became a member of the Board of Management in 1900 and Managing Director in 1912. Duisberg steered the company through the difficult times of the First World War and the economic crisis that followed. In 1925, he and Carl Bosch led the initiative to form I.G. Farbenindustrie Aktiengesellschaft.

Duisberg was a model of diligence with a sense of responsibility and duty. And he took a holistic view of the world. He believed that chemistry had a place in all areas of life: agriculture, geology, physiology, medicine, philosophy and religion. It also influenced how he saw his role as an entrepreneur. "We are not seeking the favor of the masses," he once said. "We do what we consider to be right and good in the interests of everyone." Duisberg introduced the nine-hour day in Leverkusen and built company housing and social facilities. He supported numerous organizations dedicated to training chemists, scientists and doctors. He felt that every cent had to be invested in science. He was particularly interested in young people. He told his employees: "You have an open hand to build what you think is right."

A meeting in Duisberg's office in Building Q26 in 1931: speaking with members of the Board of Management. Duisberg considered individual responsibility to be very important.

Duisberg's ability to formulate objectives was unrivaled. "It's better to think of the competition as too large than too small," he postulated, "so that we don't rest on our laurels." He abhorred lack of courage and inaction. He was also skeptical when it came to politics. He demanded that the state and municipal authorities kept out of the affairs of private business. Duisberg's philosophy: "Business requires fresh initiatives every day, rapid decisions, personal daring and commitment from the entire personality." Duisberg served his company. It was his life's fulfillment.

Carl Duisberg died on March 19, 1935. The funeral service took place three days later in the Leverkusen "Casino." The funeral procession accompanied his coffin to his last resting place in the Flora Temple in the park that now bears his name.

"Unsaleable waste"

THE COMBINATION OF WASTE AND A BRAINWAVE

At the end of the 19th century, pharmacists made medicines from natural substances. Only a few of the active substances used at the time were industrially manufactured chemicals. Chloroform was used as an anesthetic; chloral hydrate as a sedative; iodoform as an antiseptic; salicylic acid to alleviate rheumatism. The only medicine available to treat fever was quinine, which was obtained from the bark of the cinchona tree. Antipyrin was the first synthetic antipyretic.

The second such medicine was discovered by chance. Two Strasbourg doctors were treating a dog with distemper. They asked the pharmacist for naphthalene and gave this to the dog – the animal's temperature sank. The brother of one of the doctors was a chemist at Kalle & Co. in Biebrich. They sent him the naphthalene for pharmacological testing, which showed that the white powder was actually acetanilide. The pharmacist had sent the wrong thing. Kalle & Co. marketed acetanilide as Antifebrin. Its effect was undisputed but it had unpleasant side-effects.

90

Phenacetin

1888

At the time, Bayer had 30 tons of paranitrophenol in Elberfeld – a waste product from manufacturing the blue azo dyestuff Benzoazurine G. No-one knew what to do with this unsaleable waste. Carl Duisberg had an idea. If acetylizing aniline yielded acetanilide, it had to be possible to convert paranitrophenol via aminophenol (related to aniline) into a derivative of acetanilide, which was what was in Antifebrin. In 1886, Oskar Hinsberg – the chemist whom Carl Rumpff had employed three years previously together with Duisberg and Carl Herzberg – was spending his university vacation in Elberfeld. Hinsberg achieved the breakthrough with the discovery of phenetidine. When he returned to Freiburg, he had the substance put through pharmacological testing. This showed that phenetidine was more effective and better tolerated than Antifebrin. On February 19, 1888, the Supervisory Board approved production of the substance with the trade name Phenacetin – the company's first drug product.

Bayer's first drug product was Phenacetin, shown here in a bottle from 1912.

It turned out to be a kind of cure-all that reduced fever and had a broad spectrum of effect as an analgesic. The product was enthusiastically received by the medical profession. Its economic success was helped by a flu epidemic that raged between 1889 and 1892, especially in North America. Phenacetin changed an industry which had recognized that a single precursor could be used to make more than just dyestuffs.

Redder than Congo red

RESCUE AT A TIME OF NEED

From 1884, the young chemist Carl Duisberg worked in Bayer's Elberfeld laboratories. He lived in an attic room at his parents' home and traveled more than an hour by horse-drawn bus each day. It was at this time that he experimented with chemicals and dyestuffs. It was just before the weekend. As always, Duisberg was carefully tidying his workspace. He discovered a vessel whose previously brown contents were now bright red. Brighter even than Congo red. At that time, Bayer was suffering economically – as was the entire industry. The share price was at a low. The stock market journal doubted that the company would be able to survive for years.

91
Benzopurpurine 4B
1885

Unlike Congo red, Benzopurpurine 4B – as Duisberg's chance discovery was named – was resistant to acids. In 1885, it looked to be the company's rescue at its time of need. A new factory was built and business flourished. However, a competitor contested the Benzopurpurine patent and the judge decided that the product was not patentable. The company's management wanted to continue the legal battle but Duisberg, who had been corresponding with the Patent Office for some time, advised against it. Instead, the two opposing parties met with the Deutsche Bank as intermediary and came to an agreement. Duisberg suggested establishing a central scientific research laboratory in Elberfeld. And he recommended systematically evaluating all chemical patents – including those of the company's competitors.

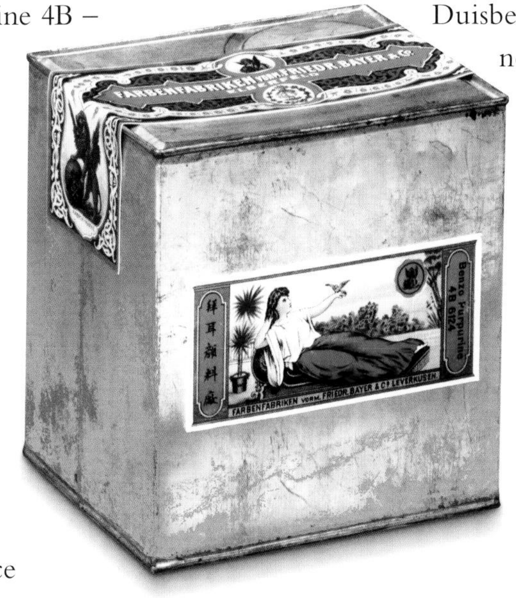

Chance gave a helping hand: Benzopurpurine 4B.

Dreamed up in his sleep

INDIGO: A DREAM SUBSTANCE

Indigo, the substance of dreams. In the late nineteenth century, little occupied the dyestuffs industry more than the deep blue dye obtained from Indigofera plants. Production was complex and expensive. "You are to test ... transforming isatin into indigo at a reasonable price." This was the instruction given by Carl Rumpff when he sent the young Carl Duisberg to Strasbourg. He was not successful. He could have given up then but he carried on. What then happened became one of the legends of the dyestuffs industry. During his lunchtime nap, he supposedly dreamed that the two methyl groups in tolidine should be replaced with two methoxy groups which would change the ugly red blue of the azo dye to the beautiful green blue that was wanted. Benzoazurine G, introduced in 1886, became one of the most successful synthetic indigo products of its time.

92
Benzoazurine G
1886

Duisberg's ingenious masterplan

A NEW DIMENSION IN SITE PLANNING

Christmas 1894. Snow was lying in Elberfeld. Carl Duisberg's five-year-old son Carl-Ludwig wanted to go sledding. Because the boy was finding this so difficult, his father decided to intervene. In doing so, he twisted his ankle so badly that he was unable to work for a few days. At home, Duisberg sat at his desk and drafted a plan for a chemical production site – 24 closely written pages entitled: "Memorandum on the construction and organization of the Farbenfabriken site at Leverkusen."

93

Memorandum

1895

There was no more room to expand at the Elberfeld site. In 1891, the company acquired the alizarine factory operated by Carl Leverkus & Söhne on the right bank of the Rhine just ten kilometers north of Cologne. It began acid production there in 1894. Leverkusen did not yet exist as a town. All that was there was a small fishing village named Wiesdorf. The employees sent to the new factory from Elberfeld were not happy with the lack of infrastructure – they saw the move as a punishment.

Dated January 1895, Duisberg's memorandum was a masterpiece of visionary planning and clarity. He organized the site in seven large sections, each with a number of sub-sections. Production units for which raw materials were delivered by barge were located directly on the riverbank. The site was divided into blocks and the buildings were arranged from the river inland depending on the production process. Related processes had to be located close together.

A futuristic design: the way Carl Duisberg planned the Leverkusen site set the standards for many decades.

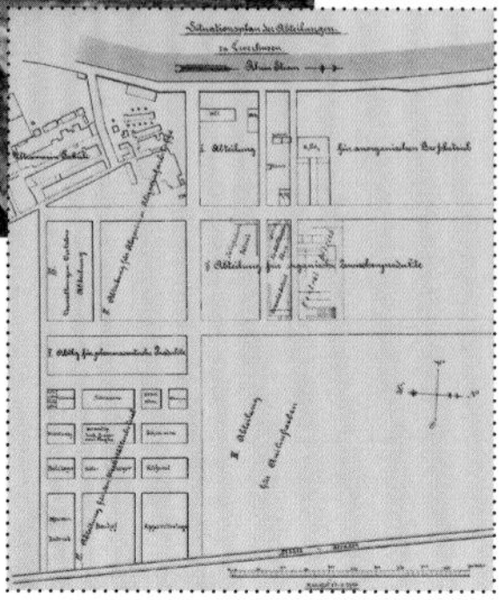

A stroke of genius caused by a sprained ankle: Duisberg's sketch

All roadways on the site were straight. The main roads were 30 meters wide and the side roads 15 meters wide so they would be able to cope with any future increase in traffic. Rail tracks were laid. All buildings were to be planned "with special consideration to light, air and cleanliness." And "the requirements of plant safety and accident prevention must take precedence over everything." What is standard today was revolutionary back then.

In a letter to a friend, Duisberg described a chemical factory of the time. He wrote of a "gloomy doorway" that "incarcerated men from early till late between bleak walls with noisy, wheezing machinery." Smoke. Dirt. Noise. Ugly red brick buildings. For this reason too, he noted in his memorandum: "The buildings are to be tasteful but with no exterior adornment." His instructions were thought through to the last detail. He not only described the size, shape and method of construction of the buildings; he also specified the thickness of the walls. His demand for industrial standards put him way ahead of his time. "We must introduce uniform dimensions for all the pipes, spigots, valves, threads, screws, boilers, vats, basins, etc. as soon as possible." And he went further still. "If at all possible, human strength should be preserved and replaced with machine power." The Leverkusen site was built almost exactly as described in Duisberg's memorandum. After the factories had been built, apartments for the workers and administrative staff, gardens, parks, playgrounds and sports fields, a restaurant, a theater, a swimming pool, a department store, a youth hostel, a library, a sanatorium and a maternity home were gradually added to the infrastructure. Duisberg himself supervised construction.

Dialogue replaces solitariness

THE DISCOVERY OF TEAM SPIRIT

T**oday we would** call it teamwork. This term didn't exist in Carl Duisberg's day. In Germany, a group that worked together was known as an "establishment." But establishments were not common in the chemical industry. Chemists were considered to be eccentric and secretive loners. Even in the cramped old laboratory in Elberfeld, Duisberg recognized the opportunities presented by focused dialogue between experts. He arranged meetings in the building's library at which specialist literature and practical experiences were discussed. Initially termed the Reading Circle, it was later renamed the Chemists' Conference. This ongoing exchange contributed significantly to many discoveries – "establishment inventions" – by the Farbenfabriken. Direct Deep Black E extra and Diamond Black PV followed Duisberg's Benzopurpurine 4B and Benzoazurine G. Under the supervision of Robert Emanuel Schmidt, Bayer became the leading producer of anthraquinone dyestuffs. Sulfur and vat dyes – like Algol, for example – were developed in joint projects. Phenacetin was followed by other drug products and then the pharmaceutical of the century: Aspirin™. And synthetic rubber, which was already produced in quantities of 2,000 tons in Leverkusen in 1916, was another classic "establishment invention" by the company.

94

"Establishment invention"

1903

Teamwork at a time when the term didn't yet exist: Aspirin™ inventor Felix Hoffmann (3rd from right) and Heinrich Dreser (2nd from right) with other chemists in 1896

A social conscience

A RELIEF FUND FOR THE COMPANY'S WORKERS

By the second half of the 19th century, industrialization had created a new social class: the proletariat. Life was characterized by hard physical work, poor hygiene, little recreation and miserable health care. There was no social security. In Central Europe, only around half of the population reached the age of 40. Bayer, however, took a different approach. The establishment of a relief fund for Bayer's employees in Elberfeld was approved by the Royal Government in Düsseldorf on February 7, 1873. More than ten years before Bismarck passed his social legislation, the company created instruments to protect its workers.

The relief fund's statutes had 39 paragraphs. Each worker paid 20 pfennigs from a weekly wage of 1.90 marks and the company paid a further 10 pfennigs. In the event of illness, a worker received 9 marks each week for up to six months and then 4.50 marks for a further six months. The relief fund's members could choose to be treated by one of two doctors. In the event of death, dependents received financial assistance of 75 marks. An illness suffered during employment with the company was not grounds for dismissal. In 1898, the first factory polyclinic was opened by Bayer in Elberfeld. Alongside a modern operating room, it had facilities for gymnastics, massage, baths, hot-air treatments and electrotherapy. It may have been in part because of the relief fund and Bayer's reputation as a socially responsible employer that the company, as determined by Barmen's chamber of commerce in 1876/77, had no difficulties in employing workers. However, illnesses caused by "drunkenness, immorality and gross negligence" were not covered. Just how employee-friendly the company was is documented by anecdotes from the relief fund's archives. One member, who felt himself too weak to take the stay in the country prescribed by the doctor, was sent 30 eggs and a bottle of brandy. A cook from the canteen was given expensive steel dentures because the conventional rubber prosthesis would have affected his sense of taste. Only the request by a worker for payment of his death benefit during his lifetime – because his children needed shoes before he died – was not approved.

95

Relief fund

1873

One of the first employee canteens: workers in Elberfeld at the beginning of the 20th century

Internal suggestions for improvement

BRIGHT IDEAS FOR A COMMON CAUSE

96

Employee suggestion plan

1903

On July 31, 1903 the management of the Farbenfabriken informed its factory managers and foremen that "from now on, we will approve cash bonuses based on the savings achieved to all those who have no interest in the company's net profit and can prove to us that they have reduced the number of men needed through the use of suitable machines and installations." The first documented suggestion was received a few months later from René Ott, head of the alizarine dye factory in Elberfeld. He improved the dyeing of flannel fabrics using a board fitted with four aluminum hooks.

What began with a letter signed by Friedrich Bayer jun. and Carl Duisberg was to become a central pillar of the company's efficiency and competitiveness that produced savings totaling many millions. From 1950, Bayer systematically advertised the suggestion plan, known at first as "Internal suggestions for improvement." In 1976, clear rules and rights were formulated for the company's employees. The Bayer Idea Pool (BIP) was established in 1995. By the time the program celebrated its centennial, employees had submitted a total of 277,362 ideas that had earned them a lot of money too.

ihm ging ein Licht auf
Das Betriebliche Vorschlagswesen
wartet auf Deine guten Gedanken
BAYER

Bayer encourages creative thinking by its employees. Thousands of suggestions for improvement are received each year. The best ones are rewarded with a bonus.

Today, BIP receives some 5,000 suggestions each year. Two employees received one of the highest bonuses ever paid (€74,000) for improving the attachment of filter cloths in titanium dioxide production. One of the highest payments to a single employee was made to a supervisor at the incineration plant in Leverkusen whose suggestion resulted in a considerable reduction in the amount of heating oil used and cut annual CO_2 emissions by 4,300 tons. One employee submitted 542 suggestions, 240 of which were implemented. From high-performance load bearers to tougher and less expensive plastic gloves – the range of ideas received from employees is as varied as it is fascinating. Above all, it is worthwhile for the company and its employees. From 1998 to 2012 alone, savings of €820 million were rewarded with bonus payments of €41 million.

Epicurean: It is not only since his stay in the French gourmet capital of Lyon that Heiko Rieck has learnt to value high-quality food. A weekly trip to his local market is almost obligatory.

97

Heiko Rieck

Fluopyram

2010

The fungicidal active substance fluopyram, approved in 2010, inhibits the respiratory chain of fungal cells, which prevents the production of energy. Alongside the conventional properties of a crop protection product, fluopyram also offers advantages in preserving the quality of the harvested produce.

A MATTER OF TASTE

Millions of tons of fruit have to be thrown away because they go moldy during transportation. A new fungicide, to which Heiko Rieck made a significant contribution, controls this problem before the fruit is even harvested.

W**e chemists call** it "cooking" when we synthesize substances in the laboratory. Instead of pots, we use flasks. We don't stir with a spoon but with a stir bar, a small magnet that looks like a piece of candy. When we talk about "cooking a preparation," it doesn't necessarily mean that we heat something for the chemical reaction. In some cases we actually cool things. In my free time, I – like many of my colleagues – am a keen cook. And that's why I sometimes have a problem with what I find in my local supermarket.

Many things look attractive but taste bland or are disappointing for other reasons. Peaches turn out to be hard as stones. Cherry tomatoes lack aroma. Vegetables have no flavor or exotic fruits go moldy soon after purchase and can no longer be eaten. Especially when it comes to fruit, I'm getting increasingly picky. Through my work with specialists in the fruit industry, I've learned what a problem pineapple looks like or what makes a melon suspect. The nice thing: with my innovation, which I worked on as a member of a global Bayer team, I've contributed to solving the problem of bland fruit. Our fungicides fluopyram, bixafen and penflufen are from a new substance class and have significant additional benefits for the health of plants. Fluopyram, for example, ensures the high quality of fruit, reduces post-harvest losses and – like the other two active substances – also protects other crops such as cereals, potatoes, oilseed rape and soybeans against harmful pathogens.

Fungal cultures are a real problem for fruit farmers because they spread through a raspberry bush or apple tree before harvest but the damage they cause only becomes visible after harvest. A nasty and unappetizing gray or brown deposit forms on shoots and leaves. And the fruit itself is also affected. This causes enormous losses, especially in the case of highly perishable produce such as berries or salad leaves. It is estimated that up to 30 percent of produce must be thrown away after transportation, which means losses of many billions of euros. What a waste of valuable food!

"My private passion is my barbecue – a giant by European standards."

Our innovation starts controlling this storage problem while the plants are growing in the field. The fungus has almost no chance of spreading. The active substance also allows the growers to harvest their fruit closer to full ripeness. I'm a little proud of how persistent we remained when so few people took any notice of our first idea. I wanted us to explore the possibility of controlling post-harvest fungal cultures while the plants are still in the field. Let me explain briefly. The active substance molecules in fluopyram penetrate the fungal cell's "power plant" where sugar is converted into energy. Fluopyram blocks an enzyme that is crucial to metabolism. If this is done efficiently, it can keep the fungus in check for a long time – it can't stop it entirely, of course. The fungicide has already been tested successfully in more than 70 crops – for example, in grapes, peaches, raspberries, tomatoes and even cut flowers. Like almost all innovations, our active substance is the result of teamwork by a fantastic group of people around the globe. An achievement to which hundreds have contributed, on almost all continents.

My private passion is international and German cuisine – and my barbecue. I have an enormous barbecue at home – a giant by European standards. I most like cooking American beef, scallops and various vegetables – not just the usual sausages. Barbecued food can be a real flavor experience and eating outdoors on a warm evening makes it even better. Taste is simply important to me.

Heiko Rieck

Dr. Heiko Rieck was born in 1969 and grew up in a village near Schwäbisch-Gmünd in southern Germany. After studying chemistry in Heidelberg, Germany; Montpellier, France; and Stanford, USA, he joined Bayer in 1998. In 2010, he was awarded the Otto Bayer Medal as a member of the research team that developed fluopyram. Heiko Rieck is married and lives with his wife and two children close to Monheim, Germany.

A universal fungicide

FOR FRUIT, VEGETABLES AND CUT FLOWERS

As well as essential vitamins, minerals and fiber, fruit and vegetables contain many different substances that protect the human body from diseases. They lower cholesterol levels, inhibit blood clotting and prevent the harmful oxidation of human cell membranes. But they have to survive a long journey before they reach the consumer. Fungi are a particular threat to the quality of fruit.

After years of intensive research and countless studies and corrections, Bayer CropScience now has a new product family that helps fruit and vegetable growers. Luna™, first approved in 2010, is based on fluopyram, an active ingredient from the chemical class of pyridinyl ethyl benzamides which has been successfully tested in more than 70 crops. It has proved to be effective in grapes, peaches, apples and raspberries – and even in tomatoes, oilseed rape, potatoes and cut flowers.

98

Luna™

2010

Producers can expect to reduce quality losses from gray mold (Botrytis), Sclerotina rot, powdery mildew and other diseases. The special feature of Luna™ is that it reliably controls the pathogens in the field, thus impeding their continued development post harvest. Even in easily spoiled fruit such as peaches and berries, fungal infestation is delayed by up to a week and more. (See also the profile of Heiko Rieck on page 250.)

Delicious vitamins: Luna™ effectively protects fruit against mold during transport.

Innovative seed

TRADITION, MODERNITY AND A CARROT CALLED IMPERATOR

The province of Limburg in the Netherlands, 1915. On a day out, Dutch businessman Herman Meddens discovered a small castle at the edge of the village of Nunhem. Meddens was delighted and bought the estate as a home for his family. He had vegetables planted on the land. At harvest time the following year, market prices were low. Meddens, the businessman, considered what to do. He decided to let his beans go to seed and established a company called "Nunhems Zaden." What sounds like a low-key decision taken in the Dutch provinces was the start of a great story.

Artichokes: also the product of healthy seed

Biotechnology for a fiery taste: Peter Keunen picks fresh chilis. The plant breeders know how hot they will taste before they grow.

Just 100 years later, the small family operation that evolved partly by chance has become Nunhems Netherlands B.V., one of the world's largest seed producers. Between 1952 and 1977 alone, the company registered 191 varieties from its own breeding and selection program. 1988 saw the introduction of Isola, one of the most successful early hybrid tomatoes, followed in 1991 by the launch in the United States of a carrot with the impressive name of Imperator (emperor). The Nunhems product range now covers 28 species and some 2,500 varieties. The company, which has belonged to Bayer CropScience since 2002, is regarded as one of the best innovators in what is traditionally a groundbreaking industry.

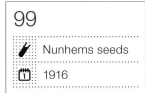

99
Nunhems seeds
1916

Using integrated breeding methods, researchers today can select plants with the properties they need from a choice of thousands. Cross-breeding processes, which once took years or even decades, can now be greatly accelerated and optimized. This has been made possible by advances in biotechnology. Researchers at Bayer CropScience are able to identify individual genes that are responsible for specific properties in vegetables – sugar content, color and disease resistance, for example. The scientists observe and analyze certain DNA sequences called molecular markers in young seedlings. They can then eliminate unwanted characteristics such as acidity or bitterness. It is also possible to reintroduce genetic information from wild plants that has been lost during years of breeding.

Research and development that serves the customer

Research at Nunhems today is interdisciplinary teamwork involving geneticists, plant disease specialists, molecular and cell biologists, bioinformaticians and breeders. The technologies are complex and detailed procedures are in place in all areas. Teamwork has replaced the lone breeder who deals with everything from pest resistance to yield improvement when developing a new vegetable variety.

One result of this teamwork was a solution to a serious problem facing the world's vegetable growers: tomato viruses. Using special markers, the scientists were able to breed seed lines with natural resistance to some of these viruses. Time and again, these had rapidly destroyed entire tomato harvests in South America, Europe and Asia. The researchers' achievement highlights what is really important: research and development that serves the customer.

Picturebook tomatoes: Francisco Martínez Granero grows a new variety in southern Spain.

Sport is his pressure valve, says Reiner Fischer. He has completed more than 20 marathons and trains regularly in the gym.

100

Reiner Fischer

Spirotetramat

1996

Reiner Fischer and his team developed an entirely new substance class to control spider mites and other insect pests – the cyclic ketoenols, which include spirotetramat (patented in 1996). They are the basis for a number of highly effective crop protection products that are kind to beneficial insects. One of these is Movento™, the first phloem-mobile insecticide which protects fruit trees from woolly aphids and scale insects. Another is Oberon™, which is used to control resistant whitefly in vegetables and cotton.

MARATHON MAN

His developments safeguard the supply of food for millions of people. Reiner Fischer feels a great sense of responsibility. He applies the same principle in the laboratory and in his free time: you need stamina to reach your goals.

S**ome people say** they can't understand what we do here, and I appreciate that. For instance, we design an active substance that moves through a plant to its shoots to control a specific pest there – and only that one particular beetle. Some people think it's magic, but it's just applied science. I know a lot about how to protect plants, especially against insect pests. Not many researchers are as experienced in this field as I am.

Some say I'm driven, because I often spend weekends and evenings at work. My desk is covered with yellow sticky notes on which I've jotted down tasks, ideas and new approaches. What we do in our research laboratories is of global interest. One of my colleagues has a satellite photo of the Earth taped to his wall, a regular legal-size sheet of paper, marked with a spot the size of a coin. That spot is a scale representation of the amount of cropland available worldwide – and as we know, the number of people who need to be fed is increasing all the time.

This is how I like to describe our work. We're like locksmiths looking for the right key to open a door. The problem is that we may have millions of possible keys but they're all blanks and only a few of them actually fit halfway. Also, the lock may change while we're working on it, because nature never stands still. So it's quite common for our search to remain fruitless – for months, for years or even forever. All researchers must have a talent for self-motivation, otherwise they won't last in this job. The secret of innovation – good powers of observation, interdisciplinary thinking, resources, tenacity, confidence and stamina, preferably all in equally large amounts.

"My teacher got me interested in chemistry."

I grew up as the son of a carpenter near the old Roman city of Xanten on the Lower Rhine, at a time when no-one cared about environmental protection. When the weather changed as a storm blew in, for example, you could smell it because the wind carried the pungent odor of the phenols in the river. I used to work for pocket money on my uncle's farm. Sometimes we'd be standing right alongside when the cereal seed was treated with mercury compounds to protect it against insect pests and fungi – and this would be done with bare hands. What is unthinkable today, was normal then.

My teacher got me interested in chemistry. I got a chemistry set for Christmas. I worked through one experiment after the other until my father, in a mix of worry and amusement, asked if I wouldn't rather do this in the attic so that if things did go wrong, I wouldn't blow up the whole house, just the roof. I abandoned my first career choice of pilot while I was still in school. I then thought of trying my luck as a sports teacher because I was pretty good at handball and track and field. When I was applying for a place at university, I checked off chemistry as my second choice and ended up in the city that was seventh on my list: Münster. Today, sport is still my stress reliever, my pressure valve. I've completed more than 20 marathons, for example in Hamburg, Berlin, Stockholm and Vienna. Without sport, I probably would have ended my career by now, because it would have been much harder to handle the pressure.

The challenges we researchers face are growing all the time. Thanks to modern means of transport, pests travel quickly to new locations where they never would have been expected. Some weeds grow several feet high in no time if nothing is done to stop them. A beetle species previously found only in China suddenly shows up in North America. Some pests are now resistant to many known products. And I think that political dictates are increasingly hindering our work in research.

Chemical crop protection research requires experience, expertise and continuity. You can't turn it on and off like a coffeemaker. My social environment is important to me, the team I work with. Money isn't everything to me. I don't let the hectic pace of modern life put me under additional pressure. There's no smartphone buzzing in my pocket every time someone sends me an e-mail. That means I've occasionally missed appointments arranged at short notice, but that's the way it is. The yellow sticky notes on my desk remind me of the important things, and also of how much there is still left to do.

Reiner Fischer

Dr. Reiner Fischer was born in 1957 and grew up in the Lower Rhine region of Germany. He studied chemistry in Münster, received his PhD in 1983 and has been a researcher at Bayer since 1985. Reiner Fischer is considered to be the discoverer of the ketoenol substance class. The awards he has received in recognition of his pioneering work include the Otto Bayer Medal. He lives near Düsseldorf, Germany.

For healthy apples

SPOILING THE WOOLLY APPLE APHID'S APPETITE

The nightmare for every apple-grower is two millimeters long and dark violet in color: Eriosoma lanigerum, the woolly apple aphid. This insect relentlessly attacks Cox's Orange Pippin, Golden Delicious or Jonathan trees, preferably at cuts and young shoots, and insatiably sucks the sap. It is protected against its enemies by a layer of wax, can penetrate even the smallest of cracks in the bark and overwinters in the vicinity of the roots. As a result, its excretions soon cover the trees like mold, while growths known as woolly aphid canker appear where the bark has been damaged, causing the shoots and fruit to wither.

101

Movento™

2007

But some years ago the nightmare came to an end, thanks to Bayer's insecticide Movento™. Unlike other substances, its active ingredient spirotetramat does not act at the surface but penetrates the transport system of the treated plant, spreading from the roots to the tips of the leaves. It is therefore also present in the plant veins that transport sugars and nutrients. The insect takes up the active substance with the nutrients, blocking an enzyme that is vital for lipid synthesis. This does not immediately kill adult insects, but makes it impossible for them to breed. Many eggs remain infertile, and larvae dry out after molting. Spirotetramat therefore functions almost like a contraceptive.

A perfect skin

Bayer researchers in a tree: specialists Dr. Reiner Fischer, Karl-Wilhelm Münks and Dr. Michael Klüken (left to right) inspect an apple orchard.

The principle is well-known. It derives from a specific group of ketoenoles that were discovered by Reiner Fischer and his team and which resulted in the insecticides Envidor™ and Oberon™. Envidor™ is, as it were, the father, Oberon™ the child and Movento™ the grandchild. That Movento™, approved in 2007, is regarded as one of the most important innovations in crop protection is due to its very high environmental compatibility and the fact that it is harmless to both plants and beneficial insects such as ichneumon wasps and ladybirds. (See also the profile of Reiner Fischer on page 256.)

Super tuber

SMART FARMERS HARVEST THE BEST POTATOES

The potato is a universe in itself. More than 5,000 varieties have been registered by the "Centro Internacional de la Papa," the international potato institute headquartered in La Molina, Peru. Solanum tuberosum is the Latin name used by plant experts. A member of the nightshade family, related to the tomato and tobacco, it is our fourth most important foodstuff. As French fries a firm favorite for kids, as potato chips a delicious accompaniment to an evening's TV viewing – and boiled a nutritious part of any meal.

New and aggressive diseases make intensive protection necessary

The tuber originated in South America, that much is clear. The oldest traces of wild potatoes – estimated at 13,000 years – were found on the Chilean island of Chiloé. It is still not really known how they came to Europe. The earliest evidence can be found in the books of the Hospital de la Sangre in Seville, Spain, documenting the purchase of potatoes back in 1573.

The potato's genome has been studied in full. A team of researchers from 14 countries published their results in the journal *Nature* in 2011: 39,000 protein-coding genes, 12 chromosomes and 800 disease resistance genes were discovered. These findings will help breeders boost potato quality, yield and nutritional value and shorten the time needed to create new varieties – a process that currently takes nearly a decade. 310 million tons of potatoes are harvested every year: one-third in Europe and 30 percent in the Asia-Pacific region.

A healthy potato

But times are tough for the good old spud. Particularly in Europe, the consumption of fresh potatoes is declining steadily. According to experts, more intensive crop protection is needed to control new and aggressive diseases. Many pests such as aphids, the Colorado potato beetle, caterpillars and wireworms have developed resistance to conventional pyrethroids.

102
Emesto™
2011

Bayer CropScience has therefore focused on the potato, with the objective of not only boosting the plant's productivity but also improving the storage stability, size and shape of potatoes and the appearance of their skin. The active substance penflufen plays a crucial role. Emesto™, a seed dressing containing penflufen, has proved to be effective although it is applied in only small quantities. First approved in 2011, it was registered in the United States and Canada in 2012 and in Belarus and Ukraine in 2013.

Penflufen belongs to a new generation of active substances which inhibit the respiration of fungi. In potatoes, the harmful fungus Rhizoctonia causes black spots, but these can be prevented by Emesto™, which also promotes germination and root growth.

Harvest time in Chile, where the potato originated: in a field belonging to the farming company Agricola Ariztia Ltda. near the town of Melipilla, Christian Benucci (left) and Carlos Cespedes Carvajal check the yield.

Active substances for the future

DELICIOUS FRUIT AND VEGETABLES

Standing still is the same as taking a step back, especially in crop protection. That's why Bayer CropScience is committed to accelerating the pace of innovation and driving forward new developments. Flupyradifurone is one of four new active substances that are to be launched by 2016.

103
Sivanto™
2015

It is effective against sucking insects such as aphids, cicadas and whitefly in fruit, vegetables and broad-acre crops, and will be marketed worldwide under the brand name Sivanto™ from 2015.

One of the most popular fruits and a real treat, picked ripe from the tree

Dreaded banana fungus

A TOUGH FUNGICIDE THAT IS KIND TO PLANTS

Baycor™ contains the active substance bitertanol and is the gentle star for controlling all kinds of fungal diseases in bananas. Unlike the chemically related substance triadimenol, bitertanol is not highly systemic and is therefore especially well-tolerated by plants. It can be used in very sensitive crops. The primary indication is apple scab, followed by many other diseases in fruit crops and ornamentals. More than ten years after the launch of Baycor™ in 1979, it was found to be the ideal product for preventing black leaf streak disease. This fungal disease in bananas is caused by Mycosphaerella fijiensis and is hard to control.

104
Baycor™
1979

Help against rot

SOLUTION FOR WINEMAKERS

A healthy harvest is the key to high-quality red and white wines. The greatest threat to grapes is Botrytis cinerea, or botrytis bunch rot. Also known as gray mold, it affects sweet and sour cherries, strawberries, plums, greenhouse tomatoes and ornamental plants too, causing fruit rot and blossom blight. Teldor™, containing the active substance fenhexamide and approved in 2000, provides a solution to these problems and makes the work of winemakers and fruit growers easier.

105
Teldor™
2000

Controlling pests

BREAKTHROUGH BY SUBSTITUTING AN ATOM

The briefing was to synthesize new active substances for the control of broadleaf weeds. For years, crop protection researcher Reiner Fischer (see his profile on page 256) had been working in this field. His experiments were based on improving known substances, which was why Fischer wasn't expecting much when he substituted a carbon atom for the nitrogen atom in a molecule. However, it was the right idea. Modifying the molecular structure fundamentally changed the mode of action. Intensive biochemical research led to the discovery of the cyclic ketoenoles, a new class of active substances – and a sensation of the kind that only happens every ten years.

106

EnvidorTM

2001

The problem was that the substance harmed both the target pests and the plants. In 1992, Fischer and his team found a new substance that kills the pests but does not harm their natural enemies, the crop plants or the user: spirodiclofen. However, it took another ten years to develop the insecticide Envidor™, which is used primarily in fruit and vines. It took comparatively little time for Fischer and his team to find out that their new substance class is also effective against whitefly. Two years after Envidor™, approved in 2001, the development of Oberon™ (active substance: spiromesifen) was concluded. Thanks to its favorable ecotoxicological properties, the product has been registered as a reduced-risk insecticide in the United States.

Independent inspector Brock Taylor (left) and Bayer employee John LeBoeuf examine freshly harvested melons.

Biological crop protection

MOTHER NATURE'S HELPERS

They are minute but effective and precise at the same time: naturally occurring microorganisms and bacteria are gaining importance in integrated crop protection. They not only use natural mechanisms to reduce fungal and pest infestation; they also make the plants more resistant to disease and promote their growth. The plants flourish better throughout the growing season and are rich in nutrients and flavor. They are resistant to heat and drought. Farmers appreciate the increased yields. Above all, biological crop protection is sustainable.

107

Biologics

1999

Mother Nature's helpers can be used to control pests with great precision. They recognize and differentiate between their targets. Because biological crop protection is based on new modes of action, there is less risk of resistance developing in growing areas – an important issue worldwide.

Experts believe the market potential of these products in 2020 will be around US$ 4 billion – three times as much as in 2010. With the acquisition of AgraQuest and Prophyta, Bayer CropScience has strengthened its core competence in the field of biological crop protection. On all continents, products such as Votivo™, Serenade™, Sonata™, Requiem™ and BioAct™ are already proving what can be achieved with this form of crop protection. If a fruit grower uses the biofungicide Serenade™, first approved in 1999, as a preventive measure on his crops, a thin protective film of Bacillus subtilis is formed around the fruit. These bacteria then compete with fungal pests for carbohydrates, which are an important source of nourishment. Bacillus subtilis also produces lipopeptides, which can destroy the cell membranes of fungi and other pathogens. The parasites themselves cause no damage.

Biological crop protection for better harvests

The right mix of options results in healthy plants.

However, no form of agriculture is possible using only biological crop protection agents. It is important to utilize the broadest possible range of products and processes. Integrated crop protection comprises biological, chemical and breeding aspects. Other options relate to crop husbandry and physical and mechanical concepts. Bayer CropScience offers farmers a broad portfolio combining optimized seed, chemical crop protection and biological control. It is the mix which makes the difference.

Quality produce: on the Rancho Granjenal in Mexico, Juan Ramón Camacho (right) and Bayer employee Gustavo Martinez Barbosa assess the harvest.

Game, set and hopefully match! In her free time, Coralie van Breukelen-Groeneveld plays tennis near her home in Neuss – primarily for fun, but with a competitive edge as a member of her club's women's team.

THE NEXT GENERATION

Coralie v. Breukelen-Groeneveld

Monheim, Germany

Bayer CropScience

ADVANTAGE VAN BREUKELEN

In the attempt to engage, Coralie van Breukelen-Groeneveld will take politicians out into the fields. She is convinced: understanding the facts always helps.

P**oliticians listen better** than one generally thinks. At least, that is my experience, which I gained around the European Parliament and European Commission during my time with Public and Governmental Affairs in Brussels. My tasks included informing decision-makers about our research work. We wanted to substantiate political debate with expertise. We sometimes took politicians out into the fields to show them what we do. My current function in Global Project Management also depends on good stakeholder management.

It's sometimes hard to get our arguments heard by the political system in Brussels. The positions we take in debates are always supported scientifically – and are also not always easy to explain. It is sometimes frustrating when the opposition argues less with reason but more with emotion and popular half-knowledge. On the other hand, I know what I'm arguing for: sustainability and environmental protection are very close to my heart.

Coralie van Breukelen-Groeneveld

Coralie van Breukelen-Groeneveld was born in Amsterdam in the Netherlands in 1972. She spent some of her childhood in South Africa. She studied environmental sciences, specializing in toxicology, and came to Bayer CropScience via a research institute and a consultancy company. In her free time she enjoys playing tennis. Coralie van Breukelen-Groeneveld is married and has two children. She lives with her family in Neuss, Germany.

Even as a child, Erwin Hacker – pictured here at a test station near Frankfurt – spent a lot of time in the fields. He comes from a farming community.

108

Erwin Hacker

Indaziflam

2010

Erwin Hacker has been involved in many developments, so many that people in his field refer to the "Hacker patents." One example is the active substance indaziflam, which was approved in 2010 (see page 271).

A FARMER AT HEART

Even as a small boy, he spent a lot of time in the fields and barns. These are experiences which help Erwin Hacker today when testing new active substances. And strengthen his understanding for the customers.

I **grew up** on a farm. Friedingen near Riedlingen in rural southern Germany, a farming community with just 300 inhabitants. Friedingen lies on the southern edge of the Swabian Jura, not far from the River Danube. My family still has a farm. Our childhood was shaped by the farming day and the seasons: working in the barn; sowing seed in spring; weeks spent digging out weeds by hand in fields of cereals, beets and potatoes; harvesting hay and cereals in the summer; digging up potatoes and beets in the fall.

The days began with school – at that time still a village school – until midday. In the afternoon, we helped in the fields. In the evening, we saw to the cows and pigs in the barn. I learned the value of real work. We rarely had any free time.

You could say that my childhood was an alternative model to today's Facebook generation. After I finished elementary school, I went to a vocational high school in Saulgau. In the summer every morning at six, I cycled ten kilometers to the rail station, returned at six in the evening and fell into bed exhausted at ten. My day left room for little other than school and farm work. I allowed myself a small luxury only on Thursdays, Fridays and Sundays: I was sweeper in a soccer team and played in a band. It was not my dream to have my own farm. But I did want to stay involved with agriculture so I studied agricultural science after graduating from high school. My areas of specialization: plant production, crop protection and weed science. In 1983, I found a job in the chemical industry.

> *"I enjoyed seeing the sun shimmer on the water in the evening light."*

For 25 years, I was responsible for the global testing of new active substances for weed control. I planned and carried out field trials worldwide to test the efficacy of new herbicides in relation to the weather conditions, precipitation, soils and competition from weeds. At peak times we had more than 100 different substances in the field each year. They had to demonstrate what they could do under natural conditions.

We often got entirely different results in glasshouses. In Central Europe and North America, we dealt mainly with cereal crops and oilseed rape; in Asia the focus was on rice; and in the United States and Latin America we concentrated on soybeans, corn, sugar cane and cotton. That didn't have much in common with working on a farm. I had a lot of paperwork to do, protocols to write, test designs and plans to create, presentations to prepare and patent applications for new findings to produce. Our work supported research and development, and I traveled a lot to other research stations around the world. My favorite crop flourishes far away from my home region in southern Germany. I liked spending time in the rice-growing areas of Asia and the United States.

I also found sugar plantations fascinating. The fact that we are in a constant race with nature is shown by the example of waterhemp, a weed that can grow up to three meters tall and threatens North America's cotton and corn fields. It's becoming increasingly resistant to known herbicides.

It's said that I've got more than one green thumb. I simply know what the plants need. That has something to do with expertise but also with a feeling that you can't learn. Like an old sailor who sometimes takes gut decisions because he knows how to interpret nature's signals. As long as I can remember, I've been roaming fields, driving tractors, sowing, tending and harvesting crop plants. This also means I can put myself in the place of our customers. I know exactly what they need.

Even today, I still help out on my family's farm in my free time. During vacation time, I sometimes take over as full-time farmer. I know the theory, but I also know the practical side just as well.

Erwin Hacker

Dr. Erwin Hacker was born in 1954 and grew up near Riedlingen on the Danube. He studied agricultural science, majoring in plant production, and did a PhD in crop protection and weed science at the University of Hohenheim in Stuttgart. Erwin Hacker contributed significantly to researching and developing the current herbicide portfolio. He was awarded the Otto Bayer Medal in 2012 for the development of indaziflam and in 2004 for his contribution to safener technology for herbicides. Erwin Hacker is married, has two daughters and divides his time between homes near Mainz and in southern Germany.

New research method

THE POWER OF BACTERIAL CELLS

Some chemical plants are just a few thousandths of a millimeter in size. Bacterial cells steer hundreds of chemical processes and produce highly complex molecular structures. Their tools are enzymes – also known as biocatalysts – which regulate cell metabolism, juggling atomic groups and constructing larger chemical compounds. Researchers from Bayer CropScience use these microorganisms to manufacture active substance molecules for crop protection agents.

109
Specticle™/Alion™
2010/2011

In the case of indaziflam, they achieved a breakthrough in solving a particularly difficult problem. Like detectives, they inched their way towards the solution using a bacterial cell which helps in the manufacture of the new herbicide. The researchers customized the minute cellular factories to produce specific chemical building blocks. It was not possible to efficiently produce the compound using a conventional chemical synthesis. However, it was possible with the enzyme. Around half a million bacteria were tested and optimization work took many months.

Indaziflam has been marketed worldwide since 2011 as Alion™ (for use in fruit, grapevines, citrus fruits and sugar cane) and since 2010 as Specticle™ (for weed control on sports fields and golf courses). The advantage of Alion™ is that it not only targets the weed but also has a particularly long-lasting effect.

A profile of Erwin Hacker, one of the inventors of indaziflam, is on page 268.

Protected by Alion™ – the herbicide is often used in citrus fruits.

Protection for vegetables

MAKING THE GARDEN A SNAIL-FREE ZONE

When hordes of large brown or black slugs invade a garden, inching their way slowly across lettuce leaves, they leave a trail of destruction. With their rough tongues, they devour everything green in their path. Biomol™ from the Bayer Garden Natria™ product family, approved in 2007, helps to control the slimy visitors. It contains a natural iron compound and bait substances like yeast, wheat and potato flakes. Once they have ingested the active substance, the slugs stop their voracious feeding and disappear. At the same time, the slug pellets are safe for important beneficial organisms such as earthworms and hedgehogs. The product is also rain-resistant so it can be applied in any weather.

110
Biomol™
2007

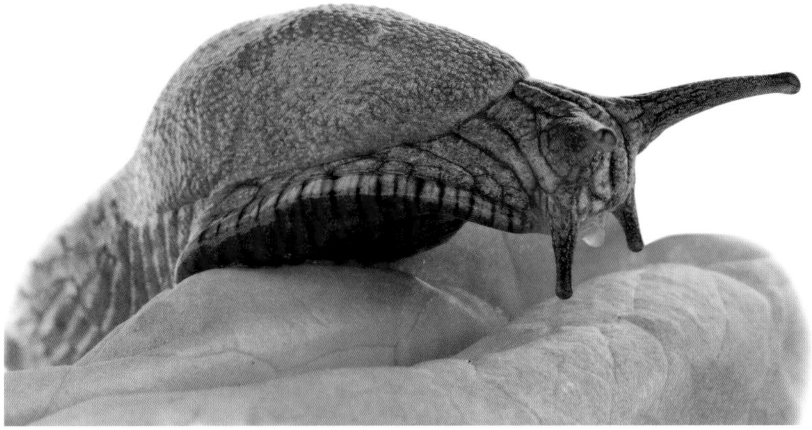

Slugs might look harmless but they can cause a lot of damage in the garden.

For amateur and professional gardeners

ON THE SAFE SIDE IN THE HOME AND GARDEN

It's a fact full of hope: around the world, people are living longer. While there may be enormous differences from country to country, the trend is the same: human life expectancy is increasing. Among the reasons for this are medical advances, improved hygiene and a healthier diet.

A growing number of people are coming to realize that juicy tomatoes, crisp lettuce and vitamin-rich capsicums are especially fresh and tasty if they are harvested from their own gardens. Home-grown fruit and vegetables are becoming increasingly popular. To ensure that harvest time is not a disappointment, voracious pests like aphids, whitefly and potato beetles must be effectively controlled. The Bayer Garden products, launched in 1972, reliably help amateur gardeners keep their fruit and vegetable plants healthy and protect them against unwanted guests. To keep the many pests in check, the Bayer Garden team has developed a range of effective products – always with an eye to protecting beneficial organisms.

111
Bayer Garden
1972

However, gardeners not only dislike insects, beetles and caterpillars. Weeds and grasses are an unsightly nuisance in hedges and rose beds and among other ornamental plants. Hoeing and simple herbicides usually bring only short-term relief from these invaders. In order to provide lasting protection, Bayer's crop protection experts are drawing on their experience of agricultural applications. In this way, gardeners can benefit from professional products. Bayer Garden and Bayer Advanced™ herbicides contain special active substance combinations that are effective longer in controlling unwanted weeds. Wet weather causes additional problems in the garden. Plants are then also susceptible to harmful fungal diseases such as late blight in potatoes. Bayer's experts have developed preventative and remedial fungicides for use in such cases. And there is also a range of natural products for amateur gardeners – the Natria™ product family from Bayer Garden.

Professional solutions for outdoors – and indoors

But unwanted guests are not only found in the garden. Mice, rats and cockroaches like to look for food in apartment blocks, warehouses and public buildings, which places them in proximity to people. And this is not without risk because these animals and insects may carry dangerous disease pathogens which they can transmit to humans.

To keep the environment in which we all live, work and play free from these pests, professional pest control operators rely on the extensive Environmental Science product portfolio. Researchers are not only trying to find new active substances but are also increasing their efforts to combine chemical and biological strategies. Bayer CropScience's focus goes beyond providing the market with highly effective products. Sustainability and environmental compatibility are just as important.

The Japanese Garden in Leverkusen, which attracts visitors from around the world, also benefits from the many Bayer Garden products.

Researching holography: the results of Friedrich-Karl Bruder's work are used in home entertainment systems, for example.

112

Friedrich-Karl Bruder

Optical data storage media

2002

The first holographic material was patented in 2002. Friedrich-Karl Bruder is working to optimize the material used for optical data storage media, which have been on the market since 1982. Polycarbonates play a key role here. Having contributed to the development of DVDs and Blu-ray Discs, the researchers at Bayer MaterialScience have now turned their attention to the displays of the future.

CROSSING FRONTIERS

Friedrich-Karl Bruder develops things that help us in our daily lives. His inventions ensure that Hollywood movies play smoothly on our screens. Bruder is a co-developer of both the DVD and Blu-ray Disc, and is already looking forward to the next quantum leap.

M**y favorite movie** is *Ice Age*, the cheerful computer-animated adventure with Manfred the mammoth and Sid the sloth that I enjoy watching with my children. We have an impressive collection of more than 250 films on DVD or Blu-ray, including many classics. As you can see, my job impacts my free time, too. I develop high-grade plastics for high-performance storage media and photostructurable films for innovative light guidance. Among the materials I work with is polycarbonate, which is used to make CDs and DVDs. In our work, we push the limits of what is possible under the laws of physics and optics. Technological advancement in our field is extremely fast. Most people don't think about all of the know-how and technical finesse that go into a CD, DVD or Blu-ray Disc. They have become everyday things. For nearly two decades, my job has been to increase storage capacities and improve the optical properties. Some years ago now, we at Bayer invented a new form of data storage in which the data are recorded optically and in three dimensions. With the DVD, for example, we seem to have reached the end of the line.

Building on our extensive experience of storage media, we applied the same chemical principle to develop special photostructurable films for use in imaging holography and light guidance in, for example, modern displays. The challenges we faced, and continue to face, are enormous.

We are looking for a material with a chemical structure that a laser beam can write data on in three dimensions. This is virgin territory – and a wonderful adventure for me as a researcher.

"Can our kids remember color film? Or typewriters?"

I always wanted to work on things that can be used in everyday life. I sometimes wonder whether my kids remember the storage media of my youth. Music came from vinyl discs spun on turntables; the color film in cameras had to be rewound by hand; offices had typewriters on the desks and meter upon meter of shelves filled with files.

Even as a child I was fascinated by all things technical. I remember how I repaired my grandfather's broken television. I read books about physical phenomena or the Big Bang and enjoyed tinkering with my electronics kit. In school, I was always better in the sciences than in subjects like German or history. There is a clarity to science that I like. Hypotheses are proven by experiments. Facts are facts.

After completing my basic study program, I decided to major in polymer physics because I was intrigued by the interdisciplinary collaboration with chemistry. I applied to various companies and accepted Bayer's offer. We moved from the Black Forest to the Lower Rhine, to Krefeld-Uerdingen. Success was immediate: I was able to prove with my physical model that polycarbonate offers substantially more favorable combinations of optical and mechanical properties when injection molding DVDs, making it superior to other materials. This led to the development of a particularly free-flowing Makrolon™ grade. I was also involved from the very start in the development of recordable DVDs and Blu-ray Discs – including, for example, the dye layer for recording the data. The first DVD Recordable we burned, by the way, held pictures from a colleague's long-service anniversary party. Today the DVD is a closed chapter, at least from a research perspective.

My dream is to make a success of light guidance using holography. Holography isn't new – it's been around for over 50 years. But implementation is a challenge, particularly with respect to the coating of the film. We are working on it. And I really mean we – a team of physicists, chemists and engineers. The field is so complex that one person could never hope to understand it all. The goal of our work is to develop light-guiding films for autostereoscopic 3D displays. I'm looking forward to the day when the results of our current research can be found on the shelf at home.

Friedrich-Karl Bruder

Dr. Friedrich-Karl Bruder was born in 1962 and grew up in Alpirsbach in the Black Forest. He was awarded the North Rhine-Westphalia Innovation Prize in recognition of his research achievements. He is married, has two children and lives in Krefeld, Germany.

Thin films for universal use

MOLECULE MODELERS

Light deflectors is how the researchers from the Holographics and Optics and Surfaces Competence Centers at Bayer MaterialScience have become known in the media. Their labs developed an extremely thin film that has the capability to forever change the world of LED televisions, displays or solar cells and has been on the market since 2010. A special plastic just a few micrometers thick could possibly soon replace expensive and sensitive lens and mirror systems. The new development could, for instance, bundle the sun's rays, glitter as colorful holograms, brighten the colors of a monitor or – in the form of a forgery-proof sticker – protect against product piracy.

One of the masters of light in his element: laboratory manager Dr. Günther Walze conducts a test in Bayer MaterialScience's laser laboratory.

113

Holographic films

2010

The expertise underlying the innovation is highly complex. Bayer's researchers alter microscopically small areas – and thus also the refractive properties – of a highly complex polymer. "Molecular modeling with light" is the name for this process, which was developed using computer simulation. Beams of light change direction when they pass through materials with different refractive indices. For example, if you combine lemon syrup and water, the mixture initially appears to contain cloudy streaks because the light is refracted between the two liquids. The scientists have utilized this effect to develop the streaks they need, which they then inscribe into the film using a laser. Two different laser beams are superimposed; their arrangement determines the distribution of the molecules in the film. Even three-dimensional faces or brand logos can be inscribed into the material – a blessing for any company seeking to protect its quality products from counterfeiters.

At present, there is no way of estimating just how large the market for holographic elements may become. Possible areas of application range from cell phones and game consoles to automotive headlamps. Electronic devices such as computers and cell phones are becoming smaller and smaller. The new film technology can be used to optimize power generation. Solar energy systems can be made more efficient by capturing the sun's rays from various directions. The "light deflectors" from Bayer's laboratories make it possible.

Zhiping Zhou enjoys the traditional cooking of a Cologne brewery restaurant.

THE NEXT GENERATION

Zhiping Zhou

Shanghai, China

Bayer MaterialScience

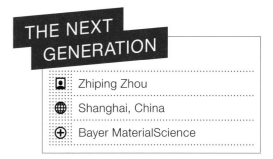

A TASTE OF TRADITION

Zhiping Zhou researches innovations.
In his free time, by contrast, he enjoys traditional things.

My dream as a researcher? That's really easy. One day, I would like to see what has come of the innovations we rack our brains over. I would like to find that our achievements have made a difference to people's lives. Sometimes it's frustrating to see how long it takes for an innovation to reach the end users. That's something which has become clearer to me in my new role at Bayer MaterialScience because I now have the opportunity to see the full horizon – from research through to marketing.

We're currently experimenting with new plastics for framing solar panels. Until now, aluminum has been used and we believe there must be a better solution. It's an area of innovation and a challenge because the main issues are extreme cost-effectiveness and matching the strength of metal. I regularly travel to Europe. When I'm there, I have a number of small rituals, like visiting one of Cologne's brewery restaurants near the cathedral. I love traditional German cuisine and German beer. My colleagues in Germany have trained me to be a real expert.

Zhiping Zhou

Dr. Zhiping Zhou was born in 1974 in Wuhan, China, where he also studied chemistry. Following a period of research in the USA, he returned to China in 2005. Today, he works in polymers research at Bayer MaterialScience. Zhiping Zhou is married, has one daughter and lives in Shanghai, China.

CHAPTER

4

PERSEVERANCE

“

YOU SIMPLY CAN’T GIVE UP. ESPECIALLY NOT WHEN YOU’VE GOT A STORM BLOWING STRAIGHT IN YOUR FACE.

”

FRITZ GESTERMANN, LEVERKUSEN, GERMANY

Page 336

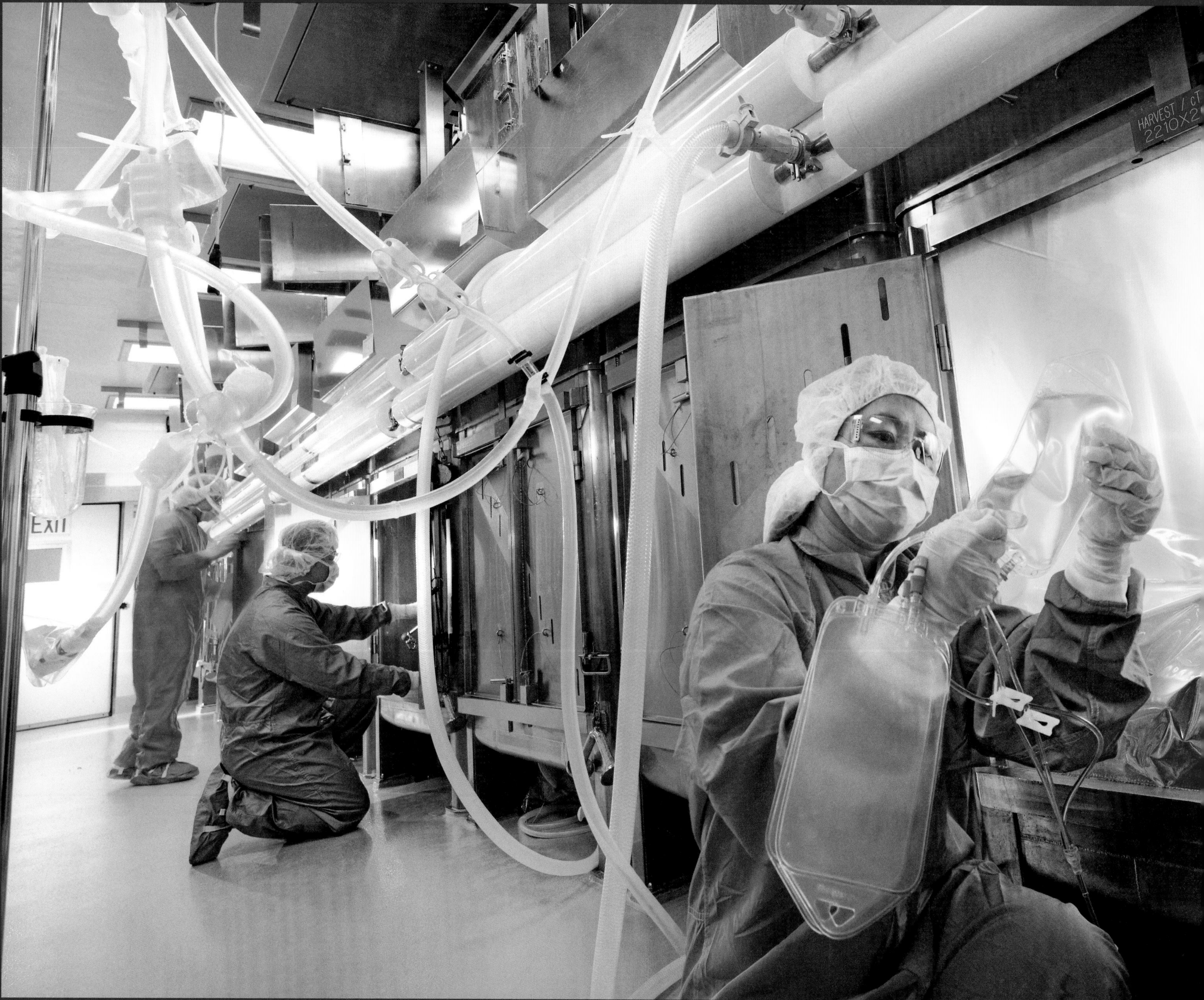
EXIT

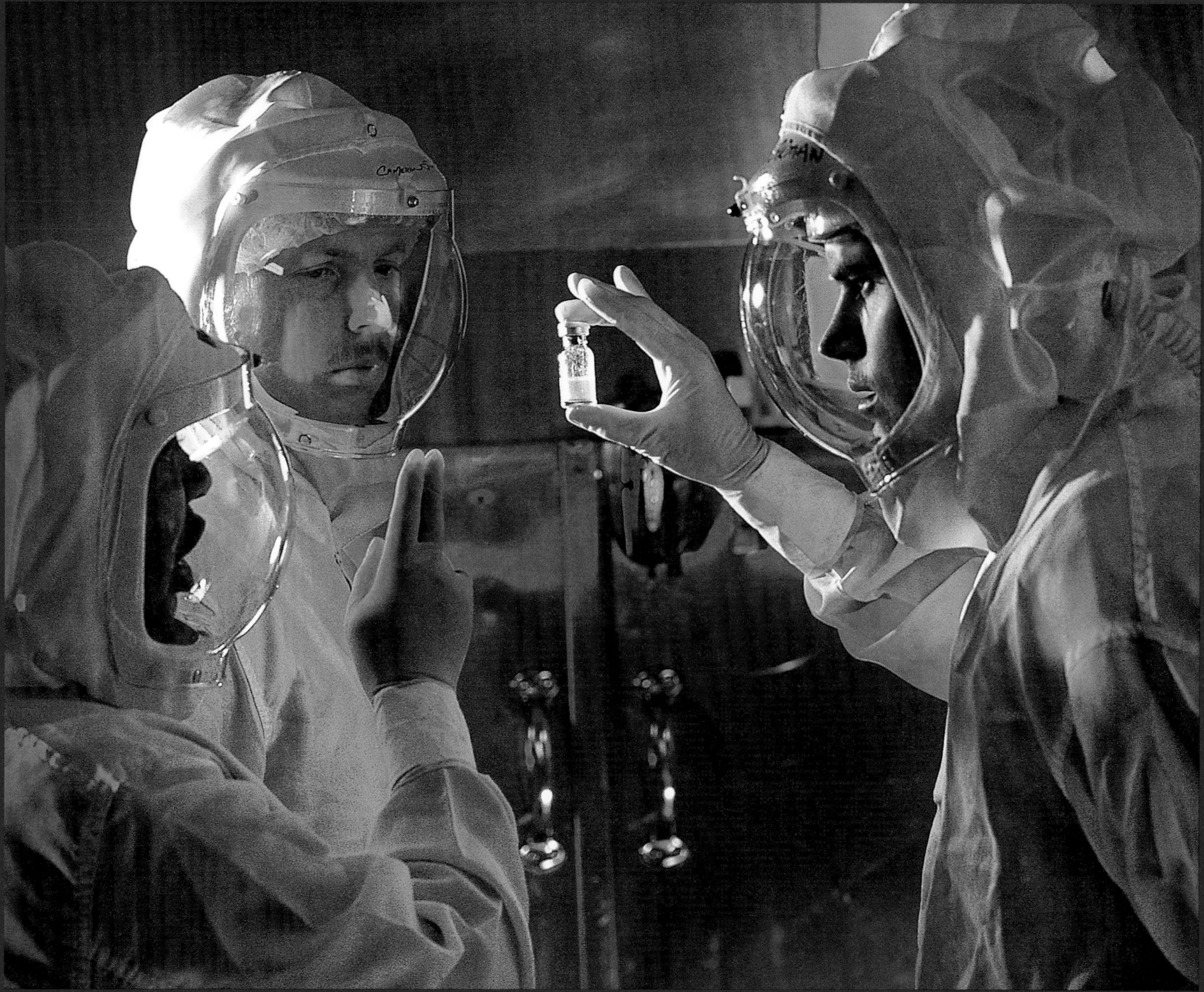

HEMOPHILIA
HIGH-TECH IN CALIFORNIA

At Bayer HealthCare's Kogenate™ production facility in Berkeley, California, USA, Mouang Gomez (front) and two colleagues test the equipment's function.

KOGENATE PRODUCTION
SCIENCE FICTION? REALITY

Not a scene from a science fiction movie but reality at the Kogenate™ production facility in Berkeley, California: special protective suits ensure optimal hygienic conditions.

Read more about hemophilia starting on page 292.

ANTIBIOTICS
BROAD SPECTRUM

Ciprobay™ tablets are pressed from these granules. In the USA, the successful antibiotic is also used to treat inhalational anthrax.

MOLECULES
CLEARING THE AIRWAYS

Bayer researcher Dr. Uwe Petersen views a computer animation of the molecular structure of Avalox™/ Avelox™. The antibiotic based on the active substance moxifloxacin can be used to treat respiratory diseases, for example.

Read more about antibiotics on page 296.

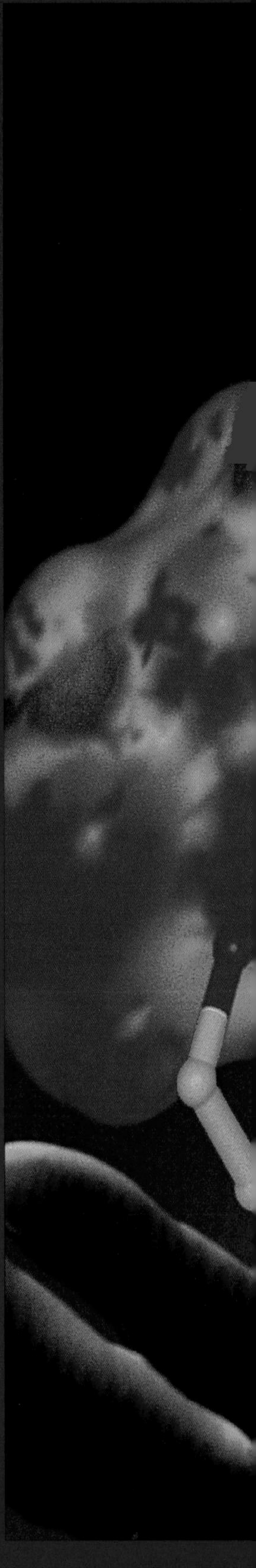

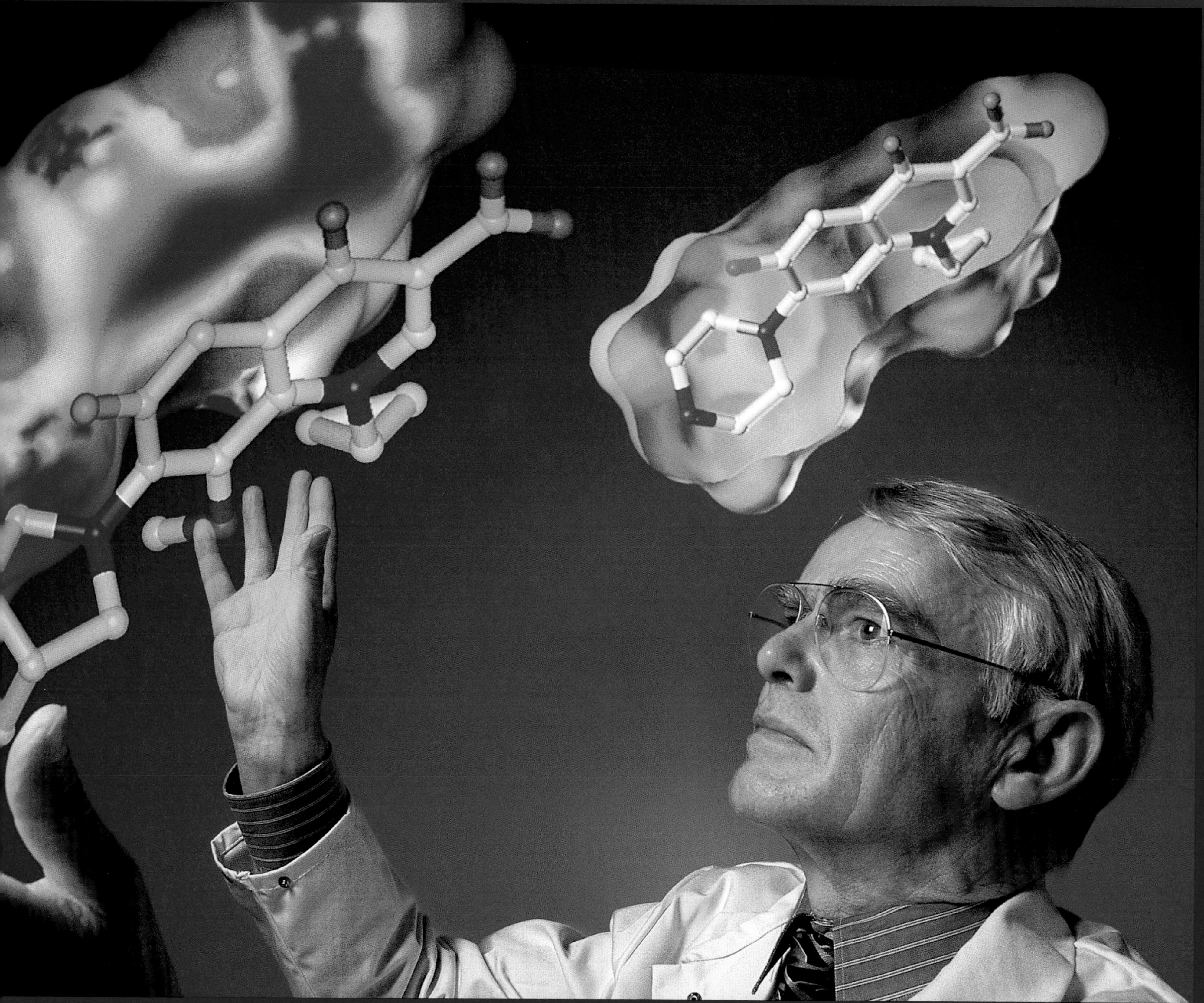

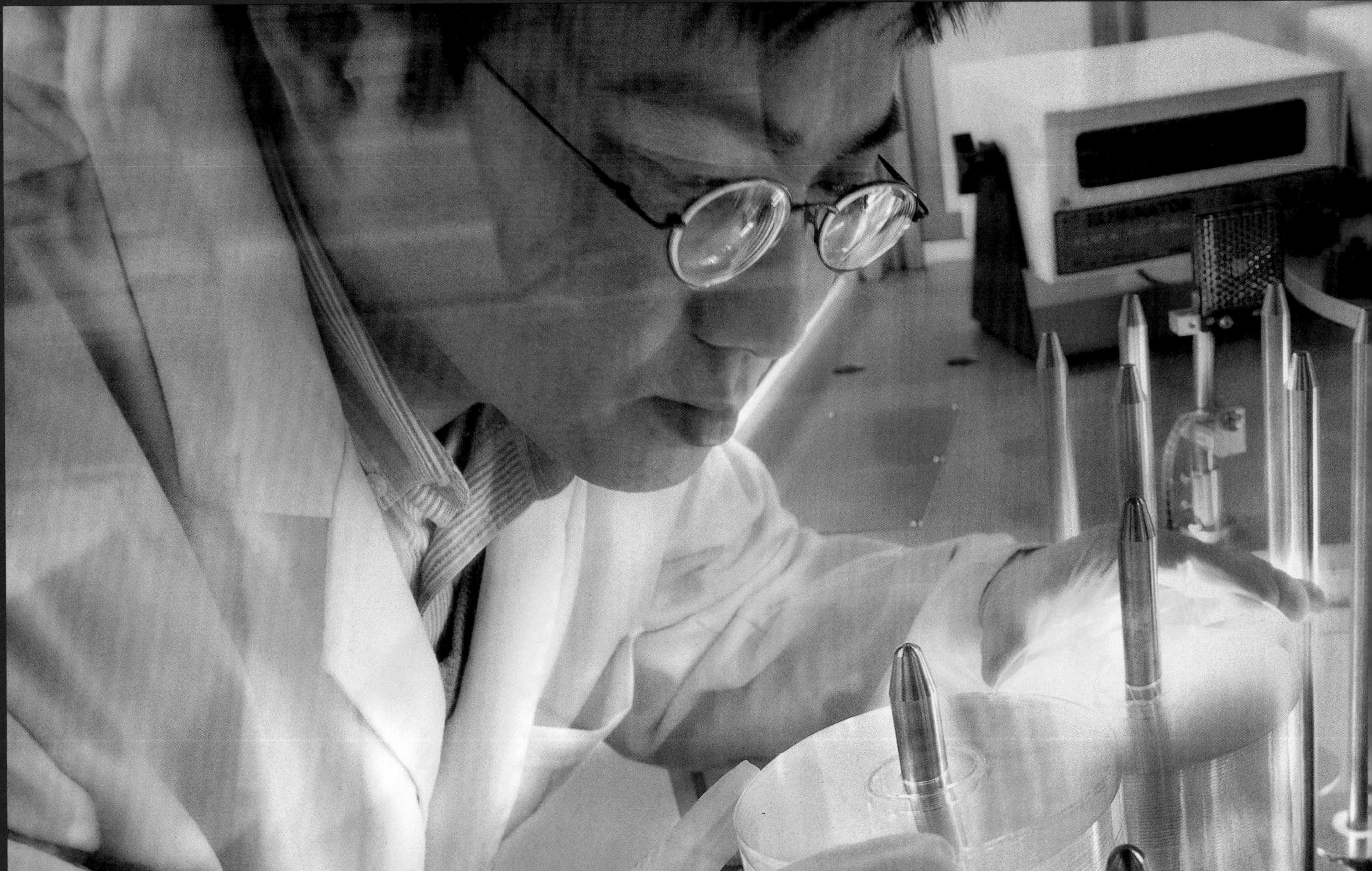

PRODUCTION FACILITIES
GLOBAL COLLABORATION

International teams are working hand in hand to build the Shanghai Chemical Industry Park in China. The photo shows Bayer employees Dr. Yun Chen (left) from China and Dr. Mark Land from the USA outside the new TDI plant.

POLYCARBONATES
DVD DEVELOPMENT

The Polymer Technical Center in Shanghai, China, supports customers with a DVD laboratory.

Read more about polycarbonates starting on page 314.

ENVIRONMENT
RESEARCHING A DREAM

Bayer scientist Dr. Thomas Müller (left) and Professor Walter Leitner of RWTH Aachen University discuss the sustainable use of carbon dioxide (CO_2). Bayer scientists are working on a visionary plan named Dream Production to use CO_2 in the manufacture of high-quality polyurethanes.

ENERGY EFFICIENCY
OXYGEN DEPOLARIZED CATHODE

Luciano Goncalves from Bayer MaterialScience checks the sodium hydroxide feed to the oxygen depolarized cathode element. This technology cuts energy consumption by around 30 percent in brine-based chlorine production.

Read more about the environment starting on page 336.

GONCALVES

RICE
MAIN SOURCE OF NUTRITION

Workers in Thailand carry mats planted with rice seedlings that will later be loaded onto a seeding machine for transplanting in the field. The photo was taken around 200 kilometers south of Bangkok.

FOR A GOOD HARVEST
CAREFUL INSPECTION

Vietnamese rice farmer Huynh Duy Chinh and Bayer employee Nguyen Thi Ngoc Anh (right) inspect the quality of rice plants.

Read about what Bayer researchers are doing to safeguard Asia's main staple food starting on page 326.

CropScience

Berthold Boedeker moved from rainy Wuppertal to the sunshine of California. One of his favorite places in San Francisco is the viewing point in the Golden Gate National Recreational Area with its vistas of the bridge and the city.

114

Berthold Boedeker

Recombinant factor VIII

1984

Factor VIII was first produced by genetic engineering in 1984. It was introduced to the market as Kogenate™. For the boys and men who suffer from hemophilia, the substance has one considerable advantage: there is no risk of infection with undetected viruses in the blood donations from which factor VIII was previously isolated.

A SUCCESSFUL RESEARCH CAREER

Berthold Boedeker moved from Wuppertal to California. He took with him from Germany his knowledge of biotechnology, which was considered pioneering. He also introduced the Factor 11 Friends.

There's one particularly impressive group photo in this book (see page 7). It shows the team of several hundred people who worked for one year to produce a small heap of active ingredient. Recombinant factor VIII, a protein that helps to control hemophilia. The white powder on the tray weighed around 200 grams. This photo gives an impression of how complex and time-consuming production of the substance is. We started working on this project in our labs in Elberfeld, right by the river with a view of Wuppertal's famous suspension railway. The small heap of powder helped tens of thousands of patients – and was worth more than €1 billion.

My photo tells another part of the story. It doesn't show me in the red-brick building by the River Wupper where I work, but in San Francisco. Because of the debate about the pros and cons of genetic engineering, the massive opposition at the time and the associated uncertainties, the production facility was built in the United States, in Berkeley. I moved from Wuppertal – which is so rainy that there have always been jokes about it – to the Golden State of California. We lived in Walnut Creek, a desert community with a communal pool. As far as the weather was concerned – and for me personally – these years meant progress, but relocating the development and production of genetically engineered biologicals was catastrophic for Germany as a research base.

Today, the debate surrounding red genetic engineering has cooled. I think this technology is now accepted by society because people understand that it benefits patients.

"In a park, we discovered a very special factor: the Factor 11 Friends."

I can claim that I wasn't only instrumental in working on factor VIII but I also introduced the Factor 11 Friends to Berkeley. I don't know if the Bay Area Biotech soccer league we established in the park still exists today. Back then, Irishmen, Mexicans and we ex-pat Germans competed passionately – destressing on the soccer pitch. Soccer has always been a constant in my life. When I was at school, my friends and I watched the victory that made Eintracht Braunschweig German League Champions.

Everyone else in my family was a teacher and I really didn't want to do that. Bernhard Grzimek and his wildlife films got me interested in biology but it was soon clear that I was never going to be able to earn my living watching animals. After three semesters, I took chemistry as well and quickly discovered my interest in biotechnology. Today I'm considered a pioneer in this field but whether I really am is something for others to judge.

In California, we worked on a groundbreaking project and the pressure was high. It wasn't only the factor VIII gene that was new but also the way we produced it in fermenters using transfected animal cell lines. We also had to develop entirely new facilities for manufacturing the substance. Researchers and engineers worked hand in hand. Ultimately, this partnership resulted in market approval for the world's first biological manufactured from a continuous perfusion cell culture – a true innovation. For patients, the result we achieved after years of hard work was a breakthrough. The product is not obtained from blood plasma, it contains no viruses and there is an adequate supply. En route to this success, I not only demanded hard work but also drew strength from a good party in the park. I regularly invited my co-workers for a barbecue. We sometimes played baseball and usually soccer, we cooked burgers and hotdogs, drank beer from cans and enjoyed our free time. The working climate afterwards was always excellent – and we sometimes came up with new ideas between the barbecue and the goal.

Today I'm back working in Wuppertal, again with a view of the suspension railway. I returned from the Pacific coast for family reasons but I often travel to California on business. I've retained my passion for soccer and rarely miss an important game. A friend has a season ticket for Borussia Dortmund. We sometimes sit below the main stand in the area they call the yellow wall – because of all the supporters' jerseys.

Berthold Boedeker

Dr. Berthold Boedeker was born in 1953 and grew up in Braunschweig, Germany. He studied at the university there, graduating at the age of 25 and obtaining his PhD at 28. Today he is Chief Scientist at Bayer Pharmaceuticals. He was awarded the Otto Bayer Medal in 1992. Berthold Boedeker is married, has two daughters and lives in Wuppertal, Germany.

Hemophilia

HAMSTER CELLS TO COMBAT THE "ROYAL DISEASE"

The **"royal disease"** was the name given to hemophilia at the beginning of the 20th century. Many members of the European aristocracy, including some members of the British royal family and of the Russian imperial family, suffered from the condition. Because of a hereditary genetic defect, hemophiliacs are unable to produce a special protein known as clotting factor VIII. This interrupts the signaling pathway which causes the platelets in the blood to clump together in the event of an injury. Sufferers are at risk of bleeding to death.

For a long time there was no treatment for hemophilia. It wasn't until in the 1950s that treatment started with what was known as the Cohn fraction, a protein mixture produced from human blood plasma which contained factor VIII, among other things. The Cohn fraction had a large volume and infusions took hours. Regular and prophylactic treatment was therefore not an option. Things improved markedly with the advent of products with a higher concentration of factor VIII, which came onto the market in 1966. However, the manufacturing process was complex and the products could be contaminated with, for example, HIV and hepatitis viruses.

115

Kogenate™

1993

The crucial advance was made in 1984 by a new field of science known as biotechnology. Scientists succeeded in identifying the factor VIII gene, making it possible to produce the factor not only from blood plasma but by genetic engineering as well. The recombinant clotting factor VIII (rFVIII, Kogenate™) has been available since 1993. To date, it is the largest molecule to be manufactured by biotechnology. A masterpiece of science.

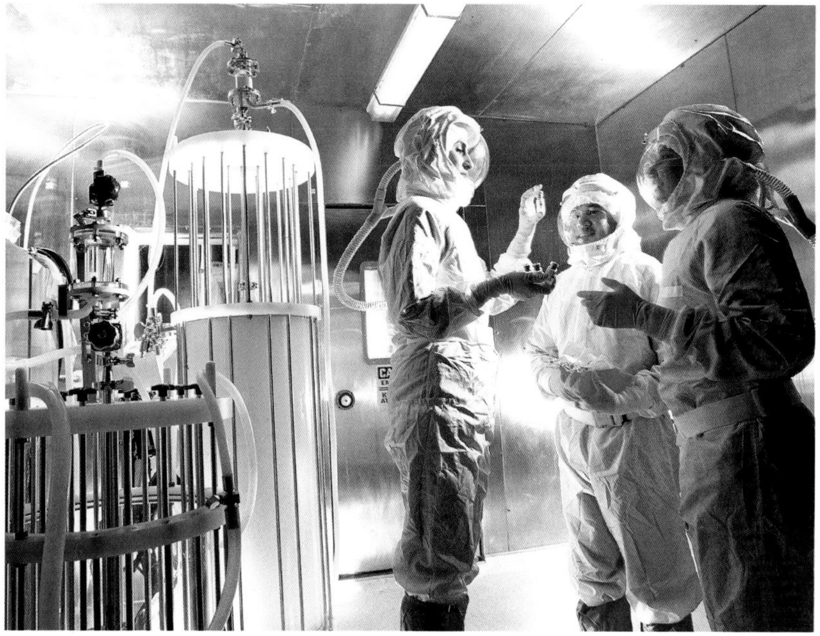

Maximum purity: the manufacture of Kogenate™ in Berkeley, USA

The production plant in Berkeley, California (near San Francisco) applies the most stringent safety precautions. Each batch takes 250 days. The complex protein is produced by genetically modified baby hamster kidney cells. An eight-stage purification process, also developed and patented by Bayer, ensures the absence of any viruses. The product is decanted, freeze-dried and packaged in a super-clean environment. Employees at the modern biotech plant wear gas-tight suits. Today, the researchers' aim is to extend the efficacy of Kogenate™ for patients.

In the laboratory: the microscope was his most important tool, which he used to test the effect of his formulations on strains of bacteria. Gerhard Domagk, shown here in his laboratory in Elberfeld, found active ingredients to combat bacteria that were known but could not be treated.

Gerhard Domagk and the story of Prontosil

DISCOVERY IN DRAMATIC CIRCUMSTANCES

For many years, Gerhard Domagk had been seeking a cure for deadly bacteria, studying them and experimenting with thousands of substances. In November 1935, these invisible enemies threatened the life of his young daughter. Six-year-old Hildegard was sewing when the needle slipped and pricked her between her thumb and index finger; a mere scratch which she forgot about immediately. But her hand soon began to swell alarmingly and her arm started throbbing. Under the skin at the wound site, Domagk found red streaks which were all too familiar to him as a bacteriologist. They indicated a streptococcal infection, which at that time could be fatal.

The Domagks rushed Hildegard to hospital in Wuppertal, but her condition deteriorated rapidly. Her arm was full of pus and the glands in her armpit were swollen. A surgeon diagnosed blood poisoning and recommended amputation as the only way to save the girl's life, showing how helpless doctors were in the face of bacterial infections.

Gerhard Domagk protested. Since 1927, he had led a team of chemists and bacteriologists in Elberfeld who were researching antibacterial drugs. In the laboratory, they treated infected mice, rats and rabbits and had recently made a breakthrough with a dyestuff component from the sulfonamide group. Was he supposed to simply look on as his daughter lost her arm?

116

Prontosil

1935

He insisted that Hildegard was injected with the new drug, which he had discovered and named Prontosil. It had only been patented for a few months and had not been tested on many humans – but Domagk felt he had no choice. Prontosil soon started to work. Sulfonamides inhibit the growth and reproduction of the pathogen, and the patient's immune system can then easily destroy the bacteria. After two days Hildegard's temperature was down and the swelling reduced. Domagk's daughter was cured and her arm saved.

Prontosil marked the beginning of a new era. It was the first antibiotic that could be used against many bacterial

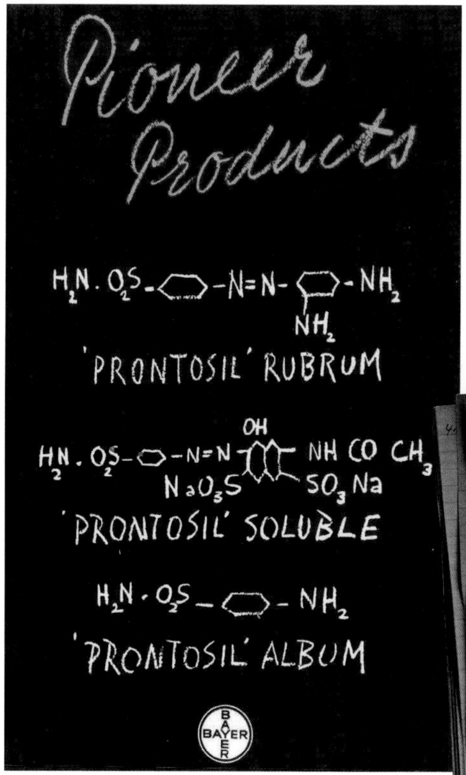

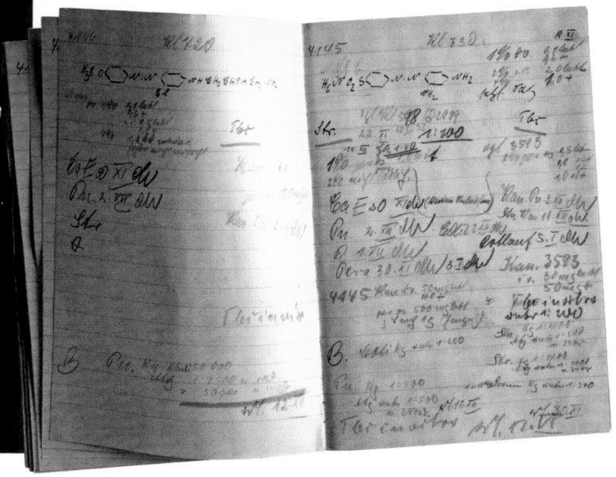

Above: Prontosil advertisement
Right: Nobel laureate Domagk's laboratory journal

infections. Pneumonia, puerperal (childbed) fever and tonsillitis were no longer fatal. In 1939, Domagk, a quiet, serious man with a high forehead and blue eyes, noted that "it is easier to destroy thousands of human lives than it is to save one." His discovery had probably already saved thousands of lives by then. But the researcher's success put him in danger.

In October 1939, the Nobel Prize Committee in Stockholm awarded the Nobel Prize in Medicine to Gerhard Domagk. He was at home in Elberfeld, suffering from influenza, when the telegram arrived from Stockholm. The news plunged him into a dilemma. Since the imprisoned publicist Carl von Ossietzky had received the Nobel Peace Prize three years earlier for his fight against the Hitler regime, all Germans had been forbidden from accepting Nobel Prizes. Domagk was to receive the highest scientific honor in the world – and he didn't know what to do.

The researcher loved traveling: the photo shows Domagk in Egypt in 1958.

He wrote to the authorities telling them of the Nobel Prize Committee's decision – he left off the "Heil Hitler" at the end of the letters. He wrote to Stockholm that he was greatly honored but didn't know whether he could accept the prize or whether he could attend the ceremony. Two weeks later, Domagk was at his desk when Gestapo officers knocked at the door. Armed men dragged the researcher into a car and took him into custody. He spent eight days in a cell without being told why he had been arrested. When a guard asked him why he was in prison, Domagk replied: "Because I won the Nobel Prize." They laughed at him. On his release, Domagk was forced to renounce the Nobel Prize. He was allowed to continue his research; his senior position in a large industrial company gave him some protection.

In 1947, Domagk finally received his Nobel Prize from the King of Sweden. His right to the prize money had lapsed, but he didn't care. "There would be no penicillin without Domagk," said Alexander Fleming, who won the Nobel Prize for his discovery of penicillin. Although Domagk's pioneering work on antibiotics is undisputed, he never became as famous during his lifetime as, for example, Alexander Fleming.

Antibacterial drugs

THE LIFE-CHANGING EXPERIENCES OF THE SOLDIER DOMAGK

117

Zephirol™

1935

Poland, December 1914. Gerhard Domagk had been a soldier at the front for three months when a bullet from a Russian machine gun hit him in the head. Like many other young Germans, Domagk, born in 1895 and the son of a teacher from Brandenburg, had gone to war as a volunteer. Now the medical student was in a field hospital. He was lucky. He soon recovered and trained as a medical orderly.

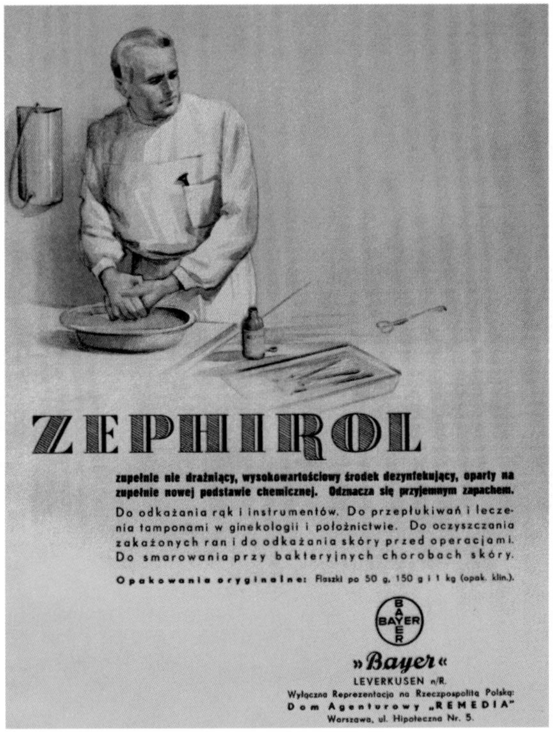

A long-awaited disinfecting agent: Zephirol™ advertisement from the 1930s

The quiet, good-natured Domagk had been plunged into a world war which he saw from its most brutal aspect. Bullet wounds and mutilated limbs were treated without surgical gloves in the dimmest of lights, with the flies circling overhead. Time and again, soldiers died after a successful operation, from wound fever or infections. Medicine seemed powerless to combat the deadly bacteria. The only things available were chlorine solution and carbolic acid, but they had only a short-term effect. Gerhard Domagk made a decision. Later, he wrote: "My desire, if I were ever to return to my homeland alive, was to work and work to make a small contribution to resolving this problem." His wish was granted. Years later, Domagk, in his early thirties, joined Bayer.

The gifted doctor set up a research institute for experimental pathology and bacteriology in Elberfeld. Chemists Fritz Mietzsch and Josef Klarer provided him with new compounds; Domagk tested their effectiveness. He firmly believed he could cure bacterial infections with drugs.

The breakthrough

In 1932, after testing thousands of substances, Domagk found one which killed bacteria like nothing previously known: benzyldimethyldodecylammonium chloride. It was ideal for disinfecting hands and instruments and preventing wound fever. In 1935, the disinfecting agent went on sale as Zephirol™. But Domagk was not satisfied just with fighting bacteria outside the body. Together with Mietzsch and Klarer, he sought a treatment for infectious diseases and was soon successful. However, Zephirol™ is still used the world over because of its long-lasting effectiveness.

A busy retiree: Klaus Grohe, shown here in the garden of his home in Leverkusen, is a man with many interests.

118

Klaus Grohe

The quinolones substance class

1987

Quinolones are one of the most important classes of antibiotics. The best-known products include Ciprobay™, Baytril™ and Avalox™/ Avelox™. Ciprofloxacin, the active ingredient of Ciprobay™, received regulatory approval in Germany in 1987.

AN UNFALTERING SPIRIT

His innovations have saved thousands of lives. In developing his active ingredient, Klaus Grohe had to demonstrate persistence and courage. A very individual success story.

The **he letter was** written by a father. Reading between the lines, it was clear that his family had been in a terrible situation. His teenage daughter Jenny had returned very ill from a trip to India: typhus, renal failure, lung and liver complications, hemorrhage. None of the known antibiotics worked. When Jenny fell into a coma, it seemed there was no more hope for her. Doctors refer to such cases as untreatable. Her death seemed to be a matter of hours. One doctor suggested trying a new product that had not yet been approved by the regulatory authorities. The father agreed. Within a few hours, Jenny's condition had improved. Just a few days later, she was able to leave the Berlin hospital where she had been treated. Completely cured.

I am the father of the Bayer quinolones, the class of substances which also includes ciprofloxacin. Letters of thanks like this were my professional motivation. I wanted to help people; that was the goal of my research. Today it is estimated that ciprofloxacin, a broad-spectrum antibiotic, has been prescribed more than one billion times and has probably saved millions of lives. Bayer donates supplies of this product after natural disasters – like those which occurred in Ecuador, Turkey and Mozambique. Following the terror attacks in the United States, millions of tablets were supplied to treat government employees, postal workers and police officers. It was the only registered drug product that is effective against the anthrax pathogen and also has a prophylactic effect. According to surveys, the name under which ciprofloxacin is sold in North America is now just as well-known as Aspirin™.

It has to be said that the active ingredient caused quite a furore. However, the history behind it was sometimes strange. It began in Ludwigshafen. My high-school teacher got me interested in chemistry. I already knew before I graduated what I wanted to be: a research scientist. After finishing high school, I studied chemistry at the University of Würzburg. After completing my PhD there as well, I worked as a scientific assistant for two years. But my goal was always to move into basic chemical and medical research, in industry.

"The process with which I initiated quinolones research at Bayer is actually referred to in literature as the Grohe Method."

Otto Bayer, the cigar-smoking patriarch, gave me a job at Bayer in 1965. Because I had several job offers from chemical companies, I was able to extract a promise from him: he would give me a certain amount of freedom to develop my own ideas. I started out in Central Research, working on organic chlorine and fluorine intermediates. In 1969, I requested a move to Pharmaceuticals. The breakthrough came in 1975 after many years of research work. Using an entirely new chemical process, I was able to synthesize antibacterial cyclopropylquinolone carbonic acids for the first time.

The process with which I initiated quinolones research at Bayer is actually referred to in literature as the Grohe Method. I was convinced I was on the right track but got no support from my supervisors during those years. On the contrary. I was transferred to a crop protection department. But I continued my research in secret. At the end of the working day and at weekends, I used the laboratory for my quinolones work. A researcher doesn't just need the spark of an idea; he also needs a flame that never goes out. I'll never forget April 15, 1981. It is the date I synthesized ciprofloxacin, the active ingredient I had already come up with in 1979, and sent it for microbiological investigation at the Institute for Chemotherapy in Elberfeld. This showed that the substance is effective against 98.3 percent of more than 20,000 different strains of bacteria. Even before clinical studies began – toxicological testing was already well advanced – I tried ciprofloxacin on myself. I had a painful infection in a tooth. The pain disappeared after just a short time and the tooth was saved. I think a researcher and inventor has to be willing to take a bit of a risk.

I take a certain degree of satisfaction from the fact that ciprofloxacin and the other quinolones enrofloxacin and moxifloxacin (see also page 309) – which subsequently followed and also became successful Bayer products – have generated enormous financial returns. I'm also proud to have received numerous awards including the Otto Bayer Medal in 1987 for ciprofloxacin, a second Otto Bayer Medal for my lifetime achievement following my retirement in 1997, the Cross of the Order of Merit of the Federal Republic of Germany (first class) and the title of scientific professor bestowed by the Innovation Ministry of North Rhine-Westphalia. However, what means most to me are letters like the one from Jenny's father. They are why I kept going.

Klaus Grohe

Professor Klaus Grohe was born in 1934 and grew up in Ludwigshafen. He is married and has two daughters. Two foundations are named after him – one at the Society of German Chemists and the other at the Berlin-Brandenburg Academy of Sciences - and support young scientists working in active ingredient research and infectology. Klaus Grohe and his family live in Leverkusen, Germany.

Anti-tuberculosis drug

WINNING THE RACE – AND NOT JUST AGAINST TIME

Two years after the Second World War, the shattered world was being ravaged by a terrible disease. Tuberculosis claimed hundreds of thousands of lives. A touch or a breath is enough to transmit the pathogen, the tuberculosis bacterium, which initially causes a mild influenza-like illness. But it then goes on to attack the organs, usually the lungs. Gerhard Domagk had been looking for a remedy for tuberculosis since the early 1930s. Now he had found it.

Domagk, who had received many job offers after being awarded the Nobel Prize in Medicine, had stayed loyal to Bayer. He tested thousands of sulfonamide variants – antibiotics he had developed himself and used against various infections. But the tuberculosis bacterium has a waxy protective layer which makes it more difficult for drugs to penetrate. An aggressive new substance called sulfathiazole yielded the first successful results. Again, it was some time before the right formulation was found and could be tested on humans.

119

Conteben

1950

It happened in August 1950. Almost as soon as the British military government had authorized Bayer's reestablishment, a hospital in Freiburg reported that several tuberculosis cases had been cured with test product Tb I/698 from Bayer's laboratory in Wuppertal. Shortly afterwards, a hospital in northern Germany also reported encouraging data: 49 of 66 patients had been cured by the drug. Soon, there were no further obstacles to the market launch of Tb I/698. From 1950, the yellow powder was sold as Conteben. It worked best against tuberculosis of the larynx, intestine and bladder but was not effective in the most widely occurring form: pulmonary tuberculosis. A tubercular lung is largely cut off from the circulation and not easily accessible for drugs.

A Conteben package from the 1950s

This all changed when Bayer chemists Hans Offe and Werner Siefken produced isonicotinic acid hydrazide in Leverkusen. The new drug is a tasteless, colorless crystalline powder which dissolves easily in water. As Domagk discovered, it inhibits the growth of tuberculosis bacilli. This success became public knowledge earlier than planned. Testing of the new drug had only just begun when the press carried reports about an American drug. Clearly, the U.S. researchers had found the same solution, independently of Domagk. Bayer's directors responded and publicized their results in the press before sharing them with other professionals. With this helping hand behind it, the new drug was rushed to market and, from 1952 onwards, was sold as Neoteben. However, the dreadful disease has still not been eradicated. Tuberculosis cases are on the rise again, claiming millions of victims. The race continues.

Fewer amputations

A POWDER CURES GAS GANGRENE

Gas gangrene is one of the worst conditions that was seen by medical orderlies during both world wars. If a wound gets dirty, bacteria enter the body, form spores and spread rapidly. The affected areas swell up, and gas collects under the skin. A speck of dust shot into an arm or a leg on a fragment of shrapnel can lead to large areas of skin being covered with rapidly spreading pustules. Until mid-way through the Second World War, the only way to stop gangrene spreading was to amputate the affected limb.

While tens of thousands of wounded soldiers waited for a cure, researchers at the Bayer site in Elberfeld, Germany found a drug combination which worked against the gas gangrene pathogen – a mixture of Marfanil, Prontalbin and Eleudron. Older surgeons advised against focusing on drug treatments and neglecting wound care. They advocated the traditional practice of quickly amputating the swollen body parts to prevent the spores spreading at all costs.

120
Marfanil
1941

However, the MPE drugs won over the critics with their potent effect: the drug cleaned the wound and prevented infection by inhibiting bacterial growth in the body. The immune system could then overcome the weakened bacteria more easily. The drug was licensed under the name Marfanil in 1941 but during the war, when it saved the lives of thousands of soldiers, it was known as MPE powder. It provided relief for a medical problem which still exists today.

Fighting drug resistance

CARRYING ON A TRADITION

Drug resistance is a phrase pharmacologists fear – and a challenge at the same time. Even the most effective drug cannot entirely eliminate a pathogen. Bacteria keep on evolving and eventually become immune, so that new drugs are needed. Antibiotics are the best example of this phenomenon. The sulfonamides, discovered by Gerhard Domagk, and penicillin, discovered by Alexander Fleming, enjoyed unparalleled success after the Second World War. They were used all over the world and saved countless human lives. But after the boom, at the end of the 1950s, came the setback. Many pathogens developed resistance to these drugs, reducing or even cancelling their effectiveness.

121
Baypen™
1977

Bayer's researchers took up the challenge. They looked for new varieties of penicillin, testing their effectiveness against bacteria and their tolerability by the human body. The first drug, Baycillin™, went on sale in 1962, followed by Baypen™ in 1977. Both are more effective and better tolerated than earlier products. Baypen™, administered intravenously, stops cell wall production in the bacteria and so gradually kills them. It is also incredibly versatile. It works against completely different pathogens, including streptococci, salmonellae and coliform bacteria. The active substance carried on the long tradition of Bayer research, which began with Gerhard Domagk (see also from page 296), and took the treatment of bacterial infections to a new level.

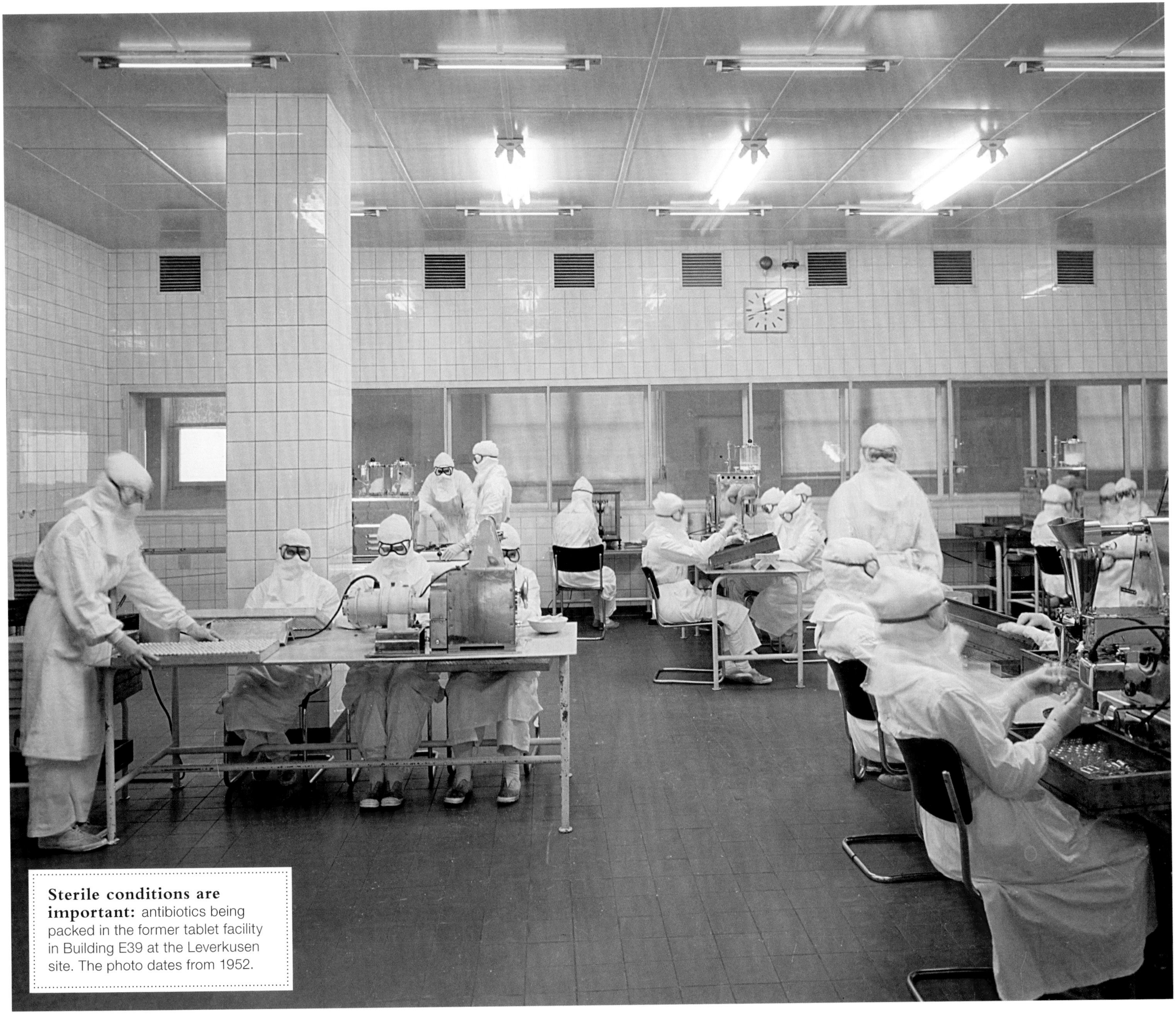

Sterile conditions are important: antibiotics being packed in the former tablet facility in Building E39 at the Leverkusen site. The photo dates from 1952.

On rough terrain:
Hans-Joachim Zeiler enjoys off-road driving, no matter what the weather.

122

Hans-Joachim Zeiler

Ciprofloxacin

1987

Ciprofloxacin, first approved in Germany in 1987 and known as Ciprobay™, is a broad-spectrum antibiotic. Like enrofloxacin and moxifloxacin, it is one of the newer fluoroquinolones.

THROUGH ROUGH TERRAIN

Hans-Joachim Zeiler is one of the inventors of important antibiotics such as ciprofloxacin. He learned that scientists are individualists. And that it's sometimes important to be tenacious.

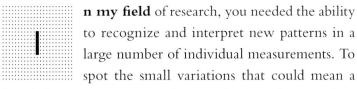

In my field of research, you needed the ability to recognize and interpret new patterns in a large number of individual measurements. To spot the small variations that could mean a big difference. My team and I were looking for new drug products. It was like a giant puzzle – we found various pieces and arranged them to create a harmonious picture. When I was a scientist – I began working in Bayer's laboratories in the mid-1970s – a researcher's intuition and eye were far more important. It may be that I have an eye for the unusual. I certainly have an eye for nature. In my free time, I'm an amateur photographer. And I enjoy off-road driving through rough terrain.

Researchers are individualists. You have to be able to put up with a lot, be patient, tenaciously keep going and believe that you will reach your goal. I joined Bayer after obtaining my PhD in microbiology. I worked on the biological aspects of anti-infectives research, which also included the search for new antibacterial agents for use in human and veterinary medicine. I tested almost all the active ingredients Bayer produced for their antibiotic effect. It really was like looking for the proverbial needle in a haystack. Most of the substances that looked promising at the start turned out to be toxic when we did more tests. I remember frustrating days when I would doubt what I was doing. I only gave up the idea of quitting and studying medicine because our third child was born. My family needed security.

We weren't getting anywhere with our research. But then we noticed a test tube containing a derivative with surprising properties. Was it something new? It was a modification of a substance class that is known for its side-effects and the tendency to form resistance. Not exactly a breakthrough then. Nevertheless, I took a closer look at the molecule and worked with my colleague Klaus Grohe in chemical research to try and produce other derivatives from related substance classes. However, we weren't able to significantly improve the antibacterial effect. When management decided to focus efforts on established substance classes, it was the end of the project. However, I couldn't forget the special biological properties and the antibacterial effect we had found.

At a congress in Chicago, I learned of a substance discovered by an Asian company that was similar to our derivatives. This news spurred me on and electrified our team. What would happen if we were able to incorporate the new substitutes into our molecule?

In spring 1981, Klaus Grohe managed to synthesize this new compound. Eight days later, I received the first results of the microbiological tests on my desk. I was excited about the compound's broad spectrum of activity – it had the most amazing antibacterial effect. The next task was to convince management about these data – and we succeeded. Things then moved very fast; we hastily conducted the next tests. However, one decision gave me sleepless nights – which of our development candidates should I propose? After carefully considering efficacy and tolerability, I selected the substance which I felt offered the best balance of all properties.

This was the crucial step in developing ciprofloxacin for indications in human medicine. Around one year later, I chose another derivative (enrofloxacin) for development as a veterinary product. Many years later, moxifloxacin became the next quinolone to enter development.

I once went into a pharmacy when I was at a congress in Tijuana, Mexico. I had to smile when I held a pack of our "Cipro" in my hand. The pharmacist saw me and asked what was wrong. I explained that I was one of the people who had invented the medicine. He almost didn't believe me. He looked at me in awe and yes, I'm proud of this achievement. We developed medicines that have saved many thousands of lives. Helping people was my main motivation. The circle had now closed and I'd fulfilled my lifetime ambition.

Even today, although I'm supposedly retired, I'm still involved in science – in cancer research. A colleague and I have established a company and are on course to finding a well-tolerated chemotherapy. My mission is not over yet.

Hans-Joachim Zeiler

Dr. Hans-Joachim Zeiler was born in 1947 in Karlsruhe. He studied microbiology and chemistry in Tübingen and joined Bayer in 1974. In 1987 he received the Otto Bayer Medal. Hans-Joachim Zeiler is married and has four children. He lives in Wuppertal, Germany.

Indicated particularly for pulmonary infections

A NEW CHAPTER IN THE HISTORY OF ANTIBIOTICS

Respiratory tract infections have major implications, not only for those affected but for the community as a whole. They are the fifth leading cause of death worldwide and the second most common reason for workers to take sick leave. And in up to two-thirds of patients, symptoms become worse after a bacterial infection. There is therefore a great need for effective therapeutic options to successfully treat acute exacerbations of chronic bronchitis, bacterial pneumonia and sinus infections. However, the problem of resistance to certain antibiotics may arise. In many countries, the most common pathogen in respiratory infections, Streptococcus pneumoniae, has become increasingly resistant to standard antibiotics such as penicillins and macrolides. As a result, these drugs can no longer be recommended unreservedly.

123
Avalox™/ Avelox™
1999

Enormous progress in just four years

In 1999, Bayer launched the quinolone antibiotic Avalox™/ Avelox™ (active ingredient: moxifloxacin), which is produced using the Grohe Method (see page 300). In less than four years, the company developed a product which is said to have enormous advantages over all previously available drugs in all significant respects – effectiveness, safety and tolerability. Avalox™/ Avelox™ is effective against all relevant bacterial pathogens of respiratory infections, killing them quickly and reliably. Another advantage for the patient is that the drug needs to be taken only once a day. It acts faster than many other antibiotics to relieve symptoms, thus shortening treatment time.

Since its market launch, Avalox™/Avelox™ has been approved in more than 120 countries. In many of them, it is successfully used to treat complex skin and soft-tissue diseases and abdominal infections, as well as respiratory infections. Worldwide, more than 160 million people have been treated with Avalox™/Avelox™ since its launch.

High-tech pharmaceuticals production: for many doctors, Avalox™/Avelox™ is the antibiotic of choice for treating acute bacterial exacerbation of chronic bronchitis.

All-around talent with a good handicap: Guido Schmitz tees off at a golf course near his home in New Jersey.

124

Guido Schmitz

Making Science Make Sense

1995

Guido Schmitz played a key role in developing new packaging designs for Aspirin™. He is also a driving force in the Making Science Make Sense program aimed at interesting young people in science, established in 1995.

BAYER PRIDE

Guido Schmitz has had an unusual career. The son of a family with strong Bayer roots worked his way up at the company – through industriousness and a talent for tinkering. Today he is also responsible for a program aimed at interesting young people in science.

I **trained as** a metalworker and I know where I come from. Taken together, my family has worked for Bayer for more than 150 years: my father put in 44 years, my grandfather spent 55 years in the leather chemicals plant, my brother works for Bayer and so do both my uncles. I joined Bayer when I was 16. We lived in the housing division for Bayer workers, on Charlottenburger Strasse in Leverkusen. Bayer 04 is our soccer club. Bayer was everything to us: our identity and our pride. Today I live in New Jersey and the title on my business card says "Head of Packaging and Technology Innovation, Global Research and Development." My license plate has "Bayer 04" on it and I am the president of the Bayer fan club in New York City. It goes without saying that I never miss a game on television. My life was even the subject of a documentary about emigrants on a German TV station.

I used to play soccer reasonably well. During my compulsory service in the German armed forces, I played together with future Germany national team players such as Olaf Thon and Thomas Hässler on the military team. And although I was never as good as they were, I practiced a signature that no one could read so it looked like a star's autograph. Thon and Hässler moved on to Schalke 04, Bayern Munich and Juventus Turin, while I began working for Bayer. My brother worked in the Pharmaceuticals division and got me a job on the air conditioning systems. Servicing the air conditioners was wonderful. To call my career path "meandering" would be a total understatement. I'm a tinkerer, I'm obsessed with details and I never give up, because I absolutely hate to lose. I'm not afraid to get my hands dirty. No matter what I did after I had worked on the air conditioning systems and my ambition had been awakened, I tirelessly continued training myself. I wanted to learn, and I learned even in my spare time. We have truly excellent skilled workers in the company. I learned what I needed to know by observing them. I'm extremely grateful to the company for that as well. I labored and tinkered my way up the ladder, for example developing machines that produce Aspirin™ tablets more simply.

"I'm not afraid to get my hands dirty."

2002 was a tough year for me. My father died. The last time I saw him was at the summer fair in Schlebusch – a district of Leverkusen – and I still reproach myself for not having drunk one last beer with him. Back then I was always stressed out, always totally immersed in work. It's still that way today, but I've learned to make space for the important things. Shortly after the funeral, the company was looking for specialists who wanted to transfer to the new Product Development Center of the Consumer Care division in Morristown, New Jersey. I was one of those invited, together with our wives. I hesitated, but my brother said: "Go ahead, it would be good for you." My wife and daughter were not so convinced at first. Then, on the last evening, we took the ferry from Manhattan to New Jersey. It was a magical evening and the big city skyline was glittering in the evening sunlight. My wife leaned up against me and said: "Okay, let's try it for three years."

America has become our home. I fit in here and I'm incredibly thankful that I'm allowed to be here. We are working on innovative product and packaging designs for the world market, such as a new bottle for Aspirin™ with a style, shape and feel that is totally different to that of our competitors – and is worthy of the drug of the century. I'm also one of the people responsible for the Making Science Make Sense program that aims to cultivate enthusiasm for chemistry in schools. Everywhere in the United States, volunteers have come forward – there are now more than 1,000 at a dozen locations – to show children and young people simple experiments and fire their interest in the natural sciences. Textbooks are all very well, but a supervised experiment where things explode, give off smoke and are lots of fun is something very different. The program gives me a great feeling: I'm able to give back some of what I've learned.

Guido Schmitz

Guido Schmitz was born in Leverkusen, Germany, in 1964. He has been appointed to the Expert Club, a network linking the company's leading minds in order to strengthen Bayer's innovative power. Today he lives with his wife and daughter in New Jersey, USA.

A top seller by accident

A TRIUMPH WITH ITS ORIGINS IN THE OFFICE

Elkhart, Indiana – winter 1928. A flu epidemic was sweeping the United States. Andrew Hubble Beardsley, known as Hub and president of pharmaceutical company Miles, was visiting his friend Tom Keene, managing editor of the local newspaper in Elkhart. While one quarter of the Miles workforce was sick, everyone at the *Elkhart Truth* was healthy and working normally. Beardsley was amazed. "Quite simple," explained Keene. "I give my people a mixture of acetylsalicylic acid and bicarbonate of soda in hot lemon juice every day."

A simple recipe with a special effect. The mixture was first tested during a cruise on passengers who were suffering from seasickness and flu – and it was a success. Miles chemist J. Maurice Treener then developed an effervescent tablet which, like Aspirin™, contained acetylsalicylic acid and so not only helped to beat the pains of colds but also headaches, aching limbs, fever, acid indigestion, hangovers and more. He called it Alka-Seltzer™, after the alkaline effect and the seltzer-like fizz made by bicarbonate of soda when it dissolves in water. It was sold for the first time in 1931 as a non-prescription OTC (over-the-counter) product.

125

Alka-Seltzer™

1931

Speedy was the face of Alka-Seltzer™ in the 1950s. Miles was acquired by Bayer in 1978.

To make Alka-Seltzer™ a commercial success, Miles invested in advertising – familiar territory for a company that since 1902 had been distributing a free almanac containing a wide range of general knowledge facts in several languages through drugstores. About a billion copies had been published by 1942.

Miles also used the radio to advertise Alka-Seltzer™ because it was the only medium that could reach even the remotest corners of the United States. Between the country music songs you could hear the tablets bubbling in the glass – "Listen to it fizz." Miles was acquired by Bayer in 1978. By then Alka-Seltzer™ was to be found in almost every household – testimony not only to the quality of the product, but also to Miles' clever advertising for Alka-Seltzer™. For the radio it created the legendary jingle "Plop, plop, fizz, fizz." And for television there were the commercials featuring the character "Speedy," whose hat and body were an Alka-Seltzer™ tablet.

Talking shop: in the laboratory in Krefeld-Uerdingen where polycarbonate was invented, Hermann Schnell (in suit) speaks with his colleagues Fritz, Bottenbruch and Krimm (from left).

Hermann Schnell's stroke of genius

BOLD DECISIONS FOR GROUND-BREAKING SUCCESS

126

Polycarbonates

1953

By the time he emerged from the shadow of his teacher, the student was 37 years old. In 1953, the year in which his former professor Hermann Staudinger was awarded the Nobel Prize for Chemistry, the chemist Hermann Schnell registered a discovery that would make him one of Bayer's greatest inventors. Polycarbonates would soon change everyday life for people all over the world.

When Schnell joined Bayer shortly after the war, the company was just starting out again. Management had to make some important decisions, including how to take the plastics business forward. It decided to focus on products with special technical properties rather than on commodities. Investment in research and development was necessary. New production facilities were needed, although no-one could foresee how the market would develop. Bold decisions were made that were typical of this era when the company restarted under the aegis of Chairman of the Board Ulrich Haberland. Haberland, a born entrepreneur, focused on innovation, and it was his visionary actions that put Bayer back on the world stage.

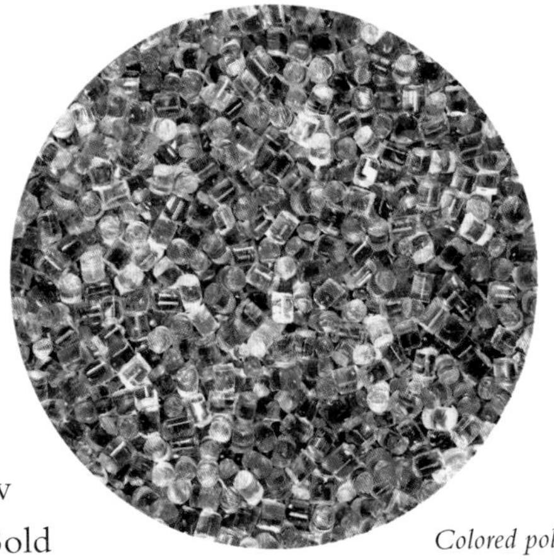

Colored polycarbonate granules

Schnell, now head of the research laboratory in Krefeld-Uerdingen, was pursuing ideas that seemed so impossible that some experts wrote him off as "crazy." Yet he stuck at it. His new plastic, which was registered with the German Patent Office on October 16, 1953, was sensational. Lightweight, transparent and flame-resistant, it could withstand extremes of heat and cold and had outstanding resistance to impact and tensile stress. It took Schnell and his colleagues five years to develop a cost-effective production path. Makrolon™ was launched onto the market.

This was the start of an incredible success story. Makrolon™ is used to make car headlights; it is molded to produce housings for electrical equipment and camping tableware; and transparent sheets of the material were used to roof Cologne's main train station. Schnell's career took off. As the head of Bayer's research department, he registered over 400 patents. He was showered with awards, including the Hermann Staudinger Prize.

Family idyll in the 1960s with Makrolon™ tableware

Dieter Freitag is a passionate amateur archeologist. He is pictured next to an excavation in Cologne's Romano-Germanic Museum.

127

Dieter Freitag

Development of Makrolon™

1982

Freitag's innovations include specially modified polycarbonates used since 1982 for products such as CDs and multiwall sheets (two sheets connected by a series of thin walls). Thanks to their high strength and good insulating properties, these sheets are often used for greenhouses or roofs. Another polycarbonate, Apec™ HT, is extremely resistant to heat. It can be found in car headlights.

THE EXCAVATOR

Dieter Freitag is considered the granddaddy of polycarbonate research. He is one of the fathers of the compact disc, having discovered the material from which they are made. A story about a "pharmacy," four billion pits and a secret of archeology

L**et's get one** thing straight right away: I am not, as is often claimed, the inventor of the CD. I helped to develop the material from which compact discs are made. Plastics are my passion. My name is on 429 patents. I have received many awards, and I have the great honor of being the first German inducted into the Plastics Academy Hall of Fame in Chicago. After joining Bayer, I had no interest in academic research, but wanted to help people. "Science For A Better Life" was my motivation. Innovation requires a good idea, the technical expertise to implement this idea, self-honesty and a good team. And a healthy portion of good luck. You have to be in the right place at the right time. That's exactly how it was when we managed to codevelop the CD.

I had been working for quite some time with colleagues from the Application Technology department on ways to improve the flowability and demolding of polycarbonate in order to accelerate the production of high-precision moldings. Because preliminary larger-scale trials were only moderately successful, the project was facing termination. Until one day in 1978, when representatives of Philips visited Bayer to present a groundbreaking innovation. They had digitized a Beethoven symphony and stored it on a metal disc. Four billion pits, each one ten-thousandth of a millimeter deep. What a sensation! They were looking for a plastic that in its liquefied state could be molded within seconds to precisely replicate these tiny pits, cure quickly and then be read by a laser. The initial reaction of my colleagues: "There isn't a plastic that can do that – and there never will be."

The problem ultimately landed on my desk. I was convinced that my new development, Makrolon™, was suitable for this application. "Are you trying to turn my production facility into a pharmacy?" asked an indignant production manager. And yes, the production facility set up a "pharmacy," in which the new material was produced in an absolutely dust-free environment. The result revolutionized music. Star conductor Herbert von Karajan considered the development of the CD to be a technological quantum leap like the switch from gas lighting to electricity.

From a stone to a plastic disc

My former boss and mentor Hermann Schnell once said: "You not only have to come up with an invention, you also have to recognize its significance – and push it through." I was a good student, but my parents, who ran a small grocery store, were against my going to high school and attending university. My teacher was able to convince my father, who was adamantly opposed to this higher form of school, to change his mind. After graduating from high school, I initially wanted to become a pharmacist. The degree program was short, and the occupation promised financial security. "You are going to study chemistry, and that's final!" countered Katharina, my childhood sweetheart to whom I have been married since 1966. My studies in Freiburg and Frankfurt went so well that the professors refunded the degree examination fees, saying it had been a pleasure to be my examiners. That same year I joined Bayer, where I worked in Krefeld-Uerdingen on optimizing polycarbonates.

The most important development was the material for the compact disc. I am particularly proud of this because it kind of fits in with my hobby: archeology. I am fascinated with how people archived information thousands of years ago using cuneiform script, hieroglyphics and coins. The oldest item in my collection dates back to 2000 B.C. and came from Iraq. The development of the CD follows in this tradition. From a stone to a plastic disc capable of storing the equivalent of 3,000 pages of information. That is progress.

Dieter Freitag

Dr. Dieter Freitag was born in Offenbach, Germany, in 1939. He has received numerous honors for his innovations, including the Otto Bayer Medal, the Hermann F. Mark Medal of the Austrian Ministry of Research and an honorary doctorate from the Russian Academy of Sciences. In 2000 he was named a corresponding member of the Accademia dei Georgofili in Florence, Italy, the world's oldest scientific academy. Induction into the Plastics Hall of Fame (2006) is one of the plastics industry's highest honors. This select circle includes Nobel laureates, chemical company founders and important inventors. Dieter Freitag is married and has two sons (one of whom died tragically following a traffic accident). His enthusiasm for the compact disc is still evident today from his car license plate, which includes the letters CD. He lives in a rural suburb of Krefeld, Germany.

The birth of the CD

THE DAY EVEN THE MAESTRO WAS FULL OF PRAISE

Salzburg, the historic city of Mozart, April 1982. Invitations were issued to a press conference that would be attended by the great conductor Herbert von Karajan. He presented a revolution in the shape of an aluminum-coated plastic disc weighing 16 grams and measuring 1.2 millimeters thick and 12 centimeters in diameter. The surface is covered with tiny pits that spiral out from the center. This disc takes sound to a whole new dimension. "Everything else is old hat," said a thrilled von Karajan. The first CD on the market featured his recording of Richard Strauss's "Alpine Symphony" with the Berlin Philharmonic. The technology came from Philips in the Netherlands, the material from Bayer's laboratories – a polycarbonate called Makrolon™ (see also the portrait of Dieter Freitag on page 316).

Initially, the innovation was met with some skepticism on the part of the public. Fans of vinyl, not wanting to part with their records, claimed CDs were too sterile, lacking color. Yet von Karajan, perfectionist and lover of pure sound that he was, was proved right. Barely five years later, the new technology had taken over. Never before had so many devices for playing music been sold, from high-end stereo systems through portable players to CD drives for computers. This was due not only to the new heights of audio quality that could be produced. The CD has also become an indispensable storage medium. The rewritable variant of the silver disc has established itself as the most important mass storage medium. Of course, development did not stop there. Hunting for ways to improve the handling of data-intensive videos, the entertainment industry worked feverishly on increasing storage capacities.

128

Compact disc

1982

In September 1995, the industry agreed on a uniform standard – the DVD. It has a capacity of 4.7 gigabytes (compared to 700 megabytes on a CD). Less than ten years later came the next advance – the Blu-ray Disc, which can store 45 gigabytes. This new medium is based on the same technology, but use lasers with shorter wavelengths so the discs can store more information in a smaller space. Bayer's researchers facilitated these developments – and thus the revolutionary advances in the entertainment industry – with new Makrolon™ grades characterized by higher purity and improved processing properties.

CDs and DVDs made from Makrolon™ are tested in Baytown, USA.

Johan Vanden Eynde loves his home city of Ghent on the banks of the Rivers Scheldt and Lys in Belgium, where his family has lived for many centuries. Here he enjoys a break in the Oude Vismijn restaurant.

129

Johan Vanden Eynde

Process technology

2006

The developments in polycarbonate production that were driven by Johan Vanden Eynde are groundbreaking in terms of energy efficiency and reductions in raw material and water consumption. They include the development of the world-scale polycarbonate plant at the Bayer Integrated Site Shanghai, China, which opened in 2006. There, polycarbonate is produced by the melt process.

THE ESTHETIC OF A FACTORY

Belgian Johan Vanden Eynde has been involved in the construction of production facilities around the world. He considers an industrial site to be a thing of beauty made from iron and steel.

I **enjoy working; I** work a lot and sleep little. In the mornings I get phone calls from colleagues in Asia, in the evenings from America. I cope well with stress. I'm responsible for the engineering, design and expansion of production facilities. Over my career, I've handled more than 50 projects ranging in size from laboratory pilot plants to industrial-scale facilities. These are all over the world – in Asia (Map Ta Phut, Thailand and Caojing, China); in North America (Baytown, Texas, United States); and in Europe (Krefeld-Uerdingen, Germany and Antwerp, Belgium). It doesn't matter how big the facility is, it's our duty to supply very high quality within a short time. If a production unit doesn't start up or breaks down, then things get expensive.

I'm also motivated to ensure the operational reliability of facilities and their compliance with the highest standards. To keep our employees safe, to protect the environment and to minimize consumption of raw materials and energy. As the member of a team, I'm involved in design, planning and commissioning. I'm also a troubleshooter for the fortunately rare problems that occur. In my job, I combine the roles of chemist (basic research), engineer (design and development), teacher (training) and psychologist (motivator). I really enjoy my job. It brings me recognition and an inner peace. I don't expect praise from supervisors or colleagues. Although that's nice, it's not particularly important. I'm convinced that we're nothing when we act alone. You need a team to get where you want to go. I was given a talent and I consider it my duty to make the best I can of it. I also enjoy mentoring young colleagues when they start out with the company.

> ***"I was given a talent and I consider it my duty to make the best I can of it. I want to develop something new, something that doesn't exist yet."***

The Vanden Eynde family has lived in Ghent for hundreds of years. My ancestors worked in artistic professions, as sculptors and painters. One of them – Balthasar – won medals from the Academy and lived in a historic building on the city's Korenmarkt. Perhaps my passion for my job has something to do with my family history. My father was a teacher and interior designer. Times weren't easy in the late 1960s. The Belgian economy was in a bad way and he didn't get many commissions. We lived in a working-class area on the edge of the city, close to a coal distribution center and the railway marshalling yard. The house had little in the way of luxury. There was no bathroom or central heating. I played soccer with the other boys in the neighborhood and we chased cows across the fields. That's how we spent our time. I have always wanted to lead a better life. Social betterment is a strong motivation. At school, I was especially good at math, physics and chemistry. I studied chemical engineering and then process engineering, which I enjoyed from the start. I'm attracted by the idea of developing something new and seeing how it takes shape. Even as a student, I worked on a new and innovative reaction vessel – fairly unusual for a student. I got more than a half-dozen job offers and chose to work for Bayer.

When producing my designs. I always have the concept and the shape in mind. Esthetics and balance are important to me. I like to have design articles and I'm fascinated by contemporary architecture. My family's home is well-designed down to the last detail and has been built in line with the principles of modern and functional architecture. In my job, I want to develop something new, something that doesn't exist yet, something that represents an improvement. The aim is to reduce energy and raw material consumption with a view to protecting the environment, achieving cost savings and ensuring sustainability. Every new facility I support from design through to start-up is a challenge. I feel a sense of responsibility.

Johan Vanden Eynde

Johan Vanden Eynde was born in Ghent, Belgium, in 1966. He received the Otto Bayer Medal in 2012 for the Melt Polycarbonate Technology project. Johan Vanden Eynde is married, has three children and lives in the city of his birth.

The evolution of Makrolon™

A NEW SUPER MATERIAL FOR BUSES, TRAMS, CARS, ...

Makrolon™ has changed the face of our world. This strong and transparent plastic is found in every car, home and office. But the potential of Hermann Schnell's invention (see page 314) is nowhere near exhausted. Bayer's researchers have mixed Makrolon™ with other polymers to produce blends, varying the properties to satisfy specific requirements. In 1975, they combined polycarbonate and acrylonitrile butadiene styrene (ABS) to create a material with very special properties: heat-resistant, tough, fire-resistant and easy to process.

130
Bayblend™
1975

Registered as a trademark in 1975, Bayblend™ became the material of choice in an era which saw a boom in computer and office technology. To this day, Bayblend™ is often used for the housings of copiers, printers and laptops. Because of its balanced property profile, it is also a favorite material of automotive engineers. Bayblend™ can be used for instrument panels and for the interior trim of buses and trams. Makrolon™ has become a major success story in the field of high-performance polymers. The future belongs to a combination of Makrolon™ and surface technologies. Bayer's scientists have optimized high-quality coatings for Makrolon™ components to produce scratch-resistant surfaces for outdoor applications. This opens an entirely new spectrum of uses for this plastic, including automotive glazing.

Thanks to new surface technologies, Makrolon™ can be used to make transparent car roofs.

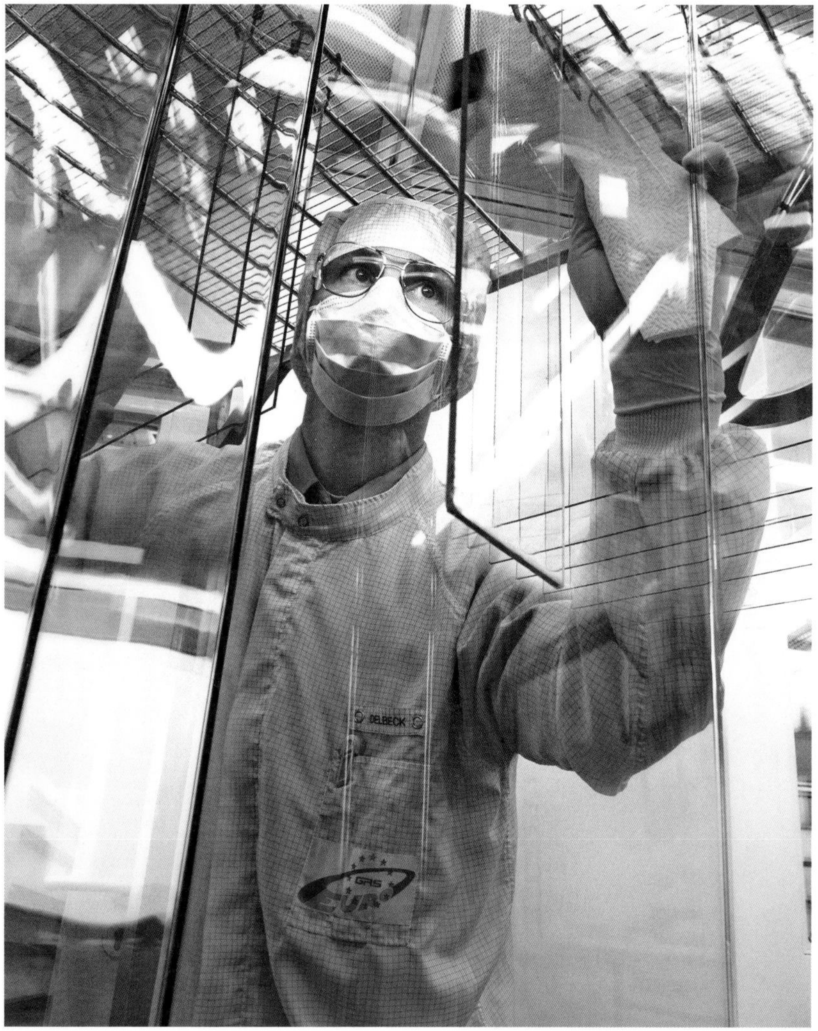

Bayer employee Michael Delbeck prepares polycarbonate sheets for a scratch-resistant coating.

Proud father: when he has time, Tobias Grömping goes for a walk with his children along the banks of the Wupper.

THE NEXT GENERATION

Tobias Grömping
Leverkusen, Germany
Bayer Technology Services

THE RESULT OF NEW PARTNERSHIPS

Cooperation is important to success in global competition. Tobias Grömping on his work for a European idea.

Research has changed. The individualist who is involved in everything from invention to production is the exception nowadays. Things are simply too complex, even for an all-round genius. We know there are many ideas out there – they're just waiting for the technology to be implemented. One example of how international companies now cooperate to achieve progress and reduce costs is the F^3 Factory. This is a project funded by the European Union, involving 26 partners from industry and research and coordinated by Bayer. It's not just a concept on paper but a project involving iron and steel. It's about process engineering and developing standardized modular production equipment in a container. The European companies are working together and learning from each other to improve their position in global competition. Yet, when it comes to details of their knowledge, they are careful to maintain the edge over their competitors. It's an interesting field and I'm the project manager. I'm a fan of the personal conversation. I'd rather sit down with a cup of coffee than send a quick message via BlackBerry. When it comes to communication, I'm old-fashioned.

Tobias Grömping

Dr. Tobias Grömping was born in Krefeld in 1975. His father and his brothers are process engineers. He is married, has two young children and lives with his family in Leverkusen, Germany.

The inventor of one of the most important crop protection products of our time: Shinzo Kagabu in historic Gifu City, close to the Nagara river

131

Shinzo Kagabu

Imidacloprid

1991

First approved for use in 1991, imidacloprid is a systemic insecticide from the group of the neonicotinoids. It can be used universally in almost all crops, including rice. Imidacloprid is taken up by the roots and transported to the leaves, which are then protected from sucking insects and some chewing insects. If applied directly to the leaves, it spreads between the upper and lower sides of the leaves and is then also transported to newly formed leaves (see also page 104).

THE VIRTUES OF THE MONKS

Shinzo Kagabu discovered one of the most important insecticides in the world. It was in a temple that he learned the discipline and perseverance with which he achieved his successes.

I**f you want** to be successful in research, you can do so almost anywhere. No matter where, no matter what the conditions. Some people wonder why I'm now a professor teaching at the education faculty of Gifu University in central Japan. I discovered one of the best-selling crop protection agents of our time: the substance class known as the neonicotinoids. Today, I train future teachers of chemistry for all types of school. The faculty is set up to train teachers and not to conduct scientific research. Our laboratory facilities are therefore somewhat modest. However, I am still researching as well. I need little to be able to achieve what I want. I tell my students: your environment is not important, your background, what you've achieved so far. You can do anything you set your mind on and there are no excuses.

My father died when I was still a baby and my mother and brother also became ill with tuberculosis. They became infected when we moved to a new company house – my father was a bank executive. Just after the end of the war, medicines were in short supply and hard times began for my family – I have two brothers and two sisters. We went to live with relatives in my mother's home city of Akita in northern Japan. I don't recall much from this time; I only remember a small room where the five of us slept. I was sent to an orphanage when I was six. After the war, there were a lot of orphans in Japan. There were 50 children in a few plain rooms. My mother also died soon after my tenth birthday. Then I was adopted by a monk from a Zen temple. Four novice monks lived with him and his family. It was my task to keep the temple clean and make sure there was hot water for bathing. I got up at six o'clock every morning, swept and cleaned, fetched firewood, went to school, then swept and cleaned again and fetched firewood. My room was small and there was no heating. It was often very cold in the winter months. I immersed myself in my books and warmed my hands on the light bulb. What I learned at that time was incredibly valuable: I learned discipline and perseverance.

The monk who adopted me died but I also got along well with his successor. He wanted me to become a monk but I didn't want to. My passion lay with the sciences, especially chemistry. I found it fascinating to observe how substances can be transformed, how they change their color or physical state. I'm not a particularly religious person, I have to say, but I do like one concept in Buddhism: a dewdrop on lotus leaves, large or small, reflects the world equally because it is spherical. My teacher visited the monk at the temple to convince him that education was the right route for me. The monk agreed and I was offered the chance to attend the prestigious Tohoku University in Sendai. During my studies, I was impressed by the work of Professor Prinzbach, whom I was able to meet at a conference in Sendai. I told him of my wish to be allowed to study in his laboratory and was on cloud nine when he agreed. The Lions Club of Akita paid my travel expenses, for which I am grateful to this day.

Feeds the world, but especially Asia: rice.

It was my first trip outside Japan. I flew via Rome to Zurich and then on to Basel. I felt like I was in a dream, shaken by a mixture of anticipation, expectation and fear. Everything was so different in Freiburg, this old city, it was like being in a fairytale. I was welcomed warmly but had problems communicating at the start. Although I found formulae easy, German grammar was very difficult for me. I did my PhD under the supervision of Prinzbach, who had good contacts with Leverkusen and put me in touch with someone at Bayer. I was very impressed by my visit to the site, the size of the company, the clear structures. My training in Elberfeld lasted one year and then I was sent back to Japan to a small laboratory on the outskirts of Tokyo. I wasn't ungrateful for this because I had met my wife Misako in Freiburg, a young woman from Japan who was studying German music there. We wanted to settle in our home country with our young family – our daughters were born in Freiburg and Wuppertal. My enthusiasm for research had now been fully kindled. I spent every day in the laboratory and worked overtime. I performed twice as many experiments as my colleagues. One could say that I lived like a monk. I was looking for an insecticide based on nithiazine to control sucking pests. We knew a group in the United States was working on the same thing.

"I'm proud that our research findings have improved the lives of many people."

February 1984: experiment number E3642 brought the breakthrough. In contrast to the Americans, who wanted to use nithiazine to control chewing insects, our small research group followed our intuition that it would be more effective against sucking pests. In tests, E3642 proved to be one hundred times more effective than comparable substances. We were so surprised that we tested it dozens of times because we just couldn't believe this high level of efficacy. Dr. Kuyama, who headed the institute at the time, came to me and cried: "Well done! You've done a fantastic job!" I was so excited, I couldn't sleep that night.

We had advanced research. One year later, we succeeded in finding a more practical derivative named imidacloprid which, since its market launch in 1991, has become the best-selling insecticide in the world. We also identified another insecticide named thiacloprid and the fungicide carpropamid. If we had complacently stopped our efforts, we would have been nothing more than a kind of generous pioneer pointing the way for others. If you want to achieve your goal, you have to stay determined.

There are areas of research which gain applause from the public. The search for pesticides is not one of them, as I've found out. I believe I've looked into cold eyes even if it was people who have praised our products. I tend to weigh up the advantages and disadvantages of each new technology and I critically question our own research activities. I'm proud to be able to say that our research findings have improved the lives of many people. When I pass a rice field, for example, I'm pleased to think I've helped the farmer. My own experiences have taught me not to simply accept other people's opinions but to make up my own mind. On the basis of facts and not prejudice.

Shinzo Kagabu

Dr. Shinzo Kagabu was born in Fukushima in 1946. In his free time, he enjoys dancing with his wife Misako. Shinzo Kagabu has received many prizes for his pioneering work, including the Otto Bayer Medal and the American Chemical Society Award. He has two daughters and lives in Gifu, Japan.

The importance of rice

SMART BREEDING FOR BETTER RICE

Rice is one of the most important grains in the world. It is traditionally the main staple food in Asia, home to half of the world's population. Oryza sativa, as it is known to scientists, provides food security and ensures political stability because it is consumed almost entirely by the countries where it is grown. Only a fraction of the world's harvest is exported. Yet, rice as a crop is facing a crisis: droughts, flooding, extreme temperature fluctuations and pests are a growing threat to harvests while, at the same time, the world's population is exploding.

132

Arize™

2012

Rice is facing a crisis but new methods offer hope.

The number of people living on Earth is expected to increase from seven billion today to more than nine billion by 2050, with disproportionately high birth rates in Asia. The Food and Agriculture Organization of the United Nations (FAO) has therefore called upon the international community and the private sector to "decisively step up investment in science and technology for food." According to estimates, an additional eight to ten million tons of rice will have to be harvested every year to safeguard the world's food supply. One product that could play a crucial role in this situation was launched by Bayer CropScience in 2012. Arize™ 6444 Gold is a hybrid rice which increases yields by 20 to 30 percent and more compared to conventional varieties. It is also resistant to bacterial leaf blight, a devastating disease which has led to serious harvest losses in India, for example.

Arize™ 6444 Gold has been developed by Bayer using marker-assisted selection (MAS) – also known as smart breeding. Molecular biological processes are used to pinpoint the gene or gene variant that is responsible for a certain property. The offspring of a crossed variety can then be tested to see whether they contain the gene that was added. Only those plants with the desired gene are left to grow. Researchers no longer have to rely on the visual assessment of a plant to determine if and to what extent it has inherited a property. Genetic analysis is more conclusive – and saves valuable time.

Bayer's researchers now have thousands of genetic markers in their database. Each one represents a specific gene sequence and is typical for certain properties in the rice plant. Many markers have been described in published literature; others were identified by the scientists themselves. Analyzing a plant's genes using biochemical methods is like analyzing fingerprints.

The new methods even have the potential to prevent plagues of biblical proportions. At present, scientists are working to develop a rice variety that will be unpalatable to a certain species of plant hoppers, swarms of which can devastate vast areas of land. Another new variety can survive under water for 14 days – when other plants would suffocate. The gene that was added is activated by a lack of oxygen and could one day protect the food source for many millions of people in flooded coastal regions.

Nativo™ – a favorite fungicide

MORE THAN JUST PROTECTION AGAINST FUNGAL DISEASES

At first, healthy green leaves turn rust-brown. Within just a few weeks, the plants lose their leaves altogether. However, farmers don't have to stand by and watch helplessly when their fields are hit by fungal diseases. There's a fungicide which can help them in the fight to control aggressive fungal pathogens.

Nativo™ is a combination of two innovative substances and has a dual mechanism of action. In the first instance, it both protects the plants and controls fungal diseases. Secondly, it has a number of other beneficial effects. Crop plants treated with Nativo™ are healthier and stronger, producing a higher yield. They also have greater tolerance to stress factors such as drought, heat and frost. The Nativo™ product family, launched in 2004, accounts for a significant proportion of the Bayer CropScience fungicides business – making it by far the most important product family. It includes the main brands Fox™ and Stratego™ YLD, which have been approved for use in 100 crops.

133

Nativo™

2004

Rice farmers in Asia, for example, rely on the positive effects of these crop protection products. And in Brazil, the world's number one exporter of orange juice, farmers use Nativo™ to keep their fruit crops healthy. It not only protects the citrus fruit against fungal infection, but also increases juice yields and sugar content.

Vietnamese farmers Huynh Thi Chieu and Phan Minh Phat (right) from Long An province are pleased with their good harvest.

Problem grasses

SECURING RICE'S FUTURE

E**chinochloa crus-galli** – or cockspur – is just one example. It shares a common ancestry with rice and has a huge resemblance to rice but it also has one crucial drawback: it likes to grow in exactly the same place as rice. Grass weeds like this are a significant threat to farmers' yields because they crowd out the rice. Cockspur can reach a height of almost two meters so it quite literally overgrows the crop.

134

Triafamone

2014

The new rice herbicide triafamone could solve this problem. Triafamone belongs to the group of sulfonanilides and was first synthesized by Bayer CropScience. It is an acetolactate synthase inhibitor that intervenes in the synthesis of amino acids and impairs the weed's protein and enzyme production. Tests conducted since 2007 have shown that triafamone successfully controls weed grasses in both directly sown and transplanted rice. It is easy to use and has good environmental compatibility. First marketing authorizations are expected in 2014.

Nutritious snack: rice is the most important food throughout Asia.

Protection against fungal pathogens

STRENGTHENING THE IMMUNE SYSTEM

I**t's cold.** Next to no sun. And very damp. Perfect conditions for the fungal pathogen Pyricularia oryzae to spread. It attaches itself to seedlings, infects stalks, panicles and grain, and causes the plant to wilt or die. Rice blast, as the disease is known, is the most economically significant disease in rice. It can occur at all growth stages and in almost all growing regions. In 2010, Bayer CropScience launched a fungicide in South Korea and Japan containing the active substance isotianil which had been jointly developed with the Japanese company Sumitomo Chemical Co. Ltd. Isotianil belongs to the chemical class of isothiazoles. It stimulates the natural defense mechanisms of rice plants, thus increasing their resistance. For the first time, a substance has been found that can be applied in small quantities yet nonetheless offers optimum protection – effective and environmentally friendly at the same time. It is all the more important given that very few substances worldwide are approved for controlling rice blast.

135

Isotianil

2010

Bayer supports Mekong rice farmers

IT'S THE QUALITY THAT MATTERS

Throughout its history, Bayer has always been innovative when it comes to attracting customers' interest for its products. When an employee survey suggested that the company should raise its consumer proximity, a large number of projects were initiated worldwide. One of these is the Much More Rice (MMR) program launched by Bayer CropScience in November 2012 and targeting rice farmers in Vietnam's Mekong Delta. It's an example of how a global enterprise can understand and address small-scale farmers' needs.

136

Much More Rice

2012

Vietnam is a major rice producer but the country's farmers repeatedly face climate-related problems – drought alternates with flooding. The MMR Program focuses on minimizing risk and maximizing return on investment. Scientifically designed and developed by Bayer's rice experts, MMR combines the efficient use of integrated crop protection and improved agronomic practices. Results have shown that Much More Rice increases yields by around 10 percent, enhances grain quality and improves farmers' profit by 20 percent compared to current farming practices. MMR benefits are derived not only from efficient protection against weeds, pests and diseases but also the plant health effects of Bayer's solutions for rice. In order to enhance yield potential, Arize™ hybrid rice seed is now included in the MMR program, thereby further improving yield and farm income. Sustainability is the lynch pin of the program, with Bayer CropScience offering partnerships to farmers and local authorities. The company's experts travel extensively through the Mekong Delta, visiting rice farmers and explaining how they can make the most effective use of their inputs. They also give practical tips for increasing yields. In these visits to the rice fields, the experts learn about the problems the farmers face on a daily basis. They also glean ideas for research projects, for example the development of new hybrid rice seed with improved resistance to pests, diseases and other stress factors. Good personal relationships are built between the farmers and experts, but the fact remains that the quality of the product is what matters. Farmers are only convinced by positive experiences – either their own or those of a neighbor.

In the first two months, more than 10,000 rice farmers actively participated in the program. The government has endorsed MMR as a preferred best practice in rice farming.

Much More Rice: with this initiative launched in 2012, Bayer supports rice farmers like Doan Thi Hong and Phan Minh Phat (right).

Marc Bots likes music and used to play in his own band. He enjoys browsing at his favorite record store in Ghent.

THE NEXT GENERATION

Marc Bots

Ghent, Belgium

Bayer CropScience

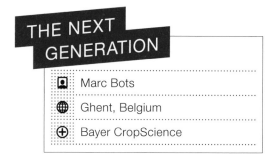

THE SOUND OF TOMORROW

Marc Bots belongs to the next generation of scientists. He doesn't want his dreams to stay that way for long.

I **don't intend** to spend my life in research. Established scientists have made a conscious decision to follow this path time and again throughout their careers. I don't have that kind of dedication. I want to get on, do something different – still related to research but more on the management side. I like bringing exciting people together and creating a good climate for innovation: an openness to ideas and creativity but also to contradiction. We're facing an enormous challenge. It's our job to safeguard the food supply for billions of people. We're capable of amazing achievements – for example, genetically modifying plants to make them resistant to insect pests. It's one thing that this is not appreciated in public debate. However, it annoys me when I have the feeling that there is a fundamental lack of trust in what we're doing. "I'm not a bad person and I'm not poisoning the world" – that's sometimes a basis for discussion with friends. My dream is to help make the world a better place and I stand by that.

Marc Bots

Born in Rotterdam, the Netherlands, in 1975, Marc Bots is Group Leader Molecular Biology at Bayer CropScience in Ghent, Belgium. In his free time he likes to play soccer and he loves music. Marc Bots lives with his girlfriend in Ghent. They have one daughter.

The deck of a tall ship is familiar territory for Fritz Gestermann. He went to sea as a young man, but then became a research scientist. The photo was taken on the four-masted bark Passat in the Baltic port of Travemünde.

137

Fritz Gestermann

Oxygen depolarized cathode

1994

The oxygen depolarized cathode cuts energy consumption in chloralkali electrolysis by around 30 percent – thus also reducing CO_2 emissions from power plants. When using hydrochloric acid electrolysis, the reduction is between 30 and 40 percent. Development of the technology started in 1994 and it has received numerous awards, including the U.S. Electrochemical Society's New Electrochemical Technology Award (Quebec, 2005) and the Environmental Prize of the Federation of German Industry in 2008. The first industrial-scale plant of this kind was commissioned at the Brunsbüttel site in 2003; others are now in operation worldwide.

THE LESSONS OF THE SEA

As a young officer cadet on the "Gorch Fock," Fritz Gestermann found out what it means to ride out a storm. They were experiences that also helped him in his career as a research scientist.

The storm is now so strong that I have to turn my face away from the wind to breathe. I'm standing on a steel cable, 45 meters above the deck of the sail training vessel "Gorch Fock." I've just secured the sail and I'm now holding on with all my strength. The three-masted bark is rolling heavily to both sides. It takes extreme concentration not to lose my grip. A force 11 in the Bay of Biscay, the dreaded sea area off the west coast of France. We've run into a really deep depression on our way home to Kiel. Some other cadets and I have volunteered to go aloft with one of our training officers. We're to take in the topmost sail, the royal, which is beating around in the wind. When we want to return to the mast, we realize with horror that one of our comrades is panicking. His eyes are wide open, he's white as a ghost and he's shivering. He's scared to death. Now it's really dangerous – for him and for us.

What if he loses his nerve? Grabs at us? Or jumps? I watch as the training officer yells something at him and holds a knife up to his face in threat. I can't understand a word because the storm is just too loud. Luckily the man relaxes slightly and stares at our trainer. He signals to us to climb past the man. We make it with the last of our strength. What I experienced at sea in December 1965 has stayed with me and also influenced my career in research and development. Keep going and don't lose your nerve. These thoughts are engraved in my mind. My family has a strong relationship with the sea. My uncle Ernst, a small man, was a well-known captain in the merchant navy who as a young sailor rounded Cape Horn on the legendary four-masted bark "Priwall." But a career at sea was not for me. I couldn't see the sense in some of the orders I heard on the "Gorch Fock."

Resorting to theory

When I went to university after my time in the Navy, I quite literally soaked up knowledge. I studied physics, did a PhD, found a job in reactor technology and worked on the development of fast breeders and pebble-bed reactors. Then the Chernobyl disaster happened and I decided that the industry had no future. I applied to Bayer and got a job in power generation. I was considered an outsider. During a chance encounter, a Management Board member gave me the brief: "Make chlorine cheaper!"

In the chlorine production plant I had no laboratory, not even a computer at the start. I resorted to theory. Chlorine – used in the production of high-quality plastics, for example – made cheaper: a virtually impossible task. Not least because I knew absolutely nothing about electrolytic processes. A chemical engineer helped and I had an idea, still quite vague: perhaps we could do something with a fuel cell. I worked out a theory, presented it and was allowed to continue working on it. I had no budget and I still had no laboratory of my own but working with some technicians I'd made friends with, we found a way. We "borrowed" some old apparatus and experimented under the simplest conditions in someone else's laboratory while the lab manager was away on a medical cure. We built a palm-sized electrolytic cell which was fed oxygen via an oxygen depolarized cathode (ODC) we had developed. At the first attempt we produced chlorine and sodium hydroxide solution without hydrogen and the voltage in the cell decreased.

In the end, it was a race against a Japanese research team which we won. Our prototype – the first on an industrial scale in the world – was working in the summer of 1998 and the initial results were overwhelming. My idea really worked! I had an incredible feeling of happiness. In the evening, the team celebrated in our garden. It was a warm summer evening, we lit a fire and cooked soup together. I saw it as a triumph for the team. All the technicians, lab assistants and plant operators who were involved in the project identified with it so strongly that they didn't care about the overtime. I was aware that my experiences at sea helped me overcome some opposition. You simply can't give up. Especially not when you've got a storm blowing straight in your face.

Fritz Gestermann

Dr. Fritz Gestermann was born in 1944 and grew up in the village of Neuenhaus near Leverkusen. His first career choice was farmer. The PhD physicist received numerous awards, including the Otto Bayer Medal (1999), for the oxygen depolarized cathode. Today he is an enthusiastic beekeeper and balloonist, he enjoys sailing and is greatly interested in astrophysics. Fritz Gestermann is married, has two children and lives in Leverkusen, Germany.

For clean wastewater

ENVIRONMENTALLY FRIENDLY, EFFICIENT AND LARGELY ODOR-FREE

E**urope's largest industrial** wastewater treatment plant in Dormagen, Germany, was put into operation by Bayer and Erdölchemie in 1971. It was followed in the same year by Bayer's communal wastewater treatment facility in the Bürrig district of Leverkusen, which is used jointly by six communities in the Wupper Regional Association (with a total of 375,000 residents). Although it reflected increased environmental awareness in both the public and industrial domains, treating biodegradable wastewater in large conventional aeration basins takes up a lot of space, is loud and stinks. A system that combined optimal effectiveness, cost-efficiency and ecological benefit did not yet exist.

In 1980 Bayer presented the solution: Tower Biology™. Four turquoise-blue clarification tanks were built in Bürrig at a cost of 127 million German marks. They are 31 meters high and look like reactors. Ringing the upper edge and hidden by silver-gray cladding are funnel-shaped overflow basins for treated water and sewage sludge. At the start, the facility's daily capacity was 90,000 tons and the annual operating costs came to 60 million marks. Bayer's Tower Biology™ technology proved that biological wastewater treatment is possible on a small surface area in a process that is largely noise- and odor-free. Moreover, the eco-friendly innovation is more efficient, costing 75 percent less than previous systems. Biological wastewater treatment uses bacteria which need oxygen and other substances to survive.

In Tower Biology™, first used in 1977 at the Bayer site in Brunsbüttel, oxygen is not fed to a large area from above, as in a conventional treatment plant. Instead, tiny oxygen bubbles are forced into the process from the base through injectors specially developed by Bayer engineers. This gives the air a larger contact area and it spends longer in the aeration tank. The result is a higher degree of efficiency, lower oxygen input and less off-gas. All of these are cost-cutting factors. The investment volume is also lower so it is little wonder that Tower Biology™ technology has been implemented at Bayer sites worldwide.

138
Tower Biology™
1977

Futuristic: Two towers for biological wastewater treatment in Leverkusen

The power plant in 1926: 12 Hanomag boilers were operated at a temperature of 380 degrees Celsius and overpressure of 30 bar, each producing 18 tons of steam per hour. They were supplemented by a Lamont boiler producing 35 tons of steam per hour. The introduction of combined heat and power technology meant that the plant generated 75 kilowatt hours of electricity in addition to heating reaction vessels. Nothing like it had been constructed before at an industrial production site.

Advanced power technology

INNOVATION IN G BLOCK

In the late 19th century, each production area at Bayer's new Leverkusen site had its own boiler house. There were 13 in all with a total of 113 steam boilers. However, wear and tear soon resulted in high maintenance costs. The different boiler types required a lot of spare parts. It was decided to construct a new power plant in G block. Critics said this would be too big, too complex and too modern. The new power plant came into service in 1926, setting new standards. It produced energy more efficiently than its predecessors, lowered fuel consumption and reduced Bayer's dependence on electricity from the public grid. Combined heat and power technology soon became the norm at all Bayer sites and at other industrial facilities. Although Power Plant G had to be supplemented in 1936 by Power Plant Y and in 1955 by Power Plant G-South, it nonetheless marked the introduction of efficiency-oriented and eco-friendly energy policies at Bayer.

139
Power plant G
1926

Creativity pays

A BRAINWAVE AT LUNCH

Summer 1988. Thomas Baumgarten, a waste incinerator foreman at Environmental Services (today: Currenta), came up with the idea during his lunch break. Baumgarten is interested in engines. He knows that an internal combustion engine with a large combustion chamber works more efficiently with twin-spark ignition – two spark plugs in each cylinder – than a system with one spark plug. If this principle works for motorcycles and cars, why shouldn't it work for his incinerator where liquid waste is burned?

Bayer established its employee suggestion plan in 1903. In 1988, this was expanded to include suggestions relating to environmental protection. According to an in-house circular at the time, the company's main objective is "to motivate all employees to greater environmental awareness." Since then, environmental protection has been an integral aspect of Bayer's training programs. Compulsory seminars are also offered, covering issues such as reducing emissions and saving energy.

140
Environmental Bonus
1988

Two are better than one.

This brings us back to Thomas Baumgarten. Even before his lunch break was over, he had completed a rough sketch. His idea was to double the number of burners in the incinerator. Whereas previously only one type of waste could be burned by the incinerator at any one time, now two types of waste could be incinerated simultaneously. This made it possible to combine liquids with a high and low calorific value. Formerly, heating oil had to be added to ensure full incineration of wastes that do not burn easily. Bayer implemented Thomas Baumgarten's idea. Thanks to this process optimization, heating oil consumption was cut by 1.2 million liters and CO_2 emissions reduced by 4,300 tons each year. Baumgarten was rewarded with the Environmental Bonus.

Bayer development sets standards worldwide

LEVERKUSEN'S CLEAN AIR

S**ulfuric acid, H_2SO_4**. Colorless, oily, viscous, hygroscopic and highly corrosive. It is one of the most important chemicals, used in the manufacture of paper, fertilizers, dyestuffs, synthetic fibers, foams, detergents, soaps and many other products besides.

Nearly 200 million tons of sulfuric acid are produced annually worldwide. To start with, pyrite, elemental sulfur or some other raw material containing sulfur is burned to obtain sulfur dioxide, which is oxidized by contact with oxygen to yield sulfur trioxide. This is combined with water to form sulfuric acid. In this method, known as the contact process, only 97 to 98 percent of the sulfur dioxide reacts. The remainder is emitted into the atmosphere with the off-gas. Or at least it was for many years, until Bayer developed a new process that largely eliminated this problem.

141

Double-contact plant

1964

Scientists and engineers worked on the innovation for ten years and spent three years testing it in a pilot plant. Finally, in 1964, the world's first double-contact plant came into operation in Leverkusen. The sulfur dioxide is exposed to the contact process twice, with the result that 99.6 percent of the chemical reacts and air pollution is reduced by about 90 percent.

Double-contact plants are now the standard in sulfuric acid production worldwide. As a result, industrial sites like Leverkusen where the substance is produced boast better air quality than most large cities.

Monitoring emissions

AN EYE FOR THE ENVIRONMENT

T**he television camera** with variable optics detects visible emissions. It was installed in Leverkusen in 1965. Air quality is monitored by a special van which tours the site. Sensors are installed on smoke stacks and outlets. Air quality at the Leverkusen and Dormagen sites is monitored at 50 checkpoints. The data are analyzed centrally by computer – standard today but innovative in 1965.

142

Environmental camera

1965

Environmental protection in the early years

RHINE WATER IN 1901

A **group of** dignified gentlemen met in Leverkusen on November 5, 1901. This was the Wastewater Commission, headed by Professor Curt Weigelt, that was to go down in history. For the first time, an industrial company voluntarily committed to monitoring its own activities. Just six months later, it issued a report criticizing the "irregular discharge of wastewater" and "the high concentration of the discharged acids." Bayer reacted by constructing collection tanks, improving the sewerage system and reducing the use of sulfuric acid in production. In 1904, the Commission registered a decrease in acid discharge of 77.3 percent compared to December 1901. Their work became a model for all Bayer sites.

143

Wastewater Commission

1901

Modern system invented in 1964: the double-contact plant reduced dust emissions from sulfuric acid production by almost 90 percent.

Smart both ecologically and economically

PRODUCING ESSENTIAL CHLORINE COST-EFFICIENTLY

H**igh-grade plastics** wouldn't exist without chlorine. At Bayer MaterialScience, chlorine is an essential component in 80 percent of all products. For many years, the chemical industry used standard membrane electrolysis to manufacture chlorine on the basis of common salt or hydrochloric acid. In this process, the raw materials are converted into chlorine, sodium hydroxide solution and hydrogen by the application of an electric current.

144

ODC technology

2003

By contrast, the oxygen depolarized cathode (ODC) technology developed by Bayer doesn't generate hydrogen as a by-product. (Read more about its inventor, Fritz Gestermann, starting on page 336.) Instead, the oxygen is added via a gas diffusion electrode (cathode). It is reduced at the cathode and hydroxide ions are produced by reaction with water. This decreases the electrode's potential and the electrolysis voltage by one-third – the same applies to the electricity consumption. As well as being economically efficient, this also benefits the environment – lower electricity consumption means lower CO_2 emissions.

The first industrial ODC facility came into operation in Brunsbüttel in 2003 with an annual capacity of 20,000 tons of chlorine. A major facility with an annual capacity of 220,000 tons was built in China in 2008. That same year, the Federation of German Industry selected this technology as winner of its Environment Award; the reduction in CO_2 at the time was in the region of 2.3 million tons in Germany alone. Manufacturing chlorine from hydrochloric acid offers an additional advantage. In the chemical industry, hydrochloric acid is often a by-product – for example, in the manufacture of polyurethanes. With this kind of recycling, the energy saving achieved using ODC technology is actually as high as 40 percent.

Bayer employee Jörg Bäther performs a routine check of the oxygen depolarized cathode at the Bayer site in Brunsbüttel, northern Germany.

Polyurethane made from CO_2

A DREAM REACTION FOR SOLVING REAL PROBLEMS

Organic chemistry is based on carbon. The primary source of this element is petroleum, which is becoming increasingly scarce worldwide. When petroleum is burned, it releases carbon dioxide which is a threat to the global climate. For this reason, chemists have long been searching for ways to replace fossil raw materials and put the greenhouse gas CO_2 to good use. Bayer researchers have succeeded in doing just that in the Dream Production project. They have incorporated carbon dioxide into the molecular structure of polyurethanes (PU).

The Dream Production project is sponsored by Bayer together with energy company RWE, RWTH Aachen University and the CAT Catalytic Center, an institute run jointly by the university and Bayer. It is another example of the potential for collaboration between industry and academia. The new process, launched in 2011, uses carbon dioxide extracted from the off-gas of an RWE power plant in Niederaussem, near Cologne. This is liquefied and transported in containers to a pilot plant in Leverkusen. There the CO_2 is combined with propylene oxide to produce a light-colored, viscous polyol, one of the two building blocks in polyurethanes. Considering that some 13 million tons of polyurethanes are currently manufactured each year, it is clear that this successful research could represent a major step forward in reducing oil consumption. But there is one problem. Carbon dioxide is very stable chemically, so it reacts with very few other substances. It is therefore extremely difficult to incorporate into polymers, which has always been the obstacle to its use in plastics manufacturing. Until a few years ago that is, when a team of researchers at Bayer succeeded in developing a zinc catalyst that facilitates the efficient use of CO_2. This was the cornerstone for the success of the Dream Production project. Industrial production is scheduled to begin in 2015. The Dream Production project took third place in the 2011 German Sustainability Award, and was ranked seventh out of ten finalists by the public vote in the "Germany – Land of Ideas" competition in 2012.

145

Dream Production

2011

Researcher Daniela d'Elia (Aachen University) and Dr. Christoph Gürtler (project manager at Bayer MaterialScience) view a scanning electron micrograph of a super-absorbent foam.

Innovative aircraft

AROUND THE WORLD IN A SOLAR PLANE

Harnessing the sun's power to fly around the world, without fuel, 100 percent emission-free. This is the ambitious goal of Swiss pioneers Bertrand Piccard and André Borschberg. They initiated the Solar Impulse project to develop an aircraft that defies all previous conventions. Bayer has been an official partner to the project since 2010 and researchers in Leverkusen, Dormagen and Krefeld-Uerdingen are working hard on product and technology solutions. One material that is to be used is Baytherm™ Microcell polyurethane foam, which is characterized by its outstanding insulating capacity. Highly efficient insulation is particularly important for the aircraft because it must withstand temperature fluctuations between minus 40 degrees Celsius at night and plus 60 degrees during the day.

146

Solar Impulse

2010

Bayer has also supplied special foams for the wing tips, engine nacelles and cockpit, as well as high-grade polycarbonate films for the cockpit windows, and adhesives and coatings for the cabin and wings. The first model, the HB-SIA, has the wingspan of an Airbus A340 (63.4 meters), but weighs only as much as a mid-range passenger car (1,600 kilograms). The revolutionary aircraft is equipped with 12,000 solar cells that power four electric motors and charge four lithium-polymer batteries, enabling the HB-SIA to also fly at night. It took off on its maiden flight in April 2010, making its first nighttime flight two months later. Since then pilot André Borschberg has journeyed to international destinations such as Brussels and Paris. A second aircraft is already planned and will be even stronger and lighter than its predecessor. The HB-SIB is scheduled to fly around the world in several stages in 2015. "I would like to encourage people to use environmentally friendly technologies," says Bertrand Piccard. "By using these technologies in a wide variety of applications, we could cut oil consumption by as much as 50 percent right now." Proof of Piccard's claim is that the technologies developed for the project can already be transferred to many areas of everyday life. They improve energy efficiency in computers, refrigerators and cars.

Pioneer: Bertrand Piccard from Switzerland with a model of his life's dream

Around the world without fuel: the Solar Impulse has a wingspan equal to that of an Airbus A340, yet is as light as a mid-sized car. The aim is to fly around the world in several stages in 2015. Here, the aircraft is shown flying over San Francisco, California, USA.

On the trail of innovative materials: at the Polymer Innovation Center in Shanghai, China, development engineer Yilan Li tests headlamp lenses made from lightweight plastics.

Cars are becoming lighter

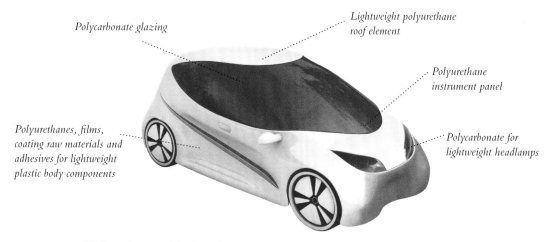

High-tech materials from Bayer for electric cars:
From coating raw materials and adhesives to body components, the experts at Bayer MaterialScience have come up with many innovative options for the electromobility of the future.

Bayer MaterialScience

SOUND INSULATION MADE FROM POLYURETHANE CAN MAKE CARS 50% QUIETER.

ISOPA

WEIGHT REDUCTION
The use of polycarbonate glazing can cut a car's weight by up to 50% compared with conventional glass components.

Bayer MaterialScience

Polycarbonates for CDs, DVDs, etc.
(in kilotons)

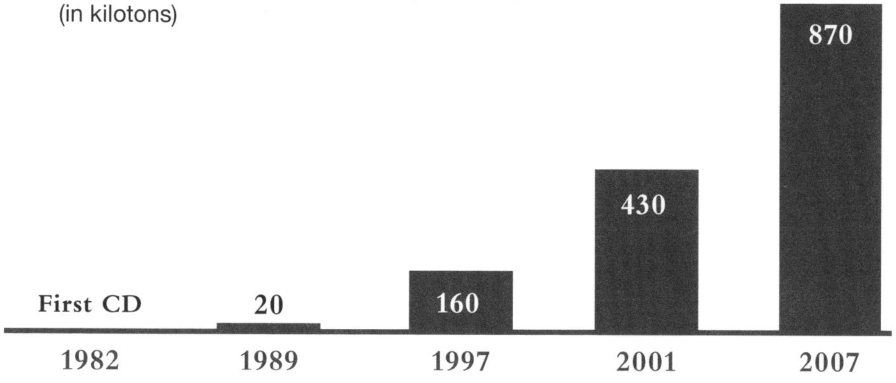

Between 1982 and 2007 alone, more than 90 billion optical data storage media were manufactured from Bayer's Makrolon™ polycarbonate.

Bayer MaterialScience

Cutting heating oil consumption (per square meter)

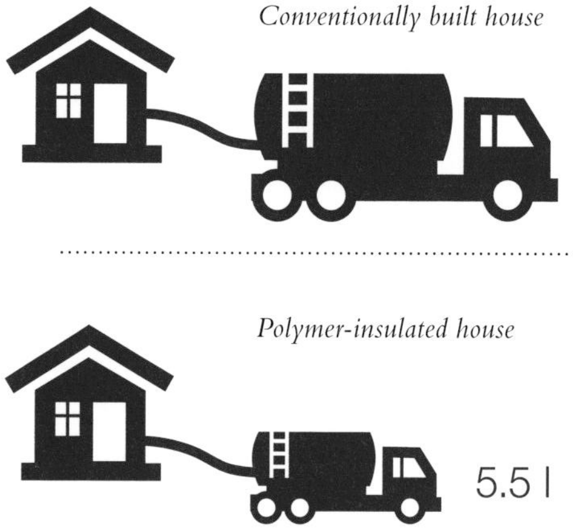

PlasticsEurope

The view across Aachen from the cathedral: Alexandra Grosse Böwing (left) and Martina Peters met as students. Today, they both work for Bayer and are still friends.

THE NEXT GENERATION

A. Grosse Böwing & M. Peters

Antwerp, Belgium & Leverkusen, Germany

Bayer MaterialScience & Bayer Technology Services

FRIENDS IN RESEARCH

They used to meet after class in a bar called "Kaktus." Today, Alexandra Grosse Böwing and Martina Peters work on key issues for the future. Two women linked by more than their job.

We met and made friends in the laboratory. The course of our lives has a number of things in common. We were both inspired by our teachers to pursue chemistry. We both liked spending our free time in Cologne and already had mutual friends before we met each other. The bars in Aachen back then were called "Kaktus," "Kittel" and "Kiste." We enjoyed our student years and life was intimate in the old city. Today, we're working together again on some projects like the major issue for the future: using carbon dioxide instead of oil as the base product for polymers. We're no longer researchers in the strictest sense of the term but operate more as ambassadors at the interface between science, production and public relations. In our area of activity, it's not always about facts but a matter of intuition. We bring the right people together at the right time. And we in particular are always pleased to see each other.

Alexandra Grosse Böwing & Martina Peters

Dr. Alexandra Grosse Böwing was born in Düsseldorf in 1977 and grew up in Dormagen. She is a technology manager in Process Development in the Polycarbonates Business Unit of Bayer MaterialScience and lives in Antwerp, Belgium.
Dr. Martina Peters was born in 1980 and comes from Bitburg in the Eifel region. She is a chemist at Bayer Technology Services in Leverkusen, where she heads the Chemical Catalysis group.

TRANSPARENCY AND A DYNAMIC TRADITION – A GLOBAL BRAND IN THE BEST LIGHT

The Bayer Cross: a symbol that is familiar around the world and not just in Leverkusen. This illuminated sign is to be found at Cologne Airport.

Leverkusen, Germany

Bellinzona, Switzerland

Osaka, Japan

Pacasmayo, Peru

Leverkusen, Germany

Cairo, Egypt

Sofia, Bulgaria

Chaux de Fonds, Switzerland

Gas station, Leverkusen site

Bayer is founded in Barmen

THE IDEA OF A DYER AND A MERCHANT

Bayer was founded on the talents of two men. Friedrich Bayer provided the commercial skills, while Johann Friedrich Weskott had the chemical knowledge. They had both already achieved some prosperity before "Friedr. Bayer et comp." was entered in the Commercial Register of Elberfeld District Court on August 7, 1863. Bayer was the son of a silk worker who started trading natural dyestuffs when he was 20. His business connections reached from New York to St. Petersburg. At the same time, Weskott – the third child of 13 whose father was a dyer of natural yarns – was making a name for himself with his dyestuffs.

When the innovative new aniline dyestuffs appeared on the market in the early 1860s, it was Bayer who recognized their commercial potential. But before they were presented to an enthusiastic public at the Great London Exposition in 1862, Bayer had obtained samples for demonstration to his customers – and had been ridiculed for "the new-fangled stuff." It was this ridicule which spurred him on. In the evenings, he sat with his friend Johann Friedrich Weskott in the Hotel zur Pfalz in Barmen (now a district of Wuppertal), trying to think of how to produce the dyestuffs. The two men spent the day in the kitchen cooking up chemicals.

147

Company founded

1863

Soon they discovered the secret to manufacturing fuchsine, named after the blue-red blossoms of the fuchsia. Bayer and Weskott decided to go into business together. The company's first headquarters was the dyestuff warehouse attached to Bayer's home. And its first employee was Daniel Preiss, who worked for Bayer for 40 years. By the end of 1863, the company already employed 12 people. However, it was not long before the first setbacks came along. On account of the growing competition, the prices for many dyestuffs fell.

The company's founders: Johann Friedrich Weskott (1821–1876, left) and Friedrich Bayer (1825–1880)

The reason the young company didn't go under like many of its rivals was that Bayer and Weskott improved their production processes and had the courage to invest at a time of economic uncertainty. Above all, however, the two owners were never content with what they had already achieved. In 1864, they employed their first trained chemist – August Siller. He was just as willing to experiment as his bosses and became the soul of the company. Weskott and Bayer died four years apart, both aged 55. They left a company that would become a global enterprise.

History of the company logo

A CROSS OF PLAIN ELEGANCE AND SIMPLICITY

The first logo in 1863 included the full company name "Farbenfabriken vorm. Friedr. Bayer & Co." but this was too long, too difficult to remember and, for non-Germans, too hard to pronounce. The winged lion, borrowed from Elberfeld's coat of arms, also meant very little to customers. The question of who actually created the Bayer Cross has not been clarified to this day (see page 358). What is known is that the new logo – registered with the Imperial Patents Office on January 6, 1904 – became a global success thanks to its clear simplicity. It has been carefully modernized several times, firstly in 1928 / 1929 when the slightly italicized letters became upright. Color was introduced in 2003 – the choice of blue and green was intended to convey the company's modernity and freshness.

148

Company logo

1863

1863

Foundation of Friedrich Bayer et comp.

1881 *1886* *1895* *1904*

1928 / 1929 *1989* *2002* *2010*

The largest illuminated sign: these workers are checking the 2,200 light bulbs in the giant Bayer Cross at the company's main site in Leverkusen, Germany. In 1933, the sign had been strung between two stacks to make the company's logo – the circle with the company name written twice to form a cross – visible to the world. With a diameter of 72 meters, it was the world's largest illuminated advertising sign. It was dismantled during the Second World War because of air raids and replaced in 1958 with a smaller version of 51 meters – that still holds the world record. Today, the Bayer Cross is the company's calling card to all travelers approaching Leverkusen – whether on the highway, by train or on the Rhine. Every spring and fall it is switched off for several nights so as not to distract migratory birds from their route.

Who created the Bayer Cross?

A MYTH BORN IN ELBERFELD – OR NEW YORK

Two legends exist concerning the creation of the Bayer Cross. Both are said to have taken place in 1900, one in Elberfeld and the other in New York City. In the first one, a group of employees from the Scientific Department were sitting in the laboratory discussing the day's problems. One of them, Hans Schneider, was idly doodling on a notepad. He wrote the letters of the company name – B A Y E R – once from left to right and once from top to bottom so they formed a cross. Suddenly he stopped and ripped the sheet of paper from the pad. A short time later, he knocked on the managing director's door and presented his brainwave.

Management liked the idea but initially saw no reason to replace the existing logo: a winged red lion with one paw resting on a globe. However, this was drawing ridicule in the company's new markets. Some people thought it looked like a flying dog, others compared it to a cat with wings. Interpretations like these were not very helpful to a company that was committed to doing business internationally. Moreover, Chinese and North American customers had problems with the lengthy company name – Elberfelder Farbenfabriken vormals Friedr. Bayer & Co. Management remembered Schneider's doodle.

The second legend concerns an employee named Dr. Schweizer at the Bayer sales office in New York. He is said to have had a stamp produced with the logo and used this for his correspondence. The clarity of the logo made it so popular that it was being used throughout the company within just a few months. In the United States it replaced the old emblem entirely, while in Germany both logos were used in parallel for some time.

It's no longer possible to establish with certainty which of these two legends is true. However, none other than Felix Hoffmann, the father of Aspirin™, served as a sort of chief witness for the New York version. After his retirement, he wrote in a company publication that Schweizer had created the characteristic logo in his efforts to get American physicians to buy Bayer's drug products. But no sooner had the article been published than a letter was received contradicting the story. It had definitely been Hans Schneider and the author of the letter claimed to remember the meeting.

149

The Bayer Cross

1904

It is a fact that the logo registered with the number 65777 at the Imperial Patents Office on January 6, 1904 became one of the best-known trademarks in the world. It has been stamped on billions of tablets, indicates the location of pharmacies and is found as an illuminated sign on the roofs or walls of buildings in more than 50 cities worldwide. The logo is omnipresent: on products and packaging, in TV commercials and on the jerseys of the Bayer 04 Leverkusen soccer players – together with the company's original red lion emblem. Studies have shown how strongly customers associate the Bayer Cross with attributes like quality and innovation. Bayer's slogan in South America has even passed into everyday language. "Si es Bayer, es bueno" means that if it's made by Bayer, it's good. A company could hardly be paid a greater compliment than this.

Pittsburgh, USA

Calamba City, Philippines

Paris, France

Santiago, Chile

Leverkusen, Germany

Moscow, Russia

Shanghai, China

Berlin, Germany

Frankfurt, Germany

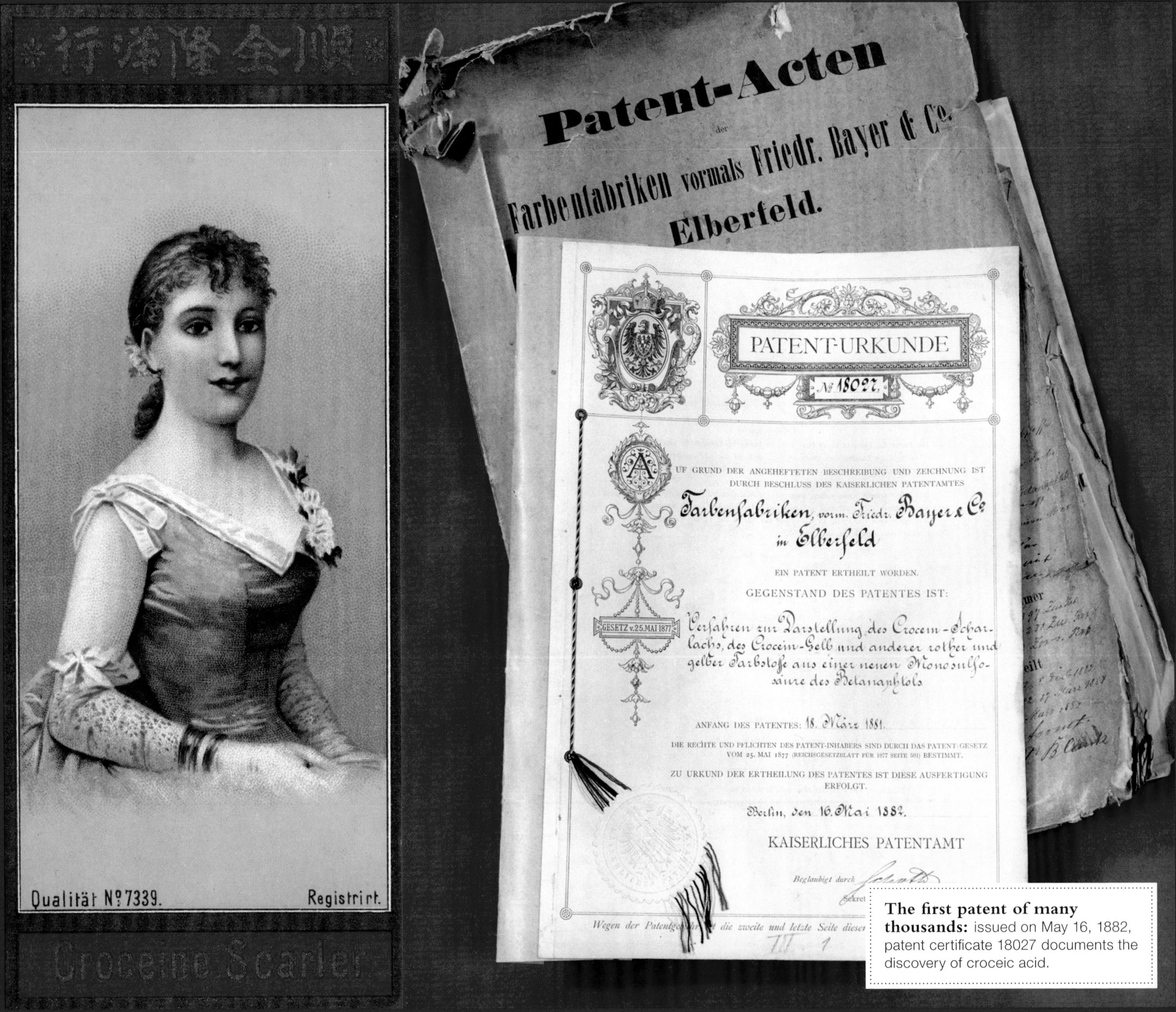

順全隆洋行
Qualität No. 7339.
Registrirt.
Croceine Scarlet
Patent-Acten
der
Farbenfabriken vormals Friedr. Bayer & Co.
Elberfeld.
PATENT-URKUNDE
№ 18027.
AUF GRUND DER ANGEHEFTETEN BESCHREIBUNG UND ZEICHNUNG IST DURCH BESCHLUSS DES KAISERLICHEN PATENTAMTES
Farbenfabriken, vorm. Friedr. Bayer & Co
in Elberfeld
EIN PATENT ERTHEILT WORDEN.
GEGENSTAND DES PATENTES IST:
Verfahren zur Darstellung des Crocein-Scharlachs, des Crocein-Gelb und anderer rother und gelber Farbstoffe aus einer neuen Monosulfosäure des Betanaphtols
GESETZ v. 25. MAI 1877
ANFANG DES PATENTES: 18. März 1881.
DIE RECHTE UND PFLICHTEN DES PATENT-INHABERS SIND DURCH DAS PATENT-GESETZ VOM 25. MAI 1877 (REICHSGESETZBLATT FÜR 1877 SEITE 501) BESTIMMT.
ZU URKUND DER ERTHEILUNG DES PATENTES IST DIESE AUSFERTIGUNG ERFOLGT.
Berlin, den 16. Mai 1882.
KAISERLICHES PATENTAMT
Beglaubigt durch

The first patent of many thousands: issued on May 16, 1882, patent certificate 18027 documents the discovery of croceic acid.

Bayer's first patent

BETTER PROTECTION FOR THE COMPANY'S IDEAS

Eugen Frank, a young chemist, was proud. Patent certificate 18027 issued by the Imperial Patents Office on May 16, 1882 not only documented his discovery but was the first patent awarded to Bayer. Frank had discovered croceic acid, often referred to as Bayer's acid, which was used to manufacture a scarlet azo dyestuff. He came across the substance during the manufacture of an existing dyestuff and initially thought it was a by-product. However, it turned out to be the breakthrough the industry had been waiting for.

His research led to a milestone in Bayer's history: chemist Eugen Frank discovered croceic acid.

In the mid-19th century, a growing number of weaving mills were being converted to machines. As a result, demand for dyestuffs increased to previously unknown levels. However, none of the traditional dyestuffs could meet the requirements of simple mass production, durability and shade consistency. Chemists all over the world were trying to find ways of synthetically producing dyestuffs. Eugen Frank's discovery, which also made it possible to dye cotton without pre-mordanting, was an important milestone for Bayer. But satisfaction with this was short-lived. A rival company started producing the same dyestuff. Bayer sued – and lost the case before the German Supreme Court. However, the company learned from its mistake. From 1885, Carl Duisberg dealt with all patent matters personally. He introduced a system for handling the company's own patents and for monitoring the patents of other companies. In 1889, he won a landmark case concerning Congo red. "I was never happier than on that evening," he wrote to Carl Rumpff, Chairman of the Supervisory Board. Duisberg conducted all important patent cases himself.

150

Croceic acid

1882

It was not his achievements as an inventor, manager or organizer that he considered to be particularly important but the protection of intellectual property. Duisberg established the Patent Department in 1896, staffing it with lawyers and experts from other departments. The Patent Department's varied and complex tasks included acquiring the industrial property rights to all inventions made or obtained by Bayer and defending these against objections or violations. In the meantime, the company has more than 70,000 patents and patent applications. The tasks of the Patent Department have now passed to Bayer Intellectual Property GmbH, which ensures that Bayer remains free to act, supporting and advising inventors in exactly formulating the technical novelty of the process they have discovered. Protection is the only way to ensure that an innovation benefits the inventor.

EPILOGUE

5

THE FUTURE

“

INNOVATION REQUIRES CURIOSITY,
PASSION AND THE
EMBRACE OF CHANGE.

”

DR. MARIJN DEKKERS, LEVERKUSEN, 2013

Dr. Marijn Dekkers,
Chairman of the Board of Management of Bayer AG

WE ARE STILL WRITING THE HISTORY OF INNOVATION

Innovation, internationalization and adaptability – these three attributes have been the cornerstones of Bayer's success across the generations. Throughout its history, the company has always been able to reinvent itself and find answers to the most pressing issues of the time. Says Marijn Dekkers: "The best is yet to come."

By Marijn Dekkers, Chairman of the Board of Management of Bayer AG.

There is a common theme in all the stories in this book – an invisible bond that holds them together. It is our company's ability to innovate. Time and again, we have responded flexibly to changes in market conditions. Time and again, we have found answers to social issues. And we have often been ahead of our time. It was Carl Rumpff, the first Chairman of the Supervisory Board, who coined the idea of the "inventor company" and was able to attract the brightest minds. Among the skills of legendary Bayer manager Carl Duisberg was his ability to turn visions into reality – visions that were to prove groundbreaking and lay the foundations for our modern enterprise. Through their passion, perseverance and willpower, many outstanding Bayer scientists have improved the lives of billions of people, bringing them relief from disease, saving many from hunger and making life easier. We are proud of these achievements.

For 150 years, Bayer has been among the world's most innovative companies. Starting from nothing in 1863, Bayer last year posted sales of around €40 billion – a remarkable performance. For 150 years, we have been creating new molecules and using them to make products people really need. To remain at the forefront of research over 150 years is an enormous achievement. If a company wants to sustain innovation and global success across many generations, it has to be able to constantly reinvent itself and adapt to new circumstances. Change as a normal state of affairs is inherent to Bayer.

"Innovation is not just a question of money."

It is an amazing feeling for me as a former researcher to head a company with such a rich scientific history. Having registered 30 patents myself, I know what it means to work in a laboratory and pursue a goal that you can never be sure of actually achieving. I know that innovation needs patience and dedication.

Although Bayer has been involved in countless inventions, few people are aware of them because they have become part of our everyday world: antibiotics that save lives; crop protection products that safeguard harvests; high-tech materials for our cars, homes and televisions. Even the material for the CD came from one of our laboratories. "Bayer: Science For A Better Life" is the mission that guides more than 110,000 employees every day throughout the company – in research and production, in marketing and administration. Worldwide, we employ almost 13,000 researchers whose work led to more than 600 patent applications in 2012. Each year, we spend around €3 billion on research and development – more than any other company in our industry. These are interesting facts. But innovation is not just a question of money.

Innovation requires curiosity, passion and the embrace of change. It demands the will to make constant improvements and go that one step further. And it requires the creation of an inspirational environment for people with ideas and the courage to pursue them. I believe that one of my central tasks as CEO of Bayer is to provide that environment. If you have read this book, you will be aware of the corporate culture that underpins our work. Our ethical foundation comprises our corporate values – known by the acronym LIFE, which stands for Leadership, Integrity, Flexibility and Efficiency. To me, innovation is about more than just developing products. It is also about new business models, optimized services and improved processes. This means not only identifying but also developing the individual strengths and talents of every employee. That is why we have stepped up our efforts in the area of employee training. As a world-ranking innovation company, we also aim to strengthen our executives' competence in innovation management. I am particularly pleased that we have recently been judged several times to be one of the best employers for scientists. Worldwide, we are also highly successful in attracting well-educated young women to Bayer. I am convinced that a diverse employee structure is a key factor in ensuring our company's competitiveness.

"The Bayer Cross stands for quality, reliability and innovation."

Bayer's success is not only measurable in terms of its financial data. We are one of the best-known and most respected companies in the world. Year after year, image

Bayer Group management in the anniversary year: the Executive Council headed by the Chairman of the Board of Management of Bayer AG and comprising the members of the Board of Management of Bayer AG and the CEOs of the three subgroups Bayer HealthCare, Bayer CropScience and Bayer MaterialScience. From left: Professor Wolfgang Plischke, Patrick Thomas, Dr. Marijn Dekkers, Dr. Richard Pott (retired on June 1, 2013), Michael König, Liam Condon and Werner Baumann.

150 YEARS OF BAYER – THE CORNERSTONES OF SUCCESS

studies in dozens of countries prove the high value of the Bayer brand. The Bayer Cross stands for quality, reliability and innovation. We are the only global enterprise that focuses on the health of people, animals and plants, and we have broad knowledge of high-performance materials. This combination gives us a unique position that we are seeking to build on. It is also confers a great responsibility. The tasks ahead of us are enormous. It is a known fact that the global population is growing at a dramatic pace. United Nations studies show that more than 9 billion people will live on our planet in 2050, many of them in fast-developing conurbations. One of the challenges facing humankind is to provide medical care for all these people. The World Health Organization (WHO) predicts a significant increase in the number of people with cardiovascular disease, cancer and diabetes. Researchers at Bayer HealthCare are working on the drug products of the future. That is what is expected of Bayer – as the company behind Aspirin™ and Ciprobay™, Kogenate™ and Xarelto™.

Our highly effective anticoagulant Xarelto™ is a good example of our success in innovation. In patients with atrial fibrillation, it can significantly reduce the risk of stroke – thus sparing many people and their families this fate. Xarelto™ is now approved in more than 120 countries. Products of this kind give hope to people worldwide, helping to diagnose, prevent and cure diseases. This is our motivation.

As the world's population increases, the amount of land available for growing food is declining. We are addressing this problem by developing innovative seeds and crop protection solutions that can provide real help for farmers worldwide. Bayer CropScience expects to bring more than 15 new projects in the areas of seeds and plant traits to market-readiness between 2011 and 2016 – for wheat, rice, oilseed rape, soybeans and cotton alone. In past agricultural crises, we have proven our capability to quickly develop solutions. We are there when we are needed.

With new and optimized products, our colleagues at Bayer MaterialScience provide crucial stimulus in automotive, electrical and construction engineering. Innovation should not be viewed in a single dimension. It is not just a matter of introducing novel products; it is also about developing processes or strategies that can advance our company and society. If, for example, our knowledge of materials can help to develop environmentally friendly energy production technologies, then we are willing to contribute our expertise. We will offer ways to save energy and preserve natural resources.

"We have always been able to adapt."

Our company's success is built on three cornerstones: innovation, internationalization and adaptability. By the time globalization became a dominant international issue, it had long been a part of Bayer's history. We have always been at home on the world's markets. In some countries, Bayer was among the first foreign companies to set up operations. For example, we produced our first dyestuffs in what was still the Russian Empire in 1876. Our company had its own agency in Shanghai as early as 1882. And a Bayer delegation traveled to Rio de Janeiro in 1896. Bayer has been a global player right from the start. This, too, has required courage and flexibility – but without ever losing sight of what the company stands for.

In our anniversary year, we are looking to the future – backed by pride in the achievements of the past 150 years. In 2013, Bayer is in a strong position going forward. We have always managed to master the challenges that arose, no matter how diverse they were. At present, we are facing generic competition in both HealthCare and CropScience; MaterialScience has to contend with price pressure from competitors in Asia and the Middle East. At the same time, we need to make substantial investments in research and development and in property, plant and equipment to ensure the continuation of our success story.

The company must take decisions today about significant capital expenditures which, if successful, will benefit the coming generations. No-one can predict the future. In an increasingly uncertain economic, political and social environment, decision-making will become more difficult. We need both foresight and very careful planning. And we also need a large dose of courage.

I'm often asked what we will be able to offer our customers 50 years from now. My answer is that it will still be molecules, just as it has been throughout our history. Bayer has always been able to create new products from scientific findings – from molecules. We have always been able to adapt. And an important factor for our success are our employees, who have shaped change across the generations. That is why they are at the focus of our anniversary year – and of this book.

The mere knowledge of our tremendous achievements isn't enough. I am concerned about whether western societies will continue to appreciate our innovations. Is acceptance of new things being weakened by an excessive and sometimes exaggerated fear of risk? Do people see innovative products as successes, as a way of improving life for everyone? Do they understand our mission or do they see it merely as a pretext for maximizing profit? We need proper appreciation as the basis for our business model and our license to operate. We need social acceptance. Creating this requires the involvement of all stakeholders: politics and business, schools and universities. And we too must contribute.

"The best is yet to come."

We at Bayer know that we all give our best at every site and apply the highest safety and sustainability standards – but this is not sufficient. We – and by this I mean every one of us – must be more effective in explaining what we do, not only for the sake of our employees and our stakeholders but also for the benefit of society as a whole. The development of a new drug product costs €1 billion on average. After 12 years, just one out of around 10,000 test substances may actually receive regulatory approval. We have to make people understand what this means. Only then will they be willing to pay a fair price for our products. And only then will we be able to finance this enormous investment. If we want people to appreciate our innovations, then we have to do more to explain what we do, why we do it and who we are.

We are facing major challenges that can only be mastered by applying our innovative capability. But, as in any other area of life, challenges always bring opportunities. I am convinced that the best is yet to come.

FOUNDERS AND CEOS SINCE 1863

Friedrich Bayer
1863–1880

Johann Friedrich Weskott
1863–1876

Prof. Dr. Carl Duisberg
1912–1925

Prof. Dr. Ulrich Haberland
1951–1961

Prof. Dr. Kurt Hansen
1961–1974

Prof. Dr. Herbert Grünewald
1974–1984

Hermann-Josef Strenger
1984–1992

Dr. Manfred Schneider
1992–2002

Werner Wenning
2002–2010

Dr. Marijn Dekkers
since 2010

An overview of the founders and CEOs of the company: between 1881 and 1912, there was no clear delineation between the functions of the Supervisory Board and the Board of Management, so no-one is pictured for this period. Likewise, between 1925 and 1951, Bayer had no CEO of its own as the company was part of I.G. Farbenindustrie AG until its re-establishment in 1951.

BAYER AND THE WORLD – IN 25 YEARS

How our employees see the future

How will the world change?
How will Bayer contribute to solving the most pressing problems in the coming decades?
What major changes will greatly improve our lives?

For 150 years, Bayer's employees have worked with great passion to create life-improving innovations. On the following pages, current employees from around the world describe how they see the future of the planet and their company's role.

"The passion for providing effective solutions continues to drive each and every one of us at Bayer in the future – with the aim of bringing smiles to faces around the world."
Manish Garg, Singapore

"Bayer is a place of diversity and inclusion. It's the global employer of choice with employees giving their best – every single day."
Jacqueline Patricio, USA

"Tiny robots will be steered through our bloodstream to rebuild cells and release substances and drugs to fight dangerous diseases much more quickly and effectively."
Priscila Mendes, Brazil

"CropScience and HealthCare will jointly develop an insecticide to control the Anopheles mosquito and a medicine for the better treatment of malaria, thus eliminating this scourge of mankind."
Ulrich Heun, Germany

"Bayer will develop new products made from renewable raw materials to make us independent of finite oil reserves."
Shirley Peh, Singapore

"What makes a difference is our active involvement with young people through educational and volunteer programs that get them interested in science."
Dennis Del Corro, USA

"Thanks to new preventative medicines from Bayer, people will lose their fear of having a stroke or heart attack."
Teresa Ilaria Savino, Italy

"At Bayer, we have learned to never stop dreaming. Dreams that helped this company and the world move forward for 150 years, dreams about a better life. In the future, we will live today's dreams."
Samy Khalil, Egypt

"It's good that my company is contributing to solving pressing problems like resource conservation. Artificial photosynthesis using chlorophyll produced in the laboratory can generate electricity, thus solving the energy problem."
Tobias Kanacher, Germany

"Population growth means we have to recycle both general materials and food waste, as well as reduce water usage. Bayer helps to produce food more efficiently, and to make it more nutritious and storable for longer."

Colin Barker, United Kingdom

"For long-term business growth and because of our corporate responsibility, we are investing in Africa, promoting children's education, offering microfinancing to farmers and supporting healthcare centers."

Boualem Saidi, South Korea

"Medical bracelets will analyze your condition, for example, during a common cold, and automatically inject the right medicine at the right time in the right dosage."

Georgy Sitnik, Russia

"When people emigrate to Mars, Bayer will supply high-performance materials for spaceships and construction. CropScience will develop a technology to grow food in a completely different environment."

Aileen Qiu, China

"New biomarker technologies will make it possible to detect the presence of diseases before symptoms appear. Then we can take early action to cure or check the progress of the diseases."

Takeshi Tanioka, Japan

"Bayer CropScience will develop a variety of rice that does not have to be planted all over again after one season, but grows again from the roots right after harvest."

Ferdinand Muyano Papio, Spain

"Bayer is still an attractive employer with a future. Success is based on enthusiastic and motivated employees."
Andrea Billert, Germany

"I would love to see Bayer's innovative capacity find ways to make effective use of the most common and available renewable energy: sunlight."
Hervé Monconduit, France

"Bayer brings many cultures closer together. As a Turk born in Germany, I can contribute to that too. My vision is of people and countries growing closer by living the company's LIFE values."
Meltem Aksoy, Turkey

"Vehicles will be made of intelligent materials that produce energy from the sun, wind and rain – making them environmentally friendly, affordable and suitable for use anywhere. Made by Bayer!"
Birgit Horns, Germany

"Looking at the growth of the world population, it will be necessary to increase crop production all over the world. Plants will have to be able to grow in areas that are currently considered to be sub-optimal for plant growth."
Wim Vriezen, Netherlands

"Bayer will develop vaccines against cancer, seeds that produce more food and new materials with even better properties. All of this is in line with our mission – for people around the world."
Manuel Palmer Alfonso, Mexico

150 YEARS OF BAYER

MILESTONES IN THE COMPANY'S HISTORY

This timeline provides an overview of key milestones in Bayer's 150-year history. Other pioneering achievements by Bayer researchers and selected inventions in the areas of health care, agriculture and high-tech materials are documented in this Anniversary Book.

1863

On August 1, merchant Friedrich Bayer (left) and master dyer Johann Friedrich Weskott (right) establish a dyestuffs factory in Barmen, now a district of the city of Wuppertal.

1865

In their first activity outside Germany, the company founders purchase an interest in a coal tar dye factory in the United States and begin exporting intermediates.

1873

A relief fund is established for all of the company's 35 employees, ten years before Bismarck's first social security law is passed.

1876

In a rented basement in Moscow, a few employees equipped with a hand mixer dissolve alizarine presscake. It doesn't deserve to be called a factory but it is a milestone in Bayer's history because it marks the start of production outside Germany.

1881

Following the founders' deaths, the company's co-owners decide to place the enterprise on a broader and sounder footing. They establish a joint stock company named "Farbenfabriken vorm. Friedr. Bayer & Co." with a capital stock of 5.4 million marks.

1882

The company receives its first patent, issued by the Imperial Patents Office in Berlin.

Meyrinck & Co. in Shanghai becomes the permanent agency of the Farbenfabriken Bayer in China.

1884

The chemist Carl Duisberg starts his career with Bayer. Under his leadership, the company's scientists make groundbreaking discoveries.

1888

The manufacture of Phenacetin, one of the first synthetic antipyretics, marks the establishment of the Pharmaceutical Department.

1891

Bayer purchases the alizarine red factory operated by "Ultramarin-Fabrik Dr. Carl Leverkus & Söhne" and other land on the right bank of the Rhine near Wiesdorf, now Leverkusen.

1897

Bayer scientist Dr. Felix Hoffmann succeeds in synthesizing a chemically pure and stable form of acetylsalicylic acid, the active ingredient of Aspirin™.

For many years, Bayer's Kekulé Library is the largest private library of chemical literature in western Europe. On the death of Friedrich August Kekulé, his collection of some 7,000 works is purchased by Carl Duisberg as the cornerstone of the library.

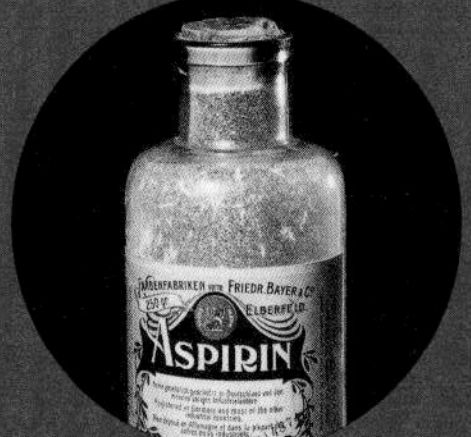

1899

Aspirin™ is registered as a trademark and soon achieves worldwide fame as a painkiller.

1904

The company sports club "Turn- und Spielverein der Farbenfabriken vorm. Friedrich Bayer & Co." is founded on July 1, 1904.

Ambassador of the skies: throughout the anniversary year, the Bayer Airship will be traveling the world. Leverkusen, Sydney, Johannesburg, Barcelona, Mexico City, Tokyo and Rio de Janeiro are just some of the destinations on its itinerary. In May, the company's ambassador of the skies flew past the Statue of Liberty in New York, USA. The Airship Tour is one of the many ways in which Bayer is celebrating its 150th anniversary. At the focus of all activities are the company's employees and their families – but neighbors, customers, other business partners and the scientific community have also been invited to participate.

2002

In June, Bayer acquires Aventis CropScience, making it a world leader in crop protection.

Bayer CropScience AG is launched in October as the first legally independent Bayer subgroup.

The Bayer Group's business has been steered from the present headquarters building since 2002 (photo).

2003

In October, the subgroups Bayer Chemicals AG and Bayer HealthCare AG and the service company Bayer Technology Services GmbH gain legal independence as part of the reorganization of the Bayer Group. The subgroup Bayer MaterialScience AG and the service companies Bayer Business Services GmbH and Bayer Industry Services GmbH & Co. OHG (now Currenta GmbH & Co. OHG) follow in December.

2004

100 years of the Bayer Cross: the Bayer Group's world-famous trademark celebrates its centennial in January.

In June, Bayer becomes the first private-sector partner to the United Nations Environment Programme (UNEP) in the area of youth and environment.

2005

In January, Bayer completes the acquisition of the Roche consumer health business, advancing to become one of the world's top three suppliers of non-prescription medicines.

Lanxess AG is spun off from the Bayer Group on January 28. This company continues Bayer's chemicals business and parts of its polymers business.

2006

In March, Bayer announces a public takeover offer for Schering AG, Berlin, Germany. In July, Bayer gains control of 92.4 percent of the approximately 191 million outstanding shares of Schering AG, Berlin, Germany. That company's activities are now assigned to Bayer HealthCare Pharmaceuticals.

2007

Bayer sells the Diagnostics Division of Bayer HealthCare to Siemens AG, Munich, for €4.2 billion.

Centennial celebration: the 100th season of the Bayer Cultural Affairs Department gets under way in September.

November sees the launch of the integrated, Group-wide Bayer Climate Program, the aims of which include reducing the company's CO_2 emissions.

2008

In June, Bayer is presented with the 2008 Environmental Award in the category "Environmentally Friendly Technologies" by the Federation of German Industries (BDI). Use of the new oxygen depolarized cathode technology saves energy and reduces CO_2 emissions.

In October, the world's largest MDI production facility goes on stream in Shanghai (photo).

2009

In November, Bayer implements its zero-emissions building concept for the first time with the opening of a children's daycare center in Monheim, Germany.

Also in November, Bayer CropScience completes the acquisition of Athenix Corp., a privately held U.S. biotechnology company (photo below).

In December, the Bayer team of Dr. Frank Misselwitz, Dr. Dagmar Kubitza and Dr. Elisabeth Perzborn (from left) are awarded the German Future Prize for the development of the new anticoagulant rivaroxaban.

2011

In February, Bayer starts up the Dream Production pilot plant in Leverkusen to manufacture high-tech plastics using carbon dioxide.

2012

With the acquisition of U.S. company AgraQuest, Bayer CropScience enters the growth market for biologicals.

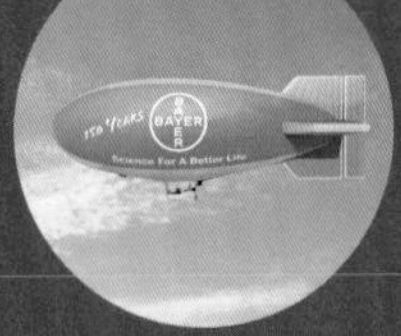

2013

Bayer celebrates its 150th anniversary.

1908

The "Erholungshaus" opens in Leverkusen, a "place for convivial and instructive events" with 1,000 seats.

1911

On April 7, Friedr. Bayer & Co. Gomei-Kaisha is entered as a general partnership in the Japanese commercial register with offices in Kobe and Yokohama. The principle place of business is Kobe.

1912

The company's headquarters are transferred to Leverkusen.

1913

Bayer is the third-largest German chemical company with 10,600 employees. It holds 8,000 German and foreign patents and has production facilities and subsidiaries in the United States, Russia, France, the United Kingdom, Austria, the Netherlands, Poland, Italy, Spain, Belgium, Portugal, India, Japan, Argentina, Brazil and China, as well as 44 of its own sales offices and 123 agencies. Alongside research and development, the establishment of a global marketing organization is a crucial pillar of the company's growth. Even in the early years, Bayer delivers dyestuffs to many countries.

1925

After the world economy has stabilized in the mid-1920s, it is clear that the German dyestuffs industry cannot regain its former position on the global market. In order to remain competitive and access new markets, Germany's leading chemical companies decide on fusion in 1925. Bayer transfers its assets to I.G. Farbenindustrie AG (I.G. Farben) and the company is deleted from the commercial register.

Yet the Bayer tradition lives on in I.G. Farben's Lower Rhine operating consortium, which comprises the Leverkusen, Dormagen, Elberfeld and Krefeld-Uerdingen sites. Leverkusen also becomes the headquarters for I.G. Farben's pharmaceutical sales consortium, which uses the Bayer Cross as its joint trademark.

1939

Bayer scientist Gerhard Domagk is awarded the Nobel Prize in Medicine for his discovery of the antibacterial effects of sulfonamides (Prontosil).

1951

Bayer is re-established as Farbenfabriken Bayer AG, changing its name to Bayer AG in 1972.

1973

Ground is broken for the Brunsbüttel production site and six years later, in 1979, for the Agricultural Center (now the corporate headquarters of Bayer CropScience) in Monheim.

1986

All Bayer's U.S. activities are consolidated under the management holding company Bayer USA Inc., Pittsburgh.

1992

With a further indication (thrombosis prophylaxis), the World Health Organization (WHO) again includes acetylsalicylic acid, the active ingredient of Aspirin™, in its List of Essential Medicines. The substance was first included in this list in 1977.

1994

The first production facility of Bayer Bitterfeld GmbH comes on stream. In the same year, Bayer acquires the North American self-medication business of Sterling Winthrop, at the same time regaining full rights to the Bayer name for all products and the Bayer Cross trademark in the United States and Canada, which had been confiscated after the First World War.

1999

To mark the 100th birthday of Aspirin™ on March 6, Bayer's former high-rise headquarters building in Leverkusen is wrapped to make it the world's biggest Aspirin™ pack, earning the company three entries in the Guinness Book of Records.

2000

Acquisition of the polyols business of U.S.-based Lyondell Chemical Company makes Bayer the world's biggest producer of raw materials for polyurethanes.

2001

On December 6, the company's management announces plans to establish independent operating subsidiaries under the umbrella of a management holding company.

Index

Masthead

Published by
Bayer AG, Communications, Leverkusen, Germany

Responsible for the contents
Michael Schade

Head of Publications
Franz Rempe

Editor
Dr. Katrin Schneider

Idea and realization
Ankerherz Verlag GmbH, Hollenstedt, Germany

Authors: Stefan Krücken (profiles), Fred Grimm, Jochen Pioch, David Schumacher, Gerhard Waldherr

Design: Julia Krücken (chief designer), Daniela Greven, Florin Preußler, Peter Löffelholz

Illustrations: Hans Baltzer

Photography
Peter Ginter, Lohmar, Germany
Jörg Klaus (profiles), Berlin, Germany

Picture editor
Frank-Michael Herzog/Medienfabrik, Leverkusen, Germany

Pictorial sources: Bayer AG, Corbis Images, Dreamstime, Fotolia, Getty Images, iStockphoto, Ros/Enfoque, Solar Impulse|Revillard|Rezo.ch, Dr. Martin Oeggerli, SPL/Agentur Focus, VectorStock

Scientific consultants
Michael Frings, Dr. Ursula Königer, Dr. Gisela Lenz, Dr. Katharina Jansen, Dr. Stephan Michael Meier, Frank Meixner, Hans-Hermann Pogarell, Michael Pohlenz, Michael Schlösser, Ulrike von Schmeling, Hans-Bernd Schmitz, Dr. Jörg Thomaier (all Bayer AG)

Typesetting
Christiane Wittich/Qualitätssicherung Wittich, Cologne, Germany
Stefan Tessun /Medienfabrik, Leverkusen, Germany

Lithography and printing
Kunst- und Werbedruck, Bad Oeynhausen, Germany

English translation
Currenta GmbH & Co. OHG, Language Service, Leverkusen, Germany

Editorial address
Bayer AG, Communications
Building W 11, 51368 Leverkusen, Germany
Bayer on the Internet: www.bayer.com

A publication for employees of the Bayer Group

Forward-Looking Statements
This publication may contain forward-looking statements based on current assumptions and forecasts made by Bayer Group or subgroup management. Various known and unknown risks, uncertainties and other factors could lead to material differences between the actual future results, financial situation, development or performance of the company and the estimates given here. These factors include those discussed in Bayer's public reports, which are available on the Bayer website at www.bayer.com. The company assumes no liability whatsoever to update these forward-looking statements or to conform them to future events or developments.

FSC
www.fsc.org
MIX
Paper from responsible sources
FSC® C011291

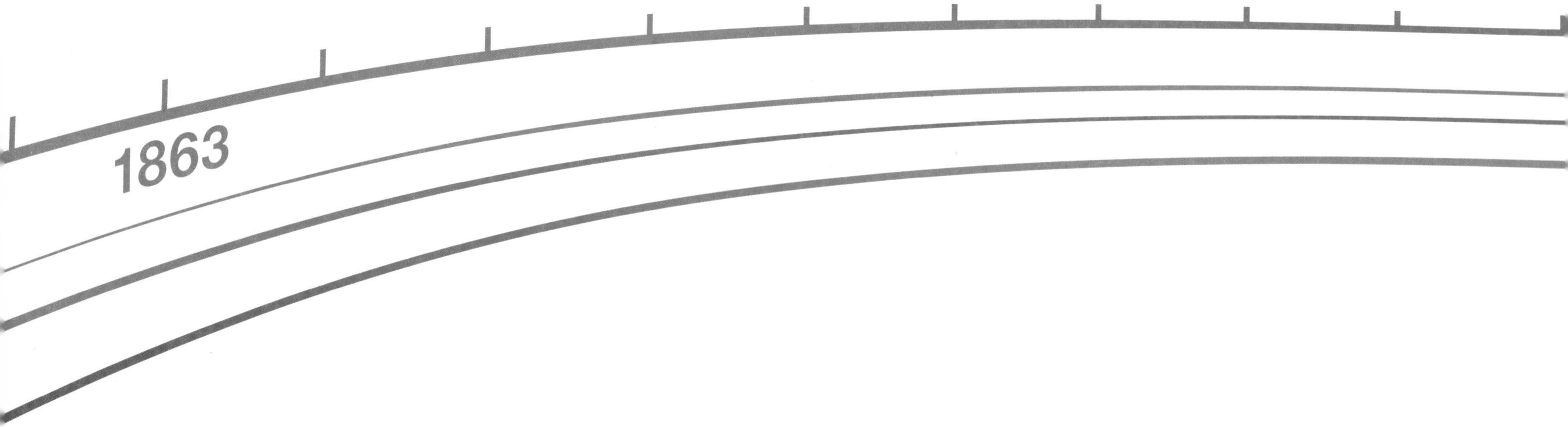
1863